WHO FOOD
ADDITIVES
SERIES: 32

Toxicological evaluation of certain food additives and contaminants

Prepared by
The forty-first meeting of the Joint FAO/WHO
Expert Committee on Food Additives (JECFA)

World Health Organization, Geneva, 1993

IPCS – International Programme on Chemical Safety

The International Programme on Chemical Safety (IPCS) is a joint venture of the United Nations Environment Programme, the International Labour Organisation, and the World Health Organization. The main objective of the IPCS is to carry out and disseminate evaluations of the effects of chemicals on human health and the quality of the environment. Supporting activities include the development of epidemiological, experimental laboratory, and risk-assessment methods that can enable production of internationally comparable results, and the development of manpower in the field of toxicology. Other activities carried out by the IPCS include the development of know-how for coping with chemical accidents, coordination of laboratory testing and epidemiological studies, and promotion of research on the mechanisms of the biological action of chemicals.

ISBN 92 4 166032 5

CONTENTS

PREFACE

The monographs contained in this volume were prepared by the forty-first Joint FAO/WHO Expert Committee on Food Additives (JECFA), which met in Geneva, Switzerland, from 9 to 18 February 1993. These monographs summarize the safety data on selected food additives and contaminants reviewed by the Committee. The data reviewed in these monographs form the basis for acceptable daily intakes (ADIs) established by the Committee.

The forty-first report of JECFA will be published by the World Health Organization in the WHO Technical Report Series. The participants in the meeting are listed in Annex 3 of the present publication and a summary of the conclusions of the Committee is included as Annex 4.

Specifications established at the forty-first meeting of JECFA will be published in the FAO Food and Nutrition Paper series. These toxicological monographs should be read in conjunction with the specifications and the report.

Reports and other documents resulting from previous meetings of the Joint FAO/WHO Expert Committee on Food Additives are listed in Annex 1.

JECFA serves as a scientific advisory body to FAO, WHO, their Member States, and the Codex Alimentarius Commission, primarily through the Codex Committee on Food Additives and Contaminants and the Codex Committee on Residues of Veterinary Drugs in Foods, regarding the safety of food additives, residues of veterinary drugs, naturally occurring toxicants, and contaminants in food. Committees serve this function by preparing reports of their meetings and publishing specifications or residues monographs and toxicological monographs, such as those contained in this volume, on substances that they have considered.

Many proprietary unpublished reports are referenced in this volume. These were voluntarily submitted to the Committee, generally by producers of the food additives under review, and in many cases these reports represent the only safety data available on these substances. The working papers used by the Committee to develop the monographs in this volume were developed by Temporary Advisers based on all the data that had been submitted, and all these studies were available to the Committee as it made its evaluations and finalized the monographs.

From 1972 to 1975 the toxicology monographs prepared by Joint FAO/WHO Expert Committees on Food Additives were published in the WHO Food Additives Series; between 1975 and 1985 this series was available in the form of unpublished WHO documents provided by the Organization upon request. WHO Food Additives Series Volume No. 20, prepared by the twenty-ninth Committee in 1985, through WHO Food Additives Series Volume No. 24, prepared by the thirty-third Committee in 1988, were published by the Cambridge University Press. Beginning with WHO Food Additives Series No. 25, prepared by the thirty-fourth Committee, WHO has produced these volumes as priced documents.

The preparation and editing of the monographs included in this volume have been made possible through the technical and financial contributions of the Participating Institutions of the International Programme on Chemical Safety (IPCS), which support the activities of JECFA. IPCS is a joint venture of the United Nations Environment Programme, the International Labour Organisation, and the World Health Organization, which is the executing agency. One of the main objectives of the IPCS is to carry out and disseminate evaluations of the effects of chemicals on human health and the quality of the environment.

The designations employed and the presentation of the material in this publication do not imply the expression of any opinion whatsoever on the part of the organizations participating in the IPCS concerning the legal status of any country, territory, city, or area or its authorities, nor concerning the delimitation of its frontiers or boundaries. The mention of specific companies or of certain manufacturers' products implies neither that they are endorsed nor recommended by those organizations in preference to others of a similar nature that are not mentioned.

Any comments or new information on the biological or toxicological data on the compounds reported in this document should be addressed to: Joint WHO Secretary of the Joint FAO/WHO Expert Committee on Food Additives, International Programme on Chemical Safety, World Health Organization, Avenue Appia, 1211 Geneva 27, Switzerland.

MONOGRAPH FORMAT

Note: Monographs in this document generally follow the format presented below. All monographs may not, however, require the use of each heading, and in some monographs the format has been modified to better present data about several substances.

1.   **EXPLANATION**

2.   **BIOLOGICAL DATA**
     2.1   Biochemical aspects
           2.1.1   Absorption, distribution and excretion.
           2.1.2   Biotransformation
           2.1.3   Effects on enzymes and other biochemical parameters
     2.2   Toxicological studies
           2.2.1   Acute toxicity studies
           2.2.2   Short-term toxicity studies
           2.2.2.1-2.2.2.X   Species tested
           2.2.3   Long-term/carcinogenicity studies
           2.2.4   Reproduction studies
           2.2.5-2.2.X   Special studies
     2.3   Observations in humans

3.   **COMMENTS**

4.   **EVALUATION**

5.   **REFERENCES**

ANTIOXIDANTS

GALLATES (PROPYL, OCTYL AND DODECYL)

First draft prepared by
Dr G.J.A. Speijers and Mrs M.E. van Apeldoorn
National Institute of Public Health and Environmental Protection
Laboratory for Toxicology
Bilthoven, The Netherlands

1.   EXPLANATION

        Propyl, octyl and dodecyl gallates have been evaluated for acceptable daily
intake at the third, sixth, eighth, tenth, fifteenth, sixteenth, seventeenth, twentieth,
twenty-fourth, and thirtieth meetings of the Committee (Annex 1, references 3, 6,
8, 13, 26, 30, 32, 41, 53 and 73). At the twenty-fourth meeting a group ADI of
0-0.2 mg/kg bw was established, based on the supposed similarity in the
biotransformation of these compounds. The Committee used a higher than normal
safety factor (250) because of concern for adverse effects shown in reproduction
studies. The gallates were again reviewed by the Committee at its thirtieth meeting.
Due to lack of adequate data, an ADI was not established for octyl or dodecyl
gallate, and more information on the hydrolysis and the biotransformation (including
lactating animals) of the different gallates was required. For propyl gallate an ADI
of 0-2.5 mg/kg bw was established.

        Since the last evaluation, additional data have become available. These
new data included four-week and 90-day toxicity studies in rats with propyl gallate
and *in vitro* studies on the hydrolysis of the gallates in different tissues. These data
are summarized and discussed in this monograph, which also includes all data from
previously published monographs. Because this monograph covers the data on
propyl, octyl and dodecyl gallates separately, a modified form of the general
monograph format has been used.

PROPYL GALLATE

2.   BIOLOGICAL DATA

2.1   Biochemical aspects

2.1.1   Absorption, distribution and excretion.

        No information available.

2.1.2 Biotransformation

The available evidence indicates that the gallate esters are hydrolyzed in the body to gallic acid. Most of the gallic acid is converted into 4-0-methyl gallic acid. Free gallic acid or a conjugated derivative of 4-0-methyl gallic acid is excreted in the urine. Conjugation of the 4-0-methyl gallic acid with glucuronic acid was demonstrated (Booth et al., 1959).

Detailed metabolic pathways for propyl gallate have been described (Dacre, 1960).

In vitro incubations with propyl, octyl and dodecyl gallate were performed using homogenates of liver, mucosa of the small intestine, and contents of caecum/colon as a source of intestinal microflora. The various homogenates were incubated at 37^0 C with the individual gallate esters. At various time points up to 24 hours, samples were taken and analysed by HPLC in order to determine the concentration of gallic acid and residual ester. From the time-course of gallic acid formation, as well as the disappearance of the specific esters, the rate of hydrolysis of the three esters was calculated.

All test substances were extensively metabolized by the homogenate of the intestinal mucosa, which was demonstrated by the appearance of peaks in the chromatograms. Furthermore, the caecum and colon contents also showed a high metabolic capacity, especially towards propyl gallate. The amount of gallic acid detected in the incubations was always much smaller than the total decrease of the amount of ester. It seems likely that apart from hydrolysis of the ester bond, other biotransformation routes (oxidation and/or conjugation) are of major importance for all three gallate esters.

The three homogenates show quantitatively different structure-activity relationships for the three esters. Homogenates of liver and of contents of caecum and colon metabolize propyl gallate most extensively, followed by octyl or dodecyl gallate. Homogenate of the mucosa of the small intestine shows the highest rates with octyl gallate, lower rates with dodecyl gallate and propyl gallate. For this homogenate, the rate of formation of gallic acid is inversely related to the chain length of the ester (de Bie & van Ommen, 1992).

2.1.3 Effects on enzymes and other biochemical parameters

Propyl gallate inhibited liver mixed function oxidase (MFO) and demethylase activity when added at concentrations of 50 to 500 μM to liver microsomal preparations obtained from male Sprague-Dawley rats. Specifically, the compound inhibited benzpyrene hydroxylase activity and demethylase activity with ethyl morphine, aminopyrene or benzphetamine as substrate. No induction of MFO activity was noted when propyl gallate was injected intraperitoneally at 300 mg/kg bw 24 hours prior to sacrifice and assay. The microsomes from the treated animals had lower demethylase activity, probably as a result of inhibitory amounts of the compound attached to the microsomes (Yang and Strickhart, 1974).

Weanling female Sprague-Dawley rats were fed high polyunsaturated fat, high saturated fat or low fat diets for one month, with or without the addition of 0.3% propyl gallate. Propyl gallate caused no measurable difference in body weights, relative liver weight or liver microsomal protein values. Liver enzyme activity of aniline hydroxylase, aminopyrene N-demethylase and cytochrome-C-reductase were not affected by treatment, nor was the liver concentration of cytochrome P-450 and microsomal protein. Rats dosed with BHT at 0.3% of the diet exhibited liver hypertrophy and induction of cytochrome P-450 microsomal protein and liver enzymes (King and McCay, 1981).

Addition of 25 or 125 μmol of propyl gallate to an MFO assay system prepared from the tissues of male Sprague-Dawley rats (liver, kidneys, stomach, colon and small intestine) inhibited the oxidation of benzo(a)pyrene (Rahimtula *et al.*, 1979).

Addition of 50 μmol of propyl gallate to a rat testis microsomal preparation in the presence of arachidonate stimulated the formation of prostaglandins PGF$_2$. Addition of 0.1 mmol vitamin E instead of propyl gallate did not result in increased production of any of the prostaglandins. Addition of propyl gallate to similar preparations from vitamin E-deficient rats resulted in an increase in production of PGF$_2$ only. In the female rat both dietary lipid and dietary propyl gallate affect prostaglandin synthesis by mammary gland preparations. These effects are concentration-dependent effects with stimulation of synthesis of some prostaglandins at one level of propyl gallate and inhibition at higher levels. The effect of propyl gallate is also dependent upon the type of fat in the rat diet. Propyl gallate stimulates formation of prostglandin PGF$_2$ in mammary gland from rats fed polyunsaturated fats, but inhibits PGF$_2$ synthesis in rats fed a saturated fat diet. Stimulation of synthesis of different prostaglandins may occur in preparations to which propyl gallate was added exogenously as compared to a dietary source of the compound. Changes in levels of PGF$_2$ have been correlated with the susceptibility of rats to mammary tumours induced by 7,12-dimethyl-benzo(a)anthracene (Carpenter, 1981).

Effects of propyl gallate on glutathione-S-transferase are described in discussion of the short-term toxicity study (Speijers et al., 1993).

2.2   Toxicological studies

2.2.1   Acute toxicity studies

The results of acute toxicity studies with propyl gallate are summarized in Table 1.

Table 1.   Acute toxicity studies - propyl gallate

Animal	Route	LD$_{50}$ (mg/kg bw)	Reference
Mouse	oral	2 - 3 000	Lehman et al., 1951
Rat	oral	3 800	Orten et al., 1948
Rat	oral	3 600	Lehman et al., 1951
Rat	i.p.	380	Orten et al., 1948

2.2.2   Short-term toxicity studies

2.2.2.1   Rats

Levels of propyl gallate of 1.2% and 2.3% in the diet of rats caused a decreased weight gain, the bitter taste of the gallate apparently making the diet unpalatable. The high dose level caused some deaths (about 40%) during the first month; the survivors continued to eat the diet for 10 - 16 months and showed retarded growth, but no pathological lesions. The animals that died exhibited renal damage (Orten et al., 1948).

Weanling rats were fed diets which contained 20% lard and 0, 0.1, 0.2, 0.3, 0.4 and 0.5% propyl gallate for six weeks. There was no effect on body weight, liver weight, liver weight to body weight ratio, left adrenal weight, total liver lipid, composition of liver polyunsaturated fatty acids, liver cholesterol, adrenal cholesterol or serum sodium (Johnson and Hewgill, 1961).

Propyl gallate was added to the dietary fat of weanling rats at levels of 0.02% in the fat for 13 weeks. The fat content of the diet provided 30% of its caloric value. There was a very slight inhibition of growth. The same rats were then placed on a partial starvation diet and kept until they died. The survival time of the animals which had received the propyl gallate was considerably reduced and the reduction in their total body protein was greater than control rats (Bukhan, 1962).

Weight gain depression of more than 10% was observed in male rats receiving diets containing 12 500 or 25 000 and in females receiving 25 000 mg propyl gallate/kg feed. Dirty tails, indicating gastrointestinal disturbance, were noted in both sexes at 25 000 mg propyl gallate/kg feed. In the 25 000 mg/kg feed groups, reddish duodenal mucosa was reported in both sexes, in addition to thickening of the stomach wall with necrosis and ulceration of the mucosal surface of the stomach, and moderate to severe granulomatous inflammatory response in the submucosa and muscular wall of the stomach. No stomach nor duodenal lesions were noted in either sex at 6 000 or 12 500 mg/kg feed (Abdo et al., 1983).

A 4-week oral toxicity study with propyl gallate was performed in rats (6 animals/group/sex) at dose levels of 0, 1 000, 5 000 and 25 000 mg/kg feed. Parameters studied comprised growth, food and water intake, biochemistry, haematology, organ weights and histopathology.

In the high-dose group both females and males gained less weight than those in the control group. Haemoglobin concentration, packed cell volume, red blood cell concentration, mean corpuscular volume and mean corpuscular haemoglobin were lowered in the high-dose group. Consistent with the anaemia, an increased extramedullary haematopoiesis and slightly decreased haemosiderosis were noted in the spleen. In kidneys hyperplastic tubuli in the outer medulla were detected. In the liver of the animals of the 5 000 and 25 000 mg/kg feed groups increases in activity of aminopyrine-N-demethylase and glucuronyl-transferase and glutathione-s-transferase and an increase in cytochrome P-450 content were detected (Strik et al., 1986).

A toxicity study with propyl gallate in SPF-derived Wistar RIVM:Tox rats (10 animals/group/sex) was performed in which they were fed a semisynthetic diet containing 0, 490, 1 910 or 7 455 mg propyl gallate/kg feed for 13 weeks. Body-weight gain was recorded weekly and food-intake twice weekly. Other parameters included haematology, biochemical analyses in urine, serum and liver and complete histopathological examinations.

Adverse effects of propyl gallate observed in the high-dose group were effects on the haematopoietic system reflected in the haematological parameters (Hb, Hct and RBC) and the morphological changes (extramedullary haematopoiesis) in the spleen. The other effects of propyl gallate comprised a decreased incidence of nephrocalcinosis normally seen in female rats on semisynthetic diet, an increased activity of ethoxy-resorufin-o-deethylase (EROD) in the high-dose group and an increased activity of the conjugating enzymes glucuronyl-transferase and glutathion-s-transferase, in the mid and high-dose groups receiving propyl gallate. The effects on the liver enzymes suggest that other biotransformation routes additional to hydrolysis of the gallate seem to be involved. The effects on nephrocalcinosis and on the conjugating enzymes were not considered adverse. Therefore the NOAEL was 1 910 mg propyl gallate/kg feed, equal to 135 mg propyl gallate/kg bw day (Speijers et al., 1993).

2.2.2.2 Guinea-pigs

Propyl gallate fed to guinea-pigs in groups of 20 at a level of 0.02% in the diet for 14 months caused no observed ill effects (Orten et al., 1948).

2.2.2.3 Dogs

A level of 0.01% propyl gallate in the diet was well tolerated by a group of seven dogs over a period of 14 months (Orten et al., 1948).

2.2.2.4 Pigs

Diets containing 0.2% propyl gallate were fed to pigs without observed ill effect; no anaemia was observed (van Esch, 1955).

2.2.3 Long-term toxicity/carcinogenicity studies

2.2.3.1 Mice

Groups of 50 mice (University Animal Breeding Station closed strain colony) equally divided by sex were maintained on diets containing 0, 0.25 or 1.0% n-propyl gallate for a period of 21 months. Water intake, food consumption and growth of test animals were comparable to controls. Treated male mice showed a greater percentage survival than control mice at termination. Haematologic measurements (haemoglobin, packed cell volume, differential white cell count) were similar for test and control animals. At autopsy, a comparison of relative organ/body weight showed a reduction in the relative spleen weight of males on the 1% diet. No compound-related histopathological changes were observed (Dacre, 1974).

Abdo and coworkers maintained groups of B6C3F$_1$ mice of each sex on diets containing 0, 6 000 or 12 000 mg propyl gallate/kg feed for 105 - 107 weeks. Lower body weights compared to controls were observed throughout most of the duration of the study in both sexes and both dose groups. At week 104, mean body weights of the male mice were 6% and 8% lower than controls in the high- and low-dose groups respectively. In the females, both dose groups had about a 12% lower body weight than the controls at week 104. Feed consumption in low and high-dose males was 91 and 100%, respectively, of that of controls while the corresponding figures for females were 109 and 106%, respectively. No other compound-related clinical signs were observed. There was no significant effect of treatment on survival. The survival rate averaged 80% in males and 75% in females. Tumour incidences of the haematopoietic system and liver in the treated groups showed significant increases, as shown in Table 2. Tumours at other sites were not significantly different from controls.

Table 2: Tumour incidence in treated mice, sites with significant increases

		Incidence					
		Males			Females		
	Group - 50 animals/group	C	L	H	C	L	H
Site	Lesion						
Haematopoietic system	Malignant lymphoma:						
	Histiocytic	0	0	4	2	0	0
	Mixed	0	1	3	4	1	3
	Lymphocytic	1	2	0	2	1	3
	Not Otherwise Specified	0	0	1	0	1	0
	All	1	3	8	8	3	6
Liver	Adenoma	3	4	1	0	2	5
	Carcinoma	14	11	9	3	1	0
	Both	17	15	10	3	3	5

C: control group, L: low dose, H: high dose.

There was a significant positive trend in the incidence of histiocytic lymphoma in male mice (8%) relative to controls. The historical control rate for histiocytic lymphomas was 3.3% (21/640). There was a significant positive trend in the incidence of all malignant lymphomas in male mice (1/3/8), and significantly increased incidence by a direct comparison between high-dose and control ($p <$ 0.028). However the high dose incidence was not statistically significant when compared to the historical control rate at the performing laboratory for all malignant lymphomas of 9.4 (60/640). In females the highest incidence was noted in the control group.

The number of male rats in which hepatic adenomas or carcinomas occurred showed a significant negative trend. Hepatocellullar adenomas in female mice occurred with a positive trend ($p <$ 0.022) and the incidence of adenoma in the high-dose females is significantly greater than in controls ($p <$ 0.039). However the incidence in the high-dose group was not different from the historical incidence of this tumour (94/3127; 3%). Further, the combined incidence of hepatocellular adenomas or carcinomas was similar in dosed and control groups (Abdo et al., 1983).

A level of 5% propyl gallate in the diet in a two-year chronic toxicity study in rats and mice gave rise to patchy hyperplasia in the proventiculus. At a level of 1%, no difference was noted between test and control animals (Lehman et al., 1951).

2.2.3.2 **Rats**

Groups of 10 male and 10 female rats were fed for two years on diets containing 0, 0.001, 0.01, 0.12, 1.2 or 2.3% propyl gallate. The groups receiving 1.17 and 2.34% propyl gallate showed stunted growth and evidence of renal damage. In the other groups, there was no detectable effect on haemoglobin, erythrocyte or leucocyte levels in the blood, nor on the histopathological appearance of the organs examined (Orten et al., 1948).

Abdo and coworkers fed groups of 50 F-344 rats of each sex diets containing 0, 6 000 or 12 000 mg propyl gallate for 105 - 107 weeks, as shown in Table 3. Throughout the study, there was a dose-related depression in body weights at both dose levels and in both sexes. Mean feed consumption was 94% and 98% of the controls in the low and high-dose males, while the corresponding values for females were 95 and 115% respectively. In males 78% of the controls, 76% of the low-dose and 88% of the high-dose group lived to the end of the study. In females the corresponding values were 78%, 76% and 84% respectively. No treatment-related clinical signs were observed. There were no significant differences in survival between the groups. For males the survival was 78%, 76% and 88%, for control, low, and high-dose groups, respectively, and the corresponding values for female rats were 78%, 76% and 84%.

As shown in Table 3, in male rats the incidence of three types of neoplasms was increased in the low-dose treatment compared to the control group, namely, phaechromocytoma of the adrenal medulla, islet cell neoplasms of the pancreas and neoplasm of preputial gland origin. Equal or greater increases were not observed in the high-dose male groups. The occurrence of these tumours was not considered to be treatment related. The combined incidence of male rats with follicular cell adenomas or carcinomas of the thyroid was significant (p < 0.05) by the trend test, but the high-dose incidence was not statistically different in any tests in direct comparison with the control. In the high-dose females there were 3 mammary adenomas while there were none in the other two groups. The trend test was statistically significant but the incidence in the high-dose group was not significantly higher than control. There was an increase in the incidence of females with endometrial stromal polyps of the uterus with a marginally significant trend. The high-dose incidence falls within the overall historical control range (4-36%).

Tumours of the brain (an astrocytoma and a glioma) were found in two low-dose female rats. None of the high-dose female rats showed this tumour. The incidence of these tumours in the brain of the low-dose females was not considered to be related to propyl gallate, since none of the high-dose females had this tumour (Abdo et al., 1983).

Table 3: Tumour incidence at sites with significant variation in rats fed propyl gallate

		Incidence					
		males			females		
Group		C	L	H	C	L	H
	Total Animals	50	50	50	50	50	50
Site	Lesion						
Pancreas	Islet cell:						
	Adenomas	0	8	2	0	0	0
	Carcinomas	2	1	2			
	Both	2	9	4			
Thyroid	Follicular cell:						
	carcinoma	0	0	2	0	0	0
	adenoma	0	0	1	0	0	0
Adrenal Gland	Phaeochromocytoma	4	12	8	4	1	3
Preputial gland	Adenoma or carcinoma	1	8	0	2	1	3
Mammary gland	Adenoma	0	0	0	0	0	3
Mammary gland	Fibroadenoma	2	0	1	11	2	5
Uterus	Endometrial stromal polyp				6	8	3
Brain	Astrocytoma	0	0	0	0	0	3
Brain	Glioma	0	0	0	0	1	0
Haematopoietic system	Leukaemia or lymphoma	16	8	6	8	5	6

C: control, L: low dose, H: high dose

2.2.4 Reproduction studies

Propyl gallate was fed to rats at concentrations of 0.035, 0.2 or 0.5% in the diet for two successive generations. Neither effects on reproduction performance nor on indices of reproduction were reported. No abnormalities were observed in the organs or tissues of the rats at autopsy (van Esch, 1955).

2.2.5 Special studies on genotoxicity

Propyl gallate was investigated *in vitro* at concentrations of 0.5, 5.0 and 50 μg/ml employing WI-38 human embryonic lung cells for anaphase abnormalities. It was also investigated *in vivo* by the cytogenetic analysis of metaphase cells from the bone marrow of rats (Sprague-Dawley C-D strain). The dosages employed were 5.0, 50.0 and 500 mg/kg bw. Propyl gallate was mutagenic in neither assay.

The genotoxic effect of propyl gallate was studied using *Salmonella typhimurium* strains TA-1530 and G-46 and *Saccharomyces* D-3 in presence or absence of metabolic activation. A 0.25% concentration was tested. Propyl gallate was non-mutagenic in all tests.

In a host-mediated assay, propyl gallate was tested at dose levels equivalent to 5, 50, 500 and 2 000 mg/kg bw in ICR Swiss mice employing, as indicator organisms, *Salmonella* G-46 and TA-1530 and *Saccharomyces* D-3. Propyl gallate was non-mutagenic under the conditions of the test.

In a dominant lethal test, Sprague-Dawley CD strain male rats were dosed at 5, 50 and 500 mg/kg bw. In an acute study, a single dose was administered with subsequent mating for each of eight weeks. Propyl gallate did not produce any significant dominant lethality. In a subacute study, five daily doses were administered (5 x 5, 5 x 50, 5 x 500 and 5 x 5 000 mg/kg bw). Males were subsequently mated for each of seven weeks. No dominant lethal effects were noted (Weir and Brusick, 1974).

2.2.6   Special studies of the effect of propyl gallate on the forestomach

Propyl gallate incorporated into the diet (0.52 and 2%) and fed to male F-344 rats, for 9 days neither affected the morphological appearance of the forestomach squamous epithelium nor induced changes in the (methyl-$_3$H) thymidine labelling index in the fundic region of the forestomach (Nera et al., 1984).

2.2.7   Special studies on the effect of propyl gallate on toxicity of chemical agents

2.2.7.1 Teratogenesis

Pregnant New Zealand white rabbits (on gestation day 12) were injected s.c. with propyl gallate (362 - 900 mg/kg bw) and hydroxyurea (600 - 750 mg/kg bw). The materials were injected either simultaneously or mixed over periods of 45 minutes. The extent of amelioration of the teratogenic effects of hydroxyurea was dependent on the dose of propyl gallate. There was a significant linear decrease in both resorptions and specific malformations with increasing doses of propyl gallate (de Sesso, 1981).

2.2.7.2 Genotoxicity

Propyl gallate inhibited the genotoxicity of benzo(*a*)pyrene for *Salmonella typhimurium* (Strain TA 98), and moderately increased the mutagenicity of aflatoxin B$_1$ for *Salmonella typhimurium* TA 100 and TA 98 (Calle and Sullivan, 1982).

Four-week old random-bred ICR Swiss male mice were fed diets containing 0, 10, 100, 1 000 or 5 000 mg propyl gallate/kg feed for 3 months.

They were exposed to 50 or 125 rad of whole gamma radiation from a ^{137}Cs source. Thirty hours after irradiation, animals were scored for micronuclei in polychromatic bone marrow erythrocytes. As compared to controls not given propyl gallate, the propyl gallate-treated animals had an increased incidence of micronuclei of about 1.6 - 2-fold. However, there was no dose dependence, 10 mg/kg of propyl gallate was as effective in producing radio-sensitization as 5 000 mg/kg feed (Kamra and Bhaskar, 1978).

Propyl gallate itself was not mutagenic towards *Salmonella typhimurium* strains TA 98 and TA 100 in the presence or absence of arochlor-induced rat liver homogenates. Treatment of bacteria (evidently without activation) with propyl gallate and N-acetoxy-AAF or N-methyl-N-nitrosoguanidine (MNNG) resulted in a reduction of mutation rate compared to that observed in the presence of N-acetoxy-AAF or MNNG alone. By contrast, mixtures of propyl gallates and 4-nitroquinoline oxide (4NQO) or N-hydroxy-AAF showed increased mutagenicity as compared to that observed with the compounds in the absence of the propyl gallate. The proceeding studies were all done using *Salmonella* strain TA 100, except that the propyl gallate-4NQO mixture was tested with both *Salmonella* strains TA 100 and TA 98. Propyl gallate was more efficient at enhancing mutagenesis for *Salmonella* TA 100 than TA 98. A propyl gallate-aflatoxin B_1 mixture was also tested using liver activation from arochlor-treated rats; the addition of propyl gallate substantially reduced the mutagenic activity of aflatoxin B_1 (Rosin and Stich, 1980).

Propyl gallate was not mutagenic to *Salmonella* strains TA-98 or TA-100 with or without activation by liver extracts from arochlor-induced rats. In contrast to the results reported above these workers observed a small increase in aflatoxin B_1 mutagenesis in TA 100 in the presence of propyl gallate (Shelef and Chin, 1980).

2.2.8   **Special studies on the effects of propyl gallate on the carcinogenic activity of carcinogens**

Lung adenomas were induced in strain A mice by chronic treatment with nitrite in drinking water and morpholine in food. Addition of gallic acid to the diet resulted in an 86% inhibition of adenoma induction. Dietary gallic acid reduced or did not affect the induction of adenomas by mononitrosopiperazine or nitrosomorpholine given in drinking water, and failed to induce lung adenomas when given alone (Mirvish et al., 1975).

Weanling (21 day old) female Sprague-Dawley rats were fed with one of three basal diets: polyunsaturated fat (20% corn oil, HPF); saturated fat (18% coconut oil and 2% linoleic acid, HSF); or low fat (2% linoleic acid, LF), with and without 0.3% propyl gallate (PG). At 50 days of age , one half of each group (30 rats/group) received 10 mg of DMBA in 1 ml corn oil p.o. as a tumour inducer. Both the amount of fat and the degree of unsaturation were found to affect the extent of protection against tumorigenesis afforded by PG, with some protection seen in all three dietary groups. Tumour incidences at 32 weeks of age were: HPF,

100%; HSF, 63%; LF, 29%; HPF+PG, 77%; HSF+PG, 11%. Tumours grew most rapidly in the HPF group. Propyl gallate did not alter the function of the hepatic mixed oxidase system by induction or inhibition under the dietary conditions used (King and McCay, 1980).

The induction of epidermal ornithine decarboxylase by 12-0-tetradecanoylphorbyl-13 acetate in mouse epidemis was inhibited by the topical application of propyl gallate. Its potency was approximately 10% of that of BHA (Kozumbo, Seed and Kensler, 1983).

Propyl gallate did not modify tumour development of 1,2-dimethylhydrazine-initiated colon carcinogenesis in F344 rats (Shirai *et al.*, 1985).

The promoting activity of 3 antioxidants, α-tocopherol, propyl gallate and tertiary butylhydroquinone (TBHQ) in urinary bladder carcinogenesis initiated by N-butyl-N-(4-hydroxybutyl)nitrosamine (BBN) in male Fischer 344 rats was examined. Rats, 6 weeks old, were treated with 0.05% BBN in the drinking water for 4 weeks and then administered 1.50, 0.75 or 0.38% α-tocopherol, 1.0% propyl gallate or 2.0% TBHQ in the diet for 32 weeks. The urinary bladder of each animal was examined histologically after the 36-week experimental period. The incidence of papillary or nodular hyperplasia (PN hyperplasia) of the urinary bladder was significantly higher in the rats treated with BBN followed by 2.0% TBHQ than in controls initiated with 0.05% BBN followed by control diet. This result indicates that TBHQ has weak promoting activity in urinary bladder carcinogenesis. α-tocopherol and propyl gallate did not demonstrate a promoting effect for urinary bladder lesions (Tamano et al., 1987).

2.2.9   **Special studies on the interactions of propyl gallate**

Propyl gallate, gallic acid and nordihydroguaiaretic acid were all potent inhibitors of the *in vitro* mouse spleen cell antibody response as assayed by anti-sheep erythrocyte plaque-forming cell response. These compounds also suppressed clone formation *in vitro* by human WISH or mouse L-cells (Blalock *et al.*, 1981).

Gallic acid was reported to suppress the *in vitro* thymus-dependent plaque forming response of mouse C57B1/6 spleen cells to sheep red blood cells. The compound also suppressed mitogen-induced DNA synthesis of 6 lymphocytes but had no effect on ß-lymphocyte function (Archer *et al.*, 1977).

2.2.10   **Special studies on sensitization**

Gallates have been shown to cause contact dermatitis in bakers and other workers handling gallates. Patch tests with lauryl gallate at 0.2% showed a weak positive response in one sensitized individual. Other individuals have suffered recurring episodes of dermatitis, presumably caused by gallates in food products (Brun, 1970).

2.2.11   Other special studies

Partial protection against liver damage by single oral doses of 2.5 or 0.25 ml/kg of chloroform was provided by i.p. injection of 150 mg/kg bw of propyl gallate (Torrielli and Ugazio, 1975).

2.3   Observations in humans

No information available.

OCTYL GALLATE

2.   BIOLOGICAL DATA

2.1   Biochemical aspects

See propyl gallate.

2.2   Toxicological studies

2.2.1   Acute toxicity studies

The results of acute toxicity studies with octyl gallate are summarized in Table 4.

Table 4.   Acute toxicity studies - octyl gallate

Animal	Sex	Route	LD_{50} mg/kg bw	Reference
Rat	?	oral	4 700	van Sluis, 1951
Rat	?	i.p.	60-80	van Esch, 1955
Rat	M	oral	2 710	Brun, 1970
Rat	F	oral	1 960	Brun, 1970
Rat	M	oral	2 710	Brun, 1970
Rat	F	oral	2 330	Brun, 1970

2.2.2   Short-term toxicity studies

2.2.2.1 Rats

Groups each of 20 rats (equally divided by sex) were maintained on diets containing 0, 1 000, 2 500 or 5 000 ppm (0%, 0.1%, 0.25% and 0.5%) octyl gallate for 13 weeks. All groups showed normal weight gains and food consumption. Haematology and blood chemistry and urinalyses revealed normal values. A complete gross and histopathologic examination showed no compound-related effects (Blackmore and Voelker, 1969a).

2.2.2.2 Dogs

Groups of eight dogs, each equally divided by sex, were fed diets containing 0, 0.1, or 0.3% n-octyl gallate for 90 days, or 1.0% n-octyl gallate for four weeks; the 1.0% level was then reduced to 0.65% for the rest of the study. All groups showed normal weight gain and food consumption, except the 1.0% group. Haematology and blood chemistry and urinalyses were normal. A complete gross and histopathologic examination showed no compound-related effects (Lindberg *et al.*, 1970).

In another study groups of eight dogs, each equally divided by sex, were maintained on diets containing 0, 0.1, 0.25 or 0.5% octyl gallate for 13 weeks. All animals showed normal food consumption and weight gain. Haematology and urinanalyses were similar for test and control animals. ASAT activity was slightly elevated in the 0.5% group. Gross and histopathologic examination of tissues and organs showed no compound-related effects (Blackmore and Voelker, 1969b).

2.2.2.3 Pigs

Diets containing 0.2% octyl gallate were fed to pigs without demonstrable ill effect; no anaemia was observed (van Esch and van Genderen, 1955).

2.2.3 Long-term toxicity/carcinogenicity studies

No information available.

2.2.4 Reproduction studies

2.2.4.1 Rats

Young rats in groups of 12 males and 12 females were fed diets containing 7% fat and 0.2% octyl gallate. There was no significant difference between test and control animals over three generations (van Sluis, 1951).

Octyl gallate was fed to rats at concentrations of 0.035, 0.2 and 0.5% in the diet for two successive generations. No effects on reproductive performance or other indices of reproduction were reported. A slight hypochromic anaemia was noticed in the 0.2% group. No abnormalities were observed in organs or tissues of the rats at autopsy (van Esch, 1955).

Groups, each of 10 male and 20 female rats, were maintained on diets containing 0, 1 000 or 5 000 mg/kg feed octyl gallate. The animals were bred twice for the first generation, and three times for the second generation. At the time of weaning of the F_{1B} litters in the 5 000 mg/kg feed group, the level was reduced to 2 500 mg/kg feed for the second generation. In the second generation, approximately 24 hours after birth, selected litters were redistributed to female parents so that control females nursed pups from test animals, and test animals nursed pups from control and other test groups. Half of the P_2 females bred for the third time (F_{2c}) were examined by Caesarean section at time of delivery and the number of implantation sites, corpora lutea and fetuses determined. One half of the pups from each litter were examined for skeletal abnormalities, and the other half for visceral abnormalities. The other parameters measured in this study were appearance, behaviour, growth of pups during the nursing and weaning process, fertility index, gestation index, live birth index, and weaning survival index. Autopsies were carried out on F_{2b} weanling pups, (control pups suckled by control dams, experimental group pups suckled by respective group dams), as well as microscopic examination of pituitary, thyroid, liver, spleen, kidneys, adrenals, stomach, pancreas, small intestine, large intestine and any unusual lesions of five males and five females from high-dose and control group. Weanling survival index and body weight at weaning were considerably reduced in the 5 000 mg/kg feed group of the F_{1a} and F_{1b} generation. Reduction of these indices was still apparent in the F_{2a} and F_{2b} generations, when the dietary level was reduced to 2 500 mg/kg feed. At 1 000 mg/kg feed, the indices were similar to control.

Redistribution of F_{2b} pups to females of control groups resulted in similar growth of all pups to weaning. Allowing pups from high level group to be nursed by control dams resulted in a marked increase in survival indices, whereas when control pups were nursed by high level dams, there was a marked decrease in survival indices. Examination of P_2 parents following the third breeding indicated a dose-dependent reduction in implantation sites, as well as a reduction in number of corpora lutea. The fertility index of high level P_2 females was depressed at the F_{2c} stage. Skeletal evaluation of F_{2c} litters showed incomplete skull ossification in some pups in the test groups, but this was not considered remarkable for the size of the fetuses. Necropsy of the pups indicated a higher incidence of gross kidney alterations than that observed in controls. No compound-related histopathological effects were reported. The NOEL was 1 000 mg/kg feed/day, equal to 17.5 mg/kg bw/day (Olson and Voelker, 1970).

n-Octyl gallate was fed in the diet to groups of eight male and 16 female rats for two successive generations at levels of 0, 0.1 or 0.3% (and 0.6% for one generation). Rats were mated to produce two litters per generation with the next generation selected from weanlings of the second litter. A dietary level of 0.1% had no effect on reproduction performance or the offspring. At 0.3 and 0.6% dietary octyl gallate, there was no significant effect on the rat fetuses during pregnancy, but a marked effect was observed on survival through weaning. In the case of the 0.6% group, return to normal diet for six weeks, prior to a third breeding, did not result in increased survival of offspring through weaning (Plank et al., 1971).

2.2.5   Special studies on sensitization

Repeated insult patch tests with 0.1% n-octyl gallate solution showed reaction in 13/445, or 2.9%, of tested individuals.   Oral mucosa irritation/ sensitization tests conducted with beer containing 20 mg/kg n-octyl gallate showed that the incidence and severity of erythema were greater with beer containing n-octyl gallate than with untreated beer.   Oedema was also greater with treated beer (Palazzolo & Fancher, 1971a,b,c).

DODECYL GALLATE

2.   BIOLOGICAL DATA

2.1   Biochemical aspects

See propyl gallate

2.2   Toxicological studies

2.2.1   Acute toxicity studies

The results of acute toxicity studies with dodecyl gallate are summarized in Table 5.

Table 5.   Acute toxicity studies - dodecyl gallate

Animal	Sex	Route	LD_{50} mg/kg bw	Reference
Rat	?	oral	6 500	van Sluis, 1951
Rat	?	i.p.	100-120	van Esch, 1955

2.2.2   Short-term toxicity studies

2.2.2.1   Rats

Weanling rats were given diets containing 2.5 or 5% dodecyl gallate.   All animals fed the smaller quantity were dead within 10 days, and all animals fed the larger quantity died within seven days (Allen & De Eds, 1951).

Male Wistar rats were administered dodecyl gallate daily by gavage, at doses equivalent to 10, 50 or 250 mg/kg bw/dy for 150 days.   In the 250 mg/kg bw/dy group, numerous deaths occurred.   Both the 250 and 50 mg/kg bw/dy dose caused changes in serum lipids and enzymes, reduction in weight of the spleen and pathological changes in the liver, kidney, and spleen.   The 10 mg/kg bw/dy level was considered to be the NOEL (Mikhailova et al., 1985).

Rats fed for 70 days on a diet containing 7% fat and 0.2% dodecyl gallate showed no effect on body weight (Tollenaar, 1957).

2.2.2.2 Pigs

Diets containing 0.2% of dodecyl gallate were fed to pigs without demonstrable ill effect; no anaemia was observed (van Esch and van Genderen, 1954).

2.2.3   Long-term toxicity/carcinogenicity studies

No information available.

2.2.4   Reproduction studies

2.2.4.1 Rats

Young rats in groups of 12 males and 12 females were fed diets containing 7% fat and 0.2% dodecyl gallate. There was no significant difference between test and control animals over three generations (van Sluis, 1951).

Dodecyl gallate was fed to rats at concentrations of 0.035, 0.2 or 0.5% in the diet, for two successive generations. There was significant retardation of growth in the 0.5% group. Some litters in this group were lost in the second generation because they were not fed sufficiently by the mothers. A slight hypochromic anaemia was observed in the 0.2% group. No abnormalities were observed in the organs or tissues at autopsy (van Esch, 1955).

2.2.5   Special studies on sensitization

See propyl gallate.

3.   COMMENTS

Although there are similarities in the metabolism of the different gallates as evidenced by earlier limited data and a newly available *in vitro* metabolism study, the Committee concluded that there was not enough evidence to allocate a group ADI for the gallates when *in vivo* pharmacokinetic and metabolic studies were not available. In addition, a 150-day gavage study with dodecyl gallate revealed a NOEL that was 10-fold lower than the dietary NOEL for propyl gallate.

4.   EVALUATION

In the 90-day toxicity study in rats at a high-dose level (7 450 mg/kg feed), changes in haematological parameters (decreased haemoglobin, haematocrit and red blood cell count), morphological changes (increased extra medullary haematopoeisis) in the spleen, and increased activity of hepatic ethoxy-resorufin-O-deethylase were observed. The Committee allocated an ADI of 0-1.4 mg propyl gallate/kg bw, which was based on the NOEL in this study of 1 910 mg propyl gallate/kg feed, equal to 135 mg propyl gallate/kg bw/day to which a 100-fold safety factor was applied.

The Committee concluded that it was unlikely that either octyl or dodecyl gallate is carcinogenic or genotoxic. Therefore, the Committee allocated temporary ADIs to both gallates based on the NOELs observed in limited toxicological studies.

With octyl gallate, a slight hypochromic anaemia was observed at 100 mg/kg bw/day in a study in rats in which the substance was administered for two generations. A temporary ADI of 0-0.1 mg octyl gallate/kg bw was allocated based on a NOEL of 17.5 mg/kg bw/day in a reproduction study with rats, to which a safety factor of 200 was applied.

With dodecyl gallate, a reduction of spleen weight and pathological changes in the liver, kidney and spleen were observed in a 150-day gavage study with rats, with a NOEL of 10 mg/kg bw/day. A temporary ADI of 0-0.05 mg/kg bw was allocated based on this study, using a 200-fold safety factor.

The Committee concluded that additional information on the pharmacokinetic and metabolic behaviour of the different gallates may help to explain the differences in toxicological potency of the different gallates and required data from such studies by 1996. If these studies do not satisfactorily resolve the issue with respect to similarity of octyl and dodecyl gallate to propyl gallate, further toxicological studies (including long-term toxicity/carcinogenicity studies and genotoxicity studies) on octyl and dodecyl gallate might be required.

5.   REFERENCES

ABDO, K.M., HUFF, J.E., HASEMAN, J.K., DIETER, M.P., BOORMAN, G.A., HILDEBRANDT, P., PREJEAN, J.D. & FARNELL, D.R. (1983), Carcinogenesis bioassay of propyl gallate in F-344 rats and B6C3F₁ mice, *J. Am. College Toxicol.*, **3(6)**, 425-33

ALLEN, C.S. & de EDS, F.D. (1951), The chronic toxicity of lauryl gallate, *J. Amer. Oil Chem. Soc.*, **28**, 304

ARCHER, D., BUKOVIC-WESS, J. & SMITH, B. (1977), Suppression of macrophage-dependent T-lymphocyte function by gallic acid, a food additive, *Proc. Soc. Exp. Bio. Med.*, **156**, 465-9

de BIE, A.Th.H.J, and van OMMEN, B., (1992) Study on the *in vitro* biotransformation of propyl, octyl, and dodecyl gallate. TNO-report V92.101, TNO Toxicology and Nutrition Institute, Zeist, The Netherlands

BLACKMORE, R.H. & VOELKER, R.W. (1969a), 13-week dietary administration, Rats, Octyl gallate, Final report (Project No. 458-115), unpublished report from Hazleton Labs., Inc., Falls Church, VA, USA, F. & M. Schaefer Brewing Co., Brooklyn, N.Y., USA

BLACKMORE, R.H. & VOELKER, R.W. (1969b), 13-week dietary feedings, Dogs, Octyl gallate, Final report (Project No. 458-117), Unpublished report from Hazleton Labs., Inc., Falls Church, Va., F. & M. Schaefer Brewing Co., Brooklyn, N.Y., USA

BLALOCK, J.E., ARCHER, D.L., & JOHNSON, H.M (1981) Anticellular and immunosuppressive activities of foodborne phenolic compounds (41185), *Proc. Soc. Exp. Bio. Med.*, **167**, 391-3

BOOTH, A.N., MASRI, M.S., ROBBINS, D.J., EMERSON, O.H., JONES, F.T. & de EDS, F. (1959), The metabolic fate of gallic acid and related compounds, *J. Biol. Chem.*, **234**, 3014-6

BRUN, R. (1970), Contact eczema due to an antioxidant of margarine (gallate) and change of occupation, *Dermatologica*, **140**, 390-394

BUKHAN, N.D. (1962), The effect of propyl gallate antioxidant on the nutritional value of fats (In Russian), *Vopr. Pitan.*, **21**, 68

CALLE, L.M. & SULLIVAN, P.D. (1982), Screening of antioxidants and other compounds for antimutagenic properties towards benzo[a]pyrene-induced mutagenicity in strain TA98 of *Salmonella typhimurium*, *Mutat. Res.*, **101**, 99-114

CARPENTER, M. (1981), Antioxidant effects on the prostaglandin endoperoxide synthetase product profile, *Fed. Proc.*, **40**, 189-194

DACRE, J.C. (1960), Metabolic pathways of phenolic antioxidants, *J. N.A. Inst. Chem.*, **24**, 161-171

DACRE, J.C. (1974), Long-term toxicity study of n-propyl gallate in mice, *Fd. Cosmet. Toxicol.*, **12**, 125-9

van ESCH, G.J. (1955), The toxicity of the antioxidants propyl-, octyl- and dodecyl gallate, *Voeding*, **16**, 683-686

van ESCH, G.J. & van GENDEREN, H. (1954), Netherlands Institute of Public Health, Report No. 481

van ESCH, G.J. & van GENDEREN, H. (1954), Netherlands Institute of Public Health, Report No. 2, 49-52

JOHNSON, A.R. & HEWGILL, F.R. (1961), The effect of the antioxidants, butylated hydroxy anisole, butylated hydroxytoluene and propyl gallate on growth, liver and serum lipids and serum sodium levels of the rat, *Aust. J. Exp. Biol. Med. Sci.*, **39**, 353-360

KAMRA, O. & BHASKAR, G. (1978), Radiosensitization of mouse bone-marrow cells by a commonly used food additive, propyl gallate, *Mutation Res.*, **53**, 207

KING, M., MCCAY, P. (1980), DMBA-induced mammary tumour incidence: Effect of propyl gallate supplementation in purified diets containing different types and amounts of fat, *Proc. Amer. Soc. Cancer Res.*, **21**, 113

KING, M., MCCAY, P. (1981), Studies on liver microsomes of female rats fed purified diets varying in fat content with and without propyl gallate, *Fd. Cosmet. Toxicol.*, **19**, 13-17

KOZUMBO, W.J., SEED, J.L. & KENSLER, T.W. (1983), Inhibition by 2(3)-tert-butyl-4-hydroxyanisole and other antioxidants of epidermal ornithine decarboxylase activity induced by 12-0-tetradecanoylphorbolacetate, *Cancer Res.*, **43**, 2555-2559

LEHMAN, A.J., FITZHUGH, O.G., NELSON, A.A. & WOODARD, G. (1951), The pharmacological evaluation of antioxidants, *Advanc. Food Res.*, **3**, 197-208

LINDBERG, D.C., KEPLINGER, M.L. & FANCHER, O.E. (1970) Ninety-day subacute oral toxicity study with Cold-Pro, GA-8 in Beagle dogs (IBT No. C8472), Unpublished report from Industrial Bio-Test Labs., Inc., Northbrook, Ill., USA, submitted to the World Health Organization by Nutrico, Inc., Milwaukee, Wisconsin, USA

MIKHAILOVA, Z. *et al.* (1985) Toxicological studies of the long term effects of the antioxidant dodecyl gallate on albino rats, *Vopr. Pitan.*, No. 2, 49-52

MIRVISH, S., CARDESS, A., WALLCAVE, L. & SHUBIK, P. (1975), Induction of lung adenomas by amines or ureas plus nitrite and by n-nitroso compounds: Effect of ascorbate, gallic acid, thiocyanate and caffeine, *J. Nat. Cancer Inst.*, **55(3)**, 633-636

NERA, E.A., LOK, E., IVERSON, F., ORMSBY, E., KARPINSKY, K.F. & CLAYSON, D.B. (1984), Short-term pathological and proliferative effects of BHA and other phenolic antioxidants in the forestomach of Fischer 344 rats, *Toxicol.*, **32**, 197-205

OLSON, W.A. & VOELKER, R.W. (1970) Modified two-generation reproduction study - Rats, Octyl Gallate, Final report (Project 458-116), Unpublished report from Hazleton Labs., Inc., Falls Church, Va., USA, submitted to the World Health Organization by F. & M. Schaefer Brewing Co., Brooklyn, N.Y., USA

ORTEN, J.M., KUYPER, A.C. & SMITH, A.H. (1948), Studies on the toxicity of propyl gallate, *Food Techn.*, **2**, 308-316

PALAZZOLO, R.J. & FANCHER, O.E. (1971a) Human repeated insult patch test with n-octyl gallate (IBT No. F9309), Unpublished report from Industrial Bio-Test Labs., Inc., Northbrook, Ill., USA, submitted to the World Health Organization by Nutrico, Inc., Milwaukee, Wisconsin, USA

PALAZZOLO, R.J. & FANCHER, O.E. (1971c) Oral mucosa irritation/sensitization test with treated beer (IBT No. F9655), Unpublished report from Industrial Bio-Test Labs., Inc., Northbrook, Ill., USA, submitted to the World Health Organization by Nutrico, Inc., Milwaukee, Wisconsin, USA

PALAZZOLO, R.J. & FANCHER, O.E. (1971b) Oral mucosa irritation/sensitization test with treated beer (IBT No. F9310), Unpublished report from Industrial Bio-Test Labs., Inc., Northbrook, Ill., USA, submitted to the World Health Organization by Nutrico, Inc., Milwaukee, Wisconsin, USA

PLANK, J.B., WRIGHT, P.L., KEPLINGER, M.L. & FANCHER, O.E. (1971) Three generation reproduction study with Cold-Pro, GA-8 in albino rats (IBT No. P84), Unpublished report from Industrial Bio-Test Labs., Inc., Northbrook, Ill., USA, submitted to the World Health Organization by Nutrico, Inc., Milwaukee, Wisconsin, USA

RAHIMTULA, A., ZACHARIAH, P. & O'BRIEN, P. (1979), Differential effects of antioxidants, steroids and other compounds on Benzo(A)Pyrene 3-hydroxylase activity in various tissues of rats, *Br. J. Cancer*, **40**, 105-112

ROSIN, M. & STICH, H. (1980), Enhancing and inhibiting effects of propyl gallate on carcinogen-induced mutagenesis, *J. Environmental Path. Toxicol.*, **4**, 159-167

de SESSO, J.M. (1981), Amelioration of teratogenesis, I. Modification of hydroxyurea-induced teratogenesis by the antioxidant propyl gallate, *Teratol.*, **24**, 19-35

SHELEF, L. & CHIN, B. (1980), Effect of phenolic anti-oxidants on the mutagenicity of aflatoxin B_1, *Applied Environ. Microbiol.*, **40**, 1039-1043

SHIRAI, T., IKAWA, E., HIROSE, M., *et al* (1985). Modification by five antioxidants of 1,2-dimethylhydrazine-initiated colon carcinogenesis in F344 rats, *Carcinogenesis* **6:4**, 637-9.

van SLUIS, K.J.H (1951), The higher alkyl gallates as antioxidants, *Food Manuf.*, **26**, 99-101

SPEIJERS, G.J.A, JANSSEN, G.B., WALLBRINK-de DRIEU, Y., van LEEUWEN, F.X.R, van LOENEN, H.A., KRAJNC-FRANKEN, M.A.M., VAESSEN, H.A.M.G & WESTER, P.W (1993) Subchronic toxicity of propyl-gallate, RIVM Report No. 618311002 (Draft) Rijksinstituut voor Volksgezondheid en Milieuhygiëne, Bilthoven, The Netherlands

STRIK, J.J.T.W.A. DANSE, L.H.J.C, HELLEMAN, P.W., van LEEUWEN, F.X.R, SPEIJERS, G.J.A, & VAESSEN, H.A.M.G (1986). Subacute toxicity of propyl gallate Report No. 618311 001 Rijksinstituut voor Volksgezondheid en Milieuhygiëne, Bilthoven, The Netherlands

TAMANO, S., FUKUSHIMA, S., SHIRAI, T., HIROSE, M & ITO, N. (1987). Modification by O-tocopherol, propyl gallate and tertiary butylhydroquinone of urinary bladder carcinogenesis in Fischer 344 rats pretreated with N-butyl-N-(4-hydroxybutyl)nitrosamine. *Cancer Letters*, **35**, 39 - 46.

TOLLENAAR, F.D. (1957) (Pub. 1963) Prevention of rancidity in edible oils and fats with special reference to the use of antioxidants, 9th Proc. Pacific Sci. Congr., Bangkok, Thailand, **5**, 92-103

TORRIELLI, M. & UGAZIO, G. (1975), Biochemical aspects of the protective action of propyl gallate on liver injury in rats poisoned with carbon tetrachloride, *Toxicol. Appl. Pharmacol.*, **34**, 151-169

WEIR, R.J. & BRUSICK, D. (1974), Mutagenic evaluation of Compound FDA 71-39, Propyl Gallate, Unpublished report from Litton Bionetics, Inc., Kensington, MD, USA, submitted to the World Health Organization by the US Food and Drug Administration

YANG, C. & STRICKHART, F. (1974), Inhibition of hepatic mixed function oxidase activity by propyl gallate, *Biochem. Pharmacol.*, **23**, 3129-35.

FLAVOURING SUBSTANCES

BENZYL ACETATE

First draft prepared by
Dr P. Olsen
Institute of Toxicology, National Food Agency of Denmark
Ministry of Health, Søborg, Denmark

1.   EXPLANATION

This compound was previously evaluated at the eleventh, twenty-seventh, twenty-ninth, thirty-first, and thirty-fifth meetings (Annex 1, references 14, 62, 70, 77, and 88). During some of these meetings the Committee also considered related substances, including benzyl alcohol, benzaldehyde, benzoic acid, and the benzoate salts.

Benzyl acetate was first evaluated by the Committee at its eleventh meeting (Annex 1, reference 14), when an ADI of 0-5 mg per kg of body weight was allocated in terms of benzoic acid, representing total benzoate from all food additive sources. At the twenty-seventh meeting (Annex 1, reference 62) the ADI for benzyl acetate was retained but made temporary because of concern raised by preliminary findings from screening tests for carcinogenicity. At its twenty-ninth meeting (Annex 1, reference 70) the Committee considered new data on the metabolism of benzyl acetate and on the occurrence of tumours in rats and mice given benzyl acetate by gavage. The Committee extended the temporary ADI of 0-5 mg per kg of body weight pending results from carcinogenicity studies with benzyl alcohol. The temporary ADI was again extended at the thirty-first meeting of the Committee (Annex 1, reference 77), as the expected data were not available. At its thirty-fifth meeting (Annex 1, reference 89) the Committee reviewed a lifetime gavage studies with benzyl alcohol and found no evidence of a tumorigenic effect. The Committee extended the temporary ADI of 0-5 mg per kg of body weight for benzyl acetate until 1993, pending the evaluation of results from ongoing long-term studies with benzyl acetate incorporated into the diet of mice and rats and requested data from and *in vivo* test for chromosomal damage to bone marrow.

Since the previous evaluation, additional toxicological data have become available and are summarized and discussed in the following monograph addendum.

2. BIOLOGICAL DATA

2.1 Toxicological studies

2.2.2 Short-term toxicity studies

2.2.2.1 Mice

Groups of 10 male and 10 female mice (B6C3F$_1$, average age at exposure 42 days; 13 days quarantine prior to test) received 0, 3 130, 6 250, 12 500, 25 000, or 50 000 mg/kg feed (equivalent to 0, 450, 900, 1 800, 3 600, or 7 200 mg/kg bw/day) of benzyl acetate (benzyl acetate, properties consistent with structure and literature references, purity: 99%; stability monitored periodically, no degradation of bulk chemical observed) in their diet for a period of 13 weeks. Feed [feed prepared weekly and stored in dark; dose formulation analyzed 4 times during study for benzyl acetate concentrations, stability, and homogeneity; contained low and biologically insignificant levels of aflatoxins, pesticides and heavy metals] and water were provided *ad libitum*. The feed consumption was recorded daily and the animals were weighed weekly. Haematology, clinical chemistry (cholesterol and triglycerides), and pancreatic enzymes (amylase, lipase, carboxypeptidase, chymotrypsin, ribonuclease), were performed at termination of the study. Histopathology examinations were performed on all control, on 25 000 mg/kg feed female, and all 50 000 mg/kg feed animals.

Statistically significant ($p < 0.01$) dose-related decreases in final body weights were observed in all treated animals compared to controls. The mean feed consumption of all exposed mice was lower, but not statistically significantly lower, than that of the control groups. Tremor was observed in female mice at a dose level of 12 500 mg/kg feed and above. At the dose level of 50 000 mg/kg feed one male died and one female mice was killed in extremis. The absolute and relative organ weights in treated animals were influenced by the lowered terminal body weight and all significant differences between treated and control groups were attributed to treatment. No dose-related effects in haematology, clinical chemistry, or pancreatic enzyme parameters were observed in treated animals.

Histopathological examination revealed hippocampal necrosis, cerebellar haemorrhage of the brain and hepatocellular necrosis in 1 male mouse receiving 50 000 mg/kg feed after 11 weeks of treatment. At termination three female mice receiving 50 000 mg/kg feed showed hippocampal necrosis and depletion of the pyramidal layer cells in the brain (NTP, 1992).

2.2.2.2 Rats

Groups of 10 male and 10 female rats (F344, average age at exposure 43 days; 13 days quarantine prior to test) received 0, 3 130, 6 250, 12 500, 25 000, or 50 000 mg/kg feed (equivalent to 0, 210, 420, 840, 1 680, or 3 360 mg/kg bw/day) of benzyl acetate (benzyl acetate, properties consistent with structure and literature references, purity: 99%; stability monitored periodically, and no

degradation of bulk chemical observed) in their diet for a period of 13 weeks.
Feed: [feed prepared weekly and stored in dark; analyzed during study for benzyl
acetate concentrations, stability, and homogeneity; contained low and biologically
insignificant levels of aflatoxins, pesticides and heavy metals] and water provided
ad libitum. The feed consumption was recorded daily and the animals were
weighed weekly. After 11 weeks of treatment haematological and clinical chemical
(cholesterol and triglycerides) parameters were determined. Pancreatic enzymes
(amylase, lipase, carboxypetidase, chymotrypsin, and ribonuclease) were determined
in all treated male and female rats except the 50 000 mg/kg feed group. At
termination liver peroxisomes morphometry were performed on female rats given
0, 25 000, or 50 000 mg/kg feed benzyl acetate. Histopathology examinations were
performed on all control, 25 000 mg/kg feed and 50 000 mg/kg feed rats.

Nine male and female rats died or were killed moribund in the 50 000
mg/kg feed group between weeks 2 and 8 of the study. Final mean body weights
of treated male and female rats were similar to or slightly lower than those of the
controls. Male rats given 25 000 mg/kg feed showed 10% decreased (p < 0.01)
terminal mean body weight. At the 50 000 mg/kg feed level the body weight of the
one surviving male and female rats was less than half of the controls. The average
feed consumption was reduced in 25 000 mg/kg feed male rats and 50 000 mg/kg
feed male and female rats. Tremor, ataxia, and urine stains were observed in the
50 000 mg/kg feed group. Serum cholesterol was significantly decreased in females
in the 12 500 mg/kg feed (p < 0.01), 25 000 mg/kg feed (p < 0.001), and 50 000
mg/kg feed (only one female rat alive after 11 weeks) groups. No other dose-
related effects were seen of the haematological, clinical chemical, or pancreatic
enzyme parameters in treated rats. The volume, surface, and numerical density of
hepatic peroxisomes in female rats (25 000 mg/kg feed) were significantly
(p < 0.001) increased. No differences in organ weights attributive to treatment were
observed. Histopathological examination of male and female rats receiving 50 000
mg/kg feed benzyl acetate revealed degeneration and necrosis of neurons and glia
cells in cerebellum and hippocampus of the brain, renal tubular degeneration, and
degeneration and sarcolemma nuclear hyperplasia in skeletal thigh muscles.
Testicular tubular atrophy was seen in a few male rats receiving 12 500 mg/kg feed
benzyl acetate or more (NTP, 1992).

2.2.3   Long-term toxicity/carcinogenicity studies

2.2.3.1   Mice

Groups of 60 male and 60 female mice (B6C3F₁, average age at initial
exposure 40 days; 11 days quarantine prior to test) received 0, 330, 1 000, or 3 000
mg/kg feed (equal to 0, 37, 112, or 346 mg/kg bw/day for males, equal to 0, 42,
132, or 382 mg/kg bw/day for females) of benzyl acetate (benzyl acetate, properties
consistent with structure and literature references, purity: 98-9%; stability monitored
periodically, and no degradation of bulk chemical observed) in their diet for a
period of 103 weeks. Interim sacrifice was carried out on 10 mice of each sex from
all groups after 15 months of exposure. Feed [feed prepared weekly and stored in

dark; analyzed during study for benzyl acetate concentrations, stability, and homogeneity; contained low and biologically insignificant levels of aflatoxins, pesticides and heavy metals] and water provided *ad libitum*. Feed consumption was measured daily per cage for 5 days once every 4 weeks. The animals were weighed weekly during the first 13 weeks of the study and every 4 weeks thereafter. Haematology and clinical chemistry (cholesterol triglycerides, alkaline phosphatase, creatinine kinase, and sorbitol dehydrogenase) were carried out on interim sacrifice mice after 15 months. Necropsy and a thorough histopathological examination were performed on all animals. Organ weights included brain, right kidney, and liver.

The survival rate of treated male mice was similar to that of the control group, while survival of treated female mice increased with dose, statistically significantly (p < 0.01) in the 3 000 mg/kg feed group. Almost all deaths occurred during the last 9 months of the study. The average feed consumption of treated mice was similar to that of the control groups. All treated mice, except 330 mg/kg feed females, showed decreased mean body weights compared to those of controls, weights were 13% and 9% lower at termination in males and females, respectively (statistics not reported). A slight decrease (inconsistent dose-related significance at the p < 0.05 level) in cholesterol, triglyceride and (females only) alkaline phosphatase levels was observed for treated mice compared to the control groups. No dose-related effects were seen in haematology. Statistically significant (p < 0.05 or lower) dose-related increased incidences and severities of non-neoplastic lesions of the nasal mucosa and glands occurred in all treated male and female mice compared to the control groups. The nasal lesions consisted of atrophy and degeneration, primarily of the olfactory epithelium, cystic hyperplasia of the nasal submucosal glands, and exudate and pigmentation of the nasal mucosal epithelium. The lesions were most pronounced in male mice and were already present in male and female mice at interim sacrifice after 15 months of exposure. No neoplasms nor pre-neoplastic dose-related lesions occurred in the nose. A dose-related negative trend in the incidence of hepatocellular carcinoma and hepatocellular adenoma, statistically significant (p < 0.01) for hepatocellular adenoma in the 3 000 mg/kg feed group, occurred in male mice. This effect was not seen in female mice (NTP, 1992).

2.2.3.2 Rats

Groups of 60 male and 60 female rats (F344; average age at initial exposure 41 days; 12 days quarantine prior to test) received 0, 3 000, 6 000, or 12 000 mg/kg feed (equal to 0, 113, 225, and 550 mg/kg bw/day) of benzyl acetate (benzyl acetate, properties consistent with structure and literature references, purity: 98-9%; stability monitored periodically, no degradation of bulk chemical was observed) in their diet for a period of 103 weeks. Interim sacrifice was carried out on 10 rats of each sex from all groups after 15 months of exposure. Feed [feed prepared weekly and stored in dark; analyzed during study for benzyl acetate concentrations, stability, and homogeneity; contained low and biologically insignificant levels of aflatoxins, pesticides and heavy metals] and water provided *ad libitum*. The feed consumption was measured daily per cage for 5 days once every 4 weeks. The animals were weighed weekly during the first 13 weeks of the study and every 4 weeks thereafter. Haematology, clinical chemistry (cholesterol triglycerides, alkaline phosphatase, creatinine kinase, and sorbitol dehydrogenase) and (in males only) analysis of pancreatic enzymes (amylase, lipase, carboxypetidase) were carried out on interim-sacrificed rats after 15 months. Necropsy and a thorough histopathological examination were performed on all animals. Organ weights included brain, right kidney, and liver.

No significant differences in the survival rate, average feed consumption, clinical findings, clinical chemistry, haematology, pancreatic enzyme assays, or incidences of neoplasms and non-neoplastic lesions were observed in treated male and female rats compared to those of the controls. The mean body weights of the 12 000 mg/kg feed males and treated females were approximately 5% lower than those of the control groups throughout most of the study (NTP, 1992).

2.2.8   **Special studies on genotoxicity**

Genotoxicity studies with benzyl acetate are summarized in Table 1.

3.   **COMMENTS**

At its present meeting, the Committee reviewed data from short-term and long-term studies in rats and mice in which benzyl acetate had been incorporated into the diet. These studies did not show any increase in the incidence of either hepatocellular or forestomach tumours in mice or of pancreatic tumours in rats, which had been observed previously in studies with benzyl acetate administered by gavage in corn oil.

The Committee noted a documented association between the use of corn oil as a vehicle control and an increased incidence of pancreatic acinar cell hyperplasia and adenomas in male rats. In addition, altered incidence of other site-specific neoplasms has been observed after administration of corn oil by gavage (see section 2.2.2).

Considering the use of both modes of administration in long-term studies, the Committee concluded that the administration of benzyl acetate in the diet was more relevant to its safety assessment as a food additive than administration by gavage in corn oil.

The Committee also reviewed data from new genotoxicity studies. These studies showed no evidence of *in vivo* genotoxicity of benzyl acetate when tested for induction of sister chromatid exchange, chromosomal aberrations or micronuclei in mouse bone marrow cells. The Committee noted the induction of necrosis of the brain involving the cerebellum and/or hippocampus in rats and mice treated with very high doses of benzyl acetate (50 000 mg/kg feed) for 13 weeks. No such effect was observed in the long-term toxicity/carcinogenicity studies in mice or rats at lower doses (3 130-25 000 mg/kg feed). In the long-term toxicity/carcinogenicity study mentioned above, of rats administered dietary benzyl acetate at levels up to 550 mg per kg of body weight per day, no adverse effects were observed.

Table 1. Results of genotoxicity tests on benzyl acetate

Test system	Test object	Concentration of benzyl acetate	Result	Reference
In vitro Bacterial mutagenicity assay (1)	*S typhimurium* TA1535, TA1537, TA100, TA98	33-10 000 µg/plate	Negative	NTP, 1992
Mammalian cell mutation assay (1)	Mouse lymphoma cells (TK locus)	0.25-1.75 µl/ml (3), 700-1 700 µg/ml	Positive (2)	NTP, 1992
Sister chromatid exchange assay (1)	Chinese hamster ovary(CHO) cells	50-5 000 µg/ml	Negative	NTP, 1992
Chromosomal aberration assay (1)	Chinese hamster ovary(CHO) cells	160-1 600 µg/ml	Negative (4)	NTP, 1992
In vivo Sex-linked recessive lethal mutation test	*Drosophilia melanogaster*	300 ppm & 20 000 ppm (5)	Negative	NTP, 1992
Sister chromatid exchange test	Mouse bone marrow cells	312-1 250 mg/kg bw	Negative	NTP, 1992
Chromosomal aberration test	Mouse bone marrow cells	325-1 700 mg/kg bw	Negative	NTP, 1992
Micronucleus test	Mouse bone marrow cells	312-1 250 mg/kg bw	Negative	NTP, 1992
Micronucleus test	Mouse peripheral blood	3130-50 000 ppm	Negative	NTP, 1992

(1)	In presence and absence of metabolic activation
(2)	Laboratory 1: positive only in presence of metabolic activation
	Laboratory 2: positive in presence of metabolic activation, test in absence of metabolic activation not conducted
(3)	Concentration unit equivocal, (laboratory 1)
(4)	Negative in presence of metabolic activation. Two out of three trials in a test showed P values of less than 0 05 in absence of metabolic activation
(5)	Feeding: 300 mg/kg feed, injection: 20 000 ppm

In the long-term toxicity/carcinogenicity study in mice given 330, 1 000, or 3 000 mg benzyl acetate per kg diet (equal to 37, 112, and 345 mg per kg body weight per day in males and 42, 132, and 382 mg per kg body weight per day in females), dose-related degeneration and atrophy of the olfactory epithelium, cystic hyperplasia of the nasal submucosal glands, and pigmentation of the nasalmucosal epithelium were observed. The Committee considered the changes of the nasal cavity to be a result of local irritant effects of the test compound and not toxicologically relevant to the assessment of food safety.

At the end of the study, treated male and female mice showed lower mean body weights than controls.

4. EVALUATION

In the absence of associated pathological lesions in the long-term toxicity/carcinogenicity study in mice and on the basis of the NOEL of 550 mg per kg of body weight per day in the long-term study in rats, the Committee included benzyl acetate in the group ADI of 0-5 mg per kg of body weight with benzyl alcohol, benzaldehyde and benzoic acid, and the benzoate salts.

The Committee noted the absence of reproduction/teratogenicity studies for substances in this group, and recommended that a full review of benzoic acid and benzoates, benzaldehyde, benzyl alcohol, and benzyl acetate be performed in 1995 to determine whether these or other studies are required.

5. REFERENCE

NTP (1992). NTP (National Toxicology Program) technical report on the toxicology and carcinogenesis studies of benzyl acetate (CAS No. 140-11-4) in F344 rats and B6C3F₁ mice, (Feed studies). NTP TR 431. Board Draft. NIH Publication 92-3162. U.S. Department of Health and Human Services, Public Health Service, National Institute of Health. Research Triangle Park, NC, USA.

2-ETHYL-1-HEXANOL

First draft prepared by
Dr K. Ekelman, Additives Evaluation Branch
Division of Health Effects Evaluation
Center for Food Safety and Applied Nutrition
Food and Drug Administration, Washington, DC, USA

1. EXPLANATION

2-Ethyl-1-hexanol (EH; also known as 2-ethylhexyl alcohol and 2-ethylhexanol) has not been reviewed previously by JECFA.

EH is a colorless liquid with a mild floral odor (Furia and Bellanca, 1975) that occurs naturally in food. EH is prepared by petrochemical synthesis and is used as a flavoring ingredient in food. Total annual consumption of EH in the United States from its natural occurrence in food is reported to be 120 kg (Stofberg and Grundschober, 1987); total annual production for use as a flavor additive is estimated to be 209 kg (NRC, 1989). Estimated intake in the United States from the use of EH as a flavoring ingredient is approximately 0.65 μg/kg bw/day (FEMA, 1993).

2. BIOLOGICAL DATA

2.1 Biochemical aspects

2.1.1 Absorption, distribution, and excretion

Two adult male CD-strain rats (300 g) were gavaged with radiolabeled 2-ethyl-1-^{14}C-hexanol (^{14}C-EH; 1 μCi; 8.8 μg) in cottonseed oil. Two others were given the same amount of ^{14}C-EH and cottonseed oil, but also were given 0.1 ml (0.64 mmol) of unlabeled EH. Following administration of the test substance, rats were housed in metabolism cages with *ad libitum* access to feed and water; expired CO_2, urine, and faeces were collected every hour for 28 hrs. Most (99.8%) of the orally administered radioactivity was accounted for by radioactivity in expired CO_2, urine, faeces, an ethanol wash of the metabolism cage at the end of the experiment, heart, brain, liver, kidneys, and "residual carcass." EH was efficiently absorbed following oral administration and rapidly excreted in respired CO_2 (6-7%), urine (80-82%), and faeces (8-9%); elimination was essentially complete by 28 hrs. The major urinary metabolite of EH in the rat was shown to be 2-ethylhexanoic acid through acid extraction of urine. This metabolite can undergo partial ß-oxidation and decarboxylation to produce $^{14}CO_2$ and 2- and 4-heptanone (in the urine). Other urinary metabolites of EH were identified as 2-ethyl-5-hydroxyhexanoic acid, 2-ethyl-5-ketohexanoic acid, and 2-ethyl-1,6-hexanedioic acid. Approximately 3% of the parent compound was excreted unchanged.

Rats and other mammals hydrolyze orally ingested DEHP (di-[2-ethylhexyl]phthalate, a plasticizer in food-contact materials) to EH and MEHP (mono-[2-ethylhexyl]phthalate) prior to absorption of MEHP by the intestine (Albro, 1975).

An *in vitro* dermal absorption study of EH and seven other compounds was conducted with full thickness rat skin and human stratum corneum. The ratio of the rate of absorption of EH through rat and human skin (rat/human) was reported to be 5.8, indicating that rat skin is more permeable to EH than is human skin. Damage to skin by dermal application of EH was defined as the ratio of the permeability constant for ^3H_2O after contact with EH to the permeability constant for ^3H_2O before application. Ratios for human skin (1.5 ± 0.4 and 3.7 ± 2.1) and rat skin (31.9 ± 5.1) indicated that dermal application of EH damages rat skin more than human skin (Barber *et al.*, 1992).

Excretion balance studies were conducted on female Fischer 344 rats (4 animals/group) following acute oral doses of 50 or 500 mg/kg bw ^{14}C-EH and repeated oral doses of 50 mg/kg bw/day ^{14}C-EH for 14 days; results of acute gavage doses of 500 mg/kg bw ^{14}C-EH administered neat and as aqueous suspensions containing 5 mg Polyoxyl 35 castor oil/100 ml were compared. Dermal exposures to ^{14}C-EH (1 g/kg bw applied dose) for 6 hours and i.v. exposures to 1 mg/kg bw ^{14}C-EH were also studied. Acute oral doses of 50 or 500 mg/kg bw and repeated oral doses of 50 mg/kg bw/day showed similar excretion balance profiles of ^{14}C, with some evidence of metabolic saturation at the high dose. No evidence of metabolic induction was reported following repeated dosing. All oral doses were rapidly eliminated during the first 24 hours after dosing, predominantly in the urine. Approximately 5% of the dermal dose was absorbed. A majority of the oral and dermal doses were eliminated as glucuronides of oxidized metabolites of EH, principally glucuronides of 2-ethyladipic acid, 2-ethylhexanoic acid, 5-hydroxy-2-ethylhexanoic acid, and 6-hydroxy-2-ethylhexanoic acid. Only trace amounts of unchanged EH were eliminated in the urine. Bioavailability of EH orally administered with the gavage vehicle was slightly greater than bioavailability of EH administered alone (Deisinger *et al.*, 1992).

2.1.2   Biotransformation

Knaak and coworkers (1966) studied the metabolism of 8 mg ^{14}C-EH in rats and 200 mg ^{14}C-EH in rabbits following i.p. injection. The major urinary metabolite in rats was 2-ethylhexanoyl glucuronide; EH and 2-ethyl hexanoic acid were also identified in rat urine. In rabbits, the major urinary metabolite also was 2-ethylhexanoyl glucuronide; 2-ethyl-2,3-dihydroxyhexanoic acid and EH were also identified in rabbit urine (Knaak *et al.*, 1966).

The metabolism, distribution and elimination of ^{14}C-DEHP following oral administration to male and female B6C3F₁ mice, Fischer 344 rats, and *Cynomolgus* monkeys was investigated. Orally administered DEHP is rapidly hydrolyzed to the monoester (MEHP), then the alcohol and acid. The GI tract had appreciable amounts of EH, and absorbed [14] C appeared to be primarily EH. The alcohol was oxidized by ß-oxidation, ω-, and ω-1-oxidation generating several major and minor products including acids, ketones, ketoacids, hydroxy acids, and diacids (such as ethylhexanoic acid [EHA], ethylhexanedioic acid [DiEHA], and 5-hydroxyethylhexanoic acid [5-OH EHA]). The three species were able to form glucuronic acid conjugates of the alcohol oxidation products, but no sulfites were detected. However, differences between species were noted: metabolism appeared to be less extensive in the monkey (which excreted largely MEHP and EH as their glucuronides) than in rodents (which excreted largely products of faster oxidation, primarily EHA, 5-OH EHA, and diEHA) (Midwest Research Institute, 1984).

2.1.3   Effects on enzymes and other biochemical parameters

Gavage administration of 1 mmol/kg bw/day EH (approximately 130 mg/kg bw/day) to five male Wistar rats for 14 days was not associated with liver peroxisome proliferation (Rhodes *et al.*, 1984).

However, in another study, administration of 2% EH in the diet (approximately 1 000 mg/kg bw/day) to five male Fischer 344 rats for three weeks was reported to cause peroxisome proliferation and significant increases in the activities of liver catalase and carnitine acetyltransferase (Moody and Reddy, 1978).

When gavage doses of 0, 100, 320, or 950 mg/kg bw/day EH were administered to male and female Fischer 344 rats (5/sex/group) for 21 days, significant hepatomegaly at 950 mg/kg bw/day, significant increases in cyanide-insensitive palmitoyl CoA oxidation (a marker for peroxisome proliferation) in males (dose-related, 320 and 950 mg/kg bw/day) and females (950 mg/kg bw/day), and significant increases in lauric acid hydroxylase activity in males and females at 950 mg/kg bw/day were shown. As well, electron microscopy showed only a slight increase in the number of peroxisomes in hepatocytes of high-dose rats (Hodgson, 1987).

Groups of five male and five female Alderley Park rats and mice were gavaged with 0, 140, 350, 700, 1050, or 1750 mg/kg bw/day EH for 14 days. Rats in the high-dose group exhibited toxic effects (not specified) and died or were killed during the course of the study. Dose-related increases in relative liver weights of rats and mice were observed; the increases were statistically significant in rats at 700 and 1050 mg/kg bw/day, in male mice at 700, 1050, and 1750 mg/kg bw/day, and in female mice at 1750 mg/kg bw/day. EH administration resulted in a nearly linear dose-related induction of peroxisomal ß-oxidation (measured as palmitoyl CoA oxidation activities) in both rats and mice, although the dose(s) at which this effect was statistically significant were not stated (Keith *et al.*, 1992).

Activity of succinic dehydrogenase was increased and activity of lactic dehydrogenase was decreased after 12 daily dermal applications of 2 ml/kg bw undiluted EH to the shaved skin of the rat. In addition, EH-treated rats had significantly lower body weights than control rats 17 days after dermal application of EH was terminated (Schmidt *et al.* 1973).

Microsomal P-450 content increased and glucose-6-phosphatase activity decreased in rat liver microsomal pellets following oral administration of EH to the intact animal. Administration of EH increased alcohol dehydrogenase activity demonstrated histochemically in the centrilobular area of the liver, the number of microbodies, the dilatation of the smooth endoplasmic reticulum, and the number of microperoxisomes in the hepatocytes of rats (Lake *et al.*, 1975).

Concentrations of EH ranging from 2.5-15 mM significantly inhibited the activities of rat liver aminopyrine N-demethylase (approximately 60% inhibition at 15 mM EH) and aniline hydroxylase (approximately 50% inhibition at 15 mM EH) *in vitro* (Seth, 1982).

Rhodes and coworkers (1984) reported that 0.1 or 0.5 mM EH did not induce palmitoyl CoA oxidase activity (a marker for peroxisome proliferation) in rat hepatocytes *in vitro* (Rhodes *et al.*, 1984).

The activity of carnitine acetyltransferase (a peroxisomal enzyme) in rat liver cells *in vitro* was significantly induced (approximately 9X level in untreated cultures) by 1mM EH but not by 0.2 mM EH (Gray *et al.*, (1982).

In an *in vitro* test system using viable plugs from periportal or pericentral regions of rat liver, Liang and coworkers (1991) demonstrated that incubation of these plugs with EH (0.1 to 3 mM) decreased urea synthesis in a dose-related manner (up to 80% inhibition at 800 μM O_2) and caused extensive cell damage (assessed by lactate dehydrogenase leakage) Liang *et al.*, 1991).

2.2   Toxicological Studies

2.2.1   Acute toxicity studies

Results of acute toxicity studies with EH are summarized in Table 1.

Rabbits given 0, 0.2, 0.4, 0.6, 0.8, 1.6 or 3.2 x 10^{-5} mol/kg EH (0.26 to 4.16 mg/kg bw i.v.) had dose-related increases in heart rate and frequency of respiration. However, when EH was administered to dogs (doses reported as 4.05 and 8.10 mol/kg i.v.), no compound-related hypotensive effects were seen. Finally, when rabbits and rats were given acute iv doses of EH (doses not provided), direct toxic damage to the heart and smooth muscle elements of the blood vessels was observed (Hollenbach *et al.*, 1972).

Table 1: Summary of Acute Toxicity Studies with EH

Species	Route	LD_{50} (mg/kg bw)	Reference
Rat	Oral	2053 (2.46 mL/kg)	Smyth et al., 1969
Rat	Oral	3730[1]	Scala and Burtis, 1973
Rat	Oral	3 250	Albro, 1975
Rat	Oral	3200 - 6400	Treon, 1963
Rat	Oral	3200	NIOSH, 1976
Rat	I.P.	650	Treon, 1963
Mice	I.P.	780	Treon, 1963
Rat	I.V.	1670	Mashkina, 1966
Mice	I.V.	1670	Mashkina, 1966
Rabbit	Dermal	1986 (2.38 mL/kg)[2]	Smyth et al., 1969
Rabbit	Dermal	>2600[3]	Scala and Burtis, 1973
Guinea pig	Dermal	>8300 (>10 mL/kg)	Treon, 1963
		LC_{50}	
Mice	Inhal.	>227 ppm (6 hr)[4]	Scala and Burtis, 1973
Rat	Inhal.	>227 ppm (6 hr)[4]	Scala and Burtis, 1973
Guinea pig	Inhal.	>227 ppm (6 hr)[4]	Scala and Burtis, 1973
Rat	Inhal.	saturated vapors (8 hr)	Smyth et al., 1969
Rat	Inhal.	>235 ppm	Treon, 1963

(1)   Gastrointestinal irritation was reported in rats after oral administration of EH undiluted or in corn oil.

(2)   Mild dermal irritation (3 on a scale of 0 [no irritation] to 10) was reported when EH was applied to the uncovered rabbit belly and moderate corneal injury in rabbits when undiluted EH was instilled in the eye (5 on a scale of 0 [no injury] to 10).

(3)   Moderate skin irritation was reported in rabbits following dermal application of EH and severe eye irritation with persistent, wide-spread corneal opacity when 0.1 ml undiluted EH was applied to the conjunctival sac.

(4)   Mice, rats and guinea pigs (10 each) were exposed for 6 hours to 227 ppm EH, then observed for 24 hours before necropsy. No deaths occurred during exposure or observation. All animals exposed to EH exhibited central nervous system depression and labored breathing and one guinea pig had a clonic convulsion. During exposure, mucous membranes of the eyes, nose, throat, and respiratory passages of animals exposed to EH were irritated, but animals recovered within one hour after exposure was terminated. Gross necropsy revealed areas of slight haemorrhage in animals exposed to EH.

2.2.2   Short-term toxicity studies

2.2.2.1 Mice

Doses of 0, 100, 330, 1 000, or 1 500 mg 2-ethyl-1-hexanol/kg bw/day were administered by gavage for 11 days (9 administrations) to groups of 10 male and 10 female C3B6F1 mice. Effects clearly related to administration of the test substance occurred in male and female mice receiving 330, 1 000, or 1 500 mg/kg bw/day. One male mouse receiving 330 mg/kg bw/day for 11 days showed ataxic gait and piloerection following the administration of the 8th dose, but these symptoms were reported to have disappeared by the next day. Two male and two female mice receiving 330 mg/kg bw/day were reported to have acanthosis in the mucous membrane of the forestomach that was usually associated with hyperkeratosis and was once associated with focal inflammatory oedema in the submucosa.

One female mouse receiving 1 000 mg 2-ethyl-1-hexanol/kg bw/day showed abdominal position and loss of consciousness; the mouse died later the same day; microscopic examination revealed tubular dilatation in the renal cortex and centrilobular fatty infiltration in the liver of this mouse. Also the following significant effects were reported to be associated with administration of 1 000 mg/kg bw/day for 11 days: 1) increased absolute stomach weights in males and females; 2) increased liver-to-bw ratio for males; 3) increased stomach-to-bw ratio for females; 4) foci in the forestomach of 3 males and 2 females; 5) hyperkeratosis and focal or multifocal acanthosis and inflammatory oedema in the submucosa of the forestomach of males and females, including focal or multifocal ulceration of the mucous membrane of a few males and females; and 6) hypertrophy of hepatocytes in one male and one female.

Males (9/10) and females (6/10) receiving 1 500 mg 2-ethyl-1-hexanol/kg bw/day for 11 days had clinical signs such as ataxia and lethargy, some animals also had piloerection, and a few animals showed abdominal or lateral position and loss of consciousness; one male and four females died during the study. Microscopic evaluation showed tubular dilatation and nephrosis in the renal cortices of males and females that died intercurrently, and centrilobular fatty infiltration in the liver of females that died intercurrently. The following statistically significant effects were reported, associated with administration of 1 500 mg 2-ethyl-1-hexanol/kg bw/day: 1) increased absolute liver and stomach weights in males and females; 2) increased organ-to-bw ratios for stomach and liver in males and females; 3) increased organ-to-brain weight ratios for stomach and liver in males and females; 4) foci in the forestomach of 7/10 males and 5/10 females; 5) hyperkeratosis and focal or multifocal acanthosis and inflammatory oedema in the submucosa of the forestomach of most males and females, including focal or multifocal ulceration of the mucous membrane in a few males and females; 6) hypertrophy of hepatocytes in the liver of males and females, including focal necrosis of liver cells in one male and one female; and 7) bilateral tubular giant cells in the testicular tubules of two males (BASF, 1992b).

Doses of 0, 25, 125, 250, or 500 mg 2-ethyl-1-hexanol/kg bw/day were administered by gavage to groups of 10 male and 10 female $B6C3F_1$ mice for 3 months. Animals in the 250 and 500 mg/kg bw/day groups showed toxic effects related to administration of the test compound. For male mice receiving 250 mg/kg bw/day, statistically significant increased stomach-to-bw ratio was observed. Statistically significant effects observed in animals receiving 500 mg 2-ethyl-1-hexanol/kg bw/day included: a) increased stomach-to-bw ratio in males and 2) slight focal or multifocal acanthosis in the mucosa of the forestomach of 2/10 males and 1/10 female (BASF, 1992b).

2.2.2.2 Rats

Doses of 0, 100, 330, 1 000, or 1 500 mg 2-ethyl-1-hexanol/kg bw/day were administered by gavage for 11 days (9 applications) to groups of 10 male and 10 female Fischer 344 rats. Clear toxic effects occurred in the male and female rats receiving 330, 1 000, or 1 500 mg/kg bw/day.

Female rats receiving 330 mg/kg bw/day for 11 days had increased kidney-to-bw ratios, but not increased absolute kidney weights or kidney-to-brain weight ratios. Microscopic findings included inflammatory oedema in the forestomach of one female rat and decreased thymus size (microscopic examination) in 1 female and 2 male rats.

Male and female rats receiving 1 000 mg 2-ethyl-1-hexanol/kg bw/day had reduced feed consumption, body weight, and body weight gain compared to control rats. Some rats in this dose group showed ataxia and apathy; a single rat showed piloerection and the genital region of one rat was smeared with urine. The following statistically significant effects were also reported to be associated with administration of 1 000 mg/kg bw/day for 11 days: a) serum cholesterol and reticulocytes in rats of both sexes were reduced; b) absolute spleen weights of rats of both sexes were reduced; c) absolute liver weights of male and female rats were increased; d) organ-to-bw ratios for stomach, liver and kidneys were increased for male and female rats; e) brain-to-bw ratio was increased in female rats; f) spleen-to-bw ratios were reduced in male and female rats; g) liver-to-brain weight ratios were increased in male and female rats; h) spleen-to-brain weight ratios were decreased in male and female rats; i) foci were reported in the forestomachs of 2 males; j) hyperkeratosis and focal or multifocal acanthosis in the mucous membrane of the forestomach of most male and female rats, as well as epithelial degeneration, ulceration and subcutaneous inflammatory oedema; k) parenchymal involution of lymphoreticular tissue in the spleens of 5 female rats; l) decreased thymus size in 2 males and 5 females (microscopic evaluation); l) lymphocyte depletion in the thymus of 5 females and lymphocyte necrosis in the thymus of 4 females.

Male and female rats receiving 1 500 mg 2-ethyl-1-hexanol/kg bw/day showed reduced feed consumption, body weight, and body weight gain compared to control rats. All animals in the dose group demonstrated ataxia and lethargy, some animals showed abdominal or lateral position and appeared to be unconscious, almost all animals had piloerection, and a few rats had genital regions smeared with urine. The following statistically significant effects were also reported to be associated with administration of 1 500 mg 2-ethyl-1-hexanol/kg bw/day: a) reduced serum cholesterol, glucose, and reticulocytes in male and female rats; b) increased serum alanine aminotransferase in male rats; c) decreased absolute spleen, brain, and adrenal weights and increased absolute liver and stomach weights in male and female rats; d) increased organ-to-body weight ratios for stomach, liver, kidney, and brain in male and female rats, decreased spleen-to-bw ratios for male and female rats, increased adrenal-to-bw ratio for male rats, and increased lung-to-bw ratio for female rats; e) increased organ-to-brain weight ratios for liver and stomach in rats of both sexes, decreased spleen-to-brain weight ratio for male and female rats, and decreased adrenal-to-brain weight ratio in female rats.

Foci were reported in the forestomach of 4 male and 7 female rats dosed with 1 500 mg 2-ethyl-1-hexanol/kg bw/day. Microscopic findings at this dose level were reported to include: a) hyperkeratosis and focal or multifocal acanthosis in the mucous membrane of the forestomach of all male and female rats, as well as epithelial degeneration, ulceration, and subcutaneous inflammatory oedema in some animals; b) slight hypertrophy of hepatocytes in the liver of 8 males and 8 females; c) focal hepatocellular necrosis in 1 female and 2 male rats; d) parenchymal involution of lymphoreticular tissue in the spleen of 9 male and 9 female rats; e) decreased thymus size in 10 male and 9 female rats; and f) lymphocyte depletion in the thymus of 9 male and 8 female rats and lymphocyte necrosis in the thymus of 1 male and 6 female rats (BASF, 1992a).

Doses of 0, 25, 125, 250, or 500 mg 2-ethyl-1-hexanol/kg bw/day were administered by gavage to groups of 10 male and 10 female Fischer 344 rats for 3 months. Animals in the 250 and 500 mg/kg bw/day groups showed toxic effects. For animals receiving 250 mg/kg bw/day, statistically significant effects were reported to include: a) decreased serum alkaline phosphatase and glucose in male rats and decreased serum alanine aminotransferase in female rats; b) increased liver-to-bw ratios in male and female rats and increased stomach-to-bw ratio in female rats; and c) decreased fat deposition of the liver cells of male rats.

Statistically significant effects observed in animals receiving 500 mg 2-ethyl-1-hexanol/kg bw/day included: a) decreased body weight and body weight gain in male and female rats; b) decreased serum alanine aminotransferase, glucose, and cholesterol in male and female rats, increased reticulocytes in male and female rats, decreased serum alkaline phosphatase in male rats, and increased serum protein and albumin in male rats; c) increased absolute liver weights in male and female rats and increased absolute stomach weights in female rats; d) increased organ-to-body weight ratios for liver and stomach in male and female rats; and e) increased organ-to-brain weight ratios for liver and stomach in male and female rats.

Slightly elevated single or multiple foci were observed in the mucosa of the forestomach of male and female rats receiving 500 mg/kg bw/day. Macroscopic findings at this dose level were reported to include: a) focal or multifocal achanthosis in the mucosa of the forestomach of 1 male and 5 female rats; b) acanthosis of the whole mucosa, ballooning degeneration of the epithelia, and inflammatory oedema in the submucosa of 1 male rat; and c) decreased fat deposition in the liver and fewer animals with fatty infiltration of the lobular periphery of the liver compared to vehicle-control rats (BASF, 1992a).

Five male Wistar-derived rats were administered 1 mmol/kg/day (approximately 130 mg/kg bw/day) EH dissolved in polyethylene glycol 300 (10 ml/kg/day) by gavage for 14 days; 10 control rats were administered the gavage vehicle alone. At the end of the treatment period, rats were killed and blood was withdrawn for analysis of plasma cholesterol and triglyceride levels; livers and testis were weighed, liver samples were taken for light and electron microscopy, and the remaining liver was homogenized for determination of total catalase and CN-insensitive palmitoyl CoA oxidation. No major pathological signs of hepatotoxicity were observed, although slight centrilobular hypertrophy (controls: 4/10 rats; EH-treated: 2/5), slight/moderate glycogen vacuolization (controls: 9/10; EH-treated: 5/5), and slight/moderate centrilobular "fat" vacuolation (controls: 9/10; EH-treated: 1/5) were reported in control and EH-treated rats. Administration of EH had no significant effect on body weight gain, liver-to-body-weight ratio, testis-to-body-weight ratio, number of peroxisomes/504 μm^2 liver, serum catalase activity, serum cholesterol, or serum triglycerides. In addition, 0.1 mM EH had no effect on acyl CoA oxidase activity after 72 hrs in *in vitro* culture with rat hepatocytes (Rhodes *et al.*, 1984).

Gavage administration of 1335 mg/kg bw/day EH in corn oil to 6 male Wistar albino rats for 7 days resulted in significantly increased liver-to-body-weight ratio (control: 3.5 ± 0.1 g/100 g bw; EH-treated: 4.9 ± 0.1 [$p < 0.001$]), decreased glucose-6-phosphatase activity (control: 24 ± 2 μg/min/mg microsomal protein; EH-treated: 15 ± 1 [$p < 0.01$]), increased biphenyl 4-hydroxylase activity (control: 1.6 ± 0.1 μmol/hr/g liver; EH-treated: 2.1 ± 0.1 [$p < 0.01$]), and increased microsomal cytochrome P-450 content (control: 0.07 ± 0.003 *delta*-E 450-500 nm/mg microsomal protein; EH-treated: 0.1 ± 0.004 [$p < 0.001$]) (Lake *et al.* 1975).

2.2.3   Long-term toxicity/carcinogenicity studies

2.2.3.1 Mice

2-ethyl-1-hexanol (0, 50, 200, or 750 mg/kg bw/day) was administered by gavage to groups of 50 male and 50 female B6C3F$_1$ mice five days per week for a period of 18 months. The purity of the test substance was reported to be greater than 99.87%. The gavage vehicle was doubly distilled water containing 5 mg Polyoxyl 35 castor oil per 100 ml. An additional control group of 50 male and 50 female rats was gavaged with double distilled water only. All rats received 10 ml/kg bw test substance emulsion, vehicle or double distilled water per dose.

The method of preparing test substance emulsions was changed after 6 months of dosing because homogeneity analyses of emulsions showed considerable variation, ranging from approximately 70% to 140% of target concentrations. However, variability in dosing during the early part of the study did not significantly affect the outcome of the study because of the "clear biological distinction between dose levels during treatment." Mice were housed singly and feed and water were available *ad libitum* throughout the study. At the initiation of dosing, mice were 49 days old; mean body weight of males was 23 g (range 21-26 g) and mean body weight of females was 19 g (range 17-23 g). At the end of the study, non-fasted mice were decapitated under CO_2 anaesthesia.

The general health of the test animals was checked daily, and test animals were examined and palpated once a week. Mice were weighed weekly during the first 13 weeks, then every four weeks for the duration of the study. Feed consumption was determined for a period of one week every four weeks during the study. Blood samples were drawn from the tail vein of all surviving animals for haematological examination at 12 months and at the end of the study. Animals that survived to the end of the study were necropsied; tissues and organs were subjected to gross and microscopic pathology examination.

No EH-related changes were observed in mice administered 50 or 200 mg/kg bw/day EH for 18 months. In mice administered 750 mg/kg bw/day, the following effects were observed: 1) decreased body weight gain in males (approximately 26%) and females (24%) that was associated with a substantial reduction in feed consumption (males: decreased from about 9% to 20%; females: decreased from about 9% to 30%); 2) increased mortality in males (vehicle controls: 4%; EH-treated: 30%) and females (vehicle controls: 8%; EH-treated: 30%); 3) treatment-related haematological changes, including slightly increased polymorphonuclear neutrophils in males and females (males: controls--$19.8 \pm 5.9\%$ [12 mo] and $20.5 \pm 7.6\%$ [18 mo]; 750 mg/kg bw/day--$26.4 \pm 9.1\%$ [12 mo] and $26.9 \pm 13.5\%$ [18 mo])(females: controls--$20.6 \pm 5.6\%$ [12 mo] and $22.6 \pm 10.7\%$ [18 mo]; 750 mg/kg bw/day--24.2 ± 5.4 [12 mo] and $25.1 \pm 9\%$ [18 mo]) and slightly decreased lymphocytes in males and females (males: controls--$77 \pm 6.9\%$ [12 mo] and $76.6 \pm 7.6\%$ [18 mo]; 750 mg/kg bw/day--$69.1 \pm 9\%$ [12 mo] and $70.6 \pm 13.2\%$ [18 mo]); and 4) treatment-related, but not statistically significant, increased focal hyperplasia of the epithelium of the forestomach in males (controls--1/50; 50 mg/kg bw/day--1/50; 200 mg/kg bw/day--1/50; 750 mg/kg bw/day--5/50) and females (controls--1/50; 50 mg/kg bw/day--1/50; 200 mg/kg bw/day--0/50; 750 mg/kg bw/day--4/50). Also, a slight increase in the incidence of hepatocellular carcinomas in high-dose females was statistically significant when compared to the incidence in vehicle control females but not when compared to the incidence in water-gavaged control females (vehicle control--0/50; 50 mg/kg bw/day--1/50; 200 mg/kg bw/day--3/50; 750 mg/kg bw/day--5/50). No statistically significant increase in tumour incidence occurred in male mice. EH is not oncogenic in the mouse under the conditions of this study (BASF, 1992b).

In a satellite study to the carcinogenicity study in mice cited above as BASF, 1992b, EH was administered by gavage (vehicle: distilled water containing 5 mg Polyoxyl 35 castor oil per 100 ml) to two groups of male and female B6C3F$_1$ mice at 750 mg/kg bw/day. A control group of 10 males and 10 females was gavaged with the vehicle only for 13 months; a second (non-recovery) group of 10 males and 10 females was gavaged with EH for 13 months, 5 days/week; a third (recovery) group of 50 males and 50 females was gavaged with EH for 13 months, 5 days/week, then gavaged with the vehicle only for 5 months, 5 days/week. Mice were killed at the end of the treatment periods--13 months for groups one and two; 18 months for group three--and subjected to gross pathological assessment. The general health of the test animals was checked daily, and animals were examined and palpated once a week. Body weights were determined once a week during the first 13 weeks of the study, then once every four weeks. Feed consumption was determined one week in every four weeks throughout the study. Microscopic examination of tissues and organs was performed only on mice that died during the study.

Administration of 750 mg/kg bw/day EH to male and female mice for 13 months caused increased mortality in males and females (males: control--0%, non-recovery--30%, recovery--22% during the first 13 months; females: control--0%, non-recovery--20%, recovery--16% during the first 13 months). For the non-recovery mice and recovery mice during treatment with EH, feed consumption was significantly decreased compared to control mice (at 13 months, males: control--4.7$\pm$0.4 g/day, non-recovery--3.7$\pm$0.5 g/day, recovery--4.4$\pm$0.6 g/day; females: control--6.0$\pm$1.3 g/day, non-recovery--5.6$\pm$1.5 g/day, recovery--5.8$\pm$1.0 g/day); following the 5 month recovery period, feed consumption for mice in the recovery group was in the same range as feed consumption for control mice (males: control--4.8$\pm$0.9 g/day, recovery--4.9$\pm$0.8 g/day; females: control--6.3$\pm$1.3 g/day, recovery--5.9$\pm$1.1 g/day). For the non-recovery mice and recovery mice during treatment with EH, body weight gain was significantly decreased (at 13 months, males: control--40.9$\pm$2.7 g, non-recovery--36.7$\pm$2.8 g, recovery--38.7$\pm$3.2 g; females: control--38.7$\pm$5.4 g, non-recovery--33.8$\pm$4.4 g, recovery--34.9$\pm$4.8 g); following the 5 month recovery period, body weight gain of female mice that had been gavaged with EH for 13 weeks was still significantly decreased compared to control mice (males: control--42.7$\pm$3.5 g, recovery--42.4$\pm$3.6 g; females: control--41.1$\pm$5.6 g, recovery--36.9+5.1 g). Some statistically significant changes in organ weights and masses or foci in liver and stomach were observed to be associated with EH administration; these were similar to changes noted in the results of the carcinogenicity study (BASF, 1992d).

2.2.3.2 Rats

2-ethyl-1-hexanol (0, 50, 100, or 150 mg/kg bw/day) was administered by gavage to groups of 50 male and 50 female Fischer 344 rats five days/week for a period of 24 months. The purity of the test substance was reported to be greater than 99.3%. The gavage vehicle was doubly distilled water containing 5 mg Polyoxyl 35 castor oil per 100 ml. An additional control group of 50 male and 50 female rats was gavaged with double distilled water only. All rats received 10 ml/kg bw/day test substance emulsion, vehicle or double distilled water per dose.

The method of preparing test substance emulsions was changed after 6 months of dosing because homogeneity analyses of emulsions showed considerable variation, ranging from approximately 70% to 140% of target concentrations.

However, the report concluded that variability in dosing during the early part of the study did not significantly affect the outcome of the study because of the "clear biological distinction between dose levels during treatment."

Rats were housed singly and food and water were available *ad libitum* throughout the study. At the initiation of dosing, rats were 42 days old; mean body weight of males was 103 g (range 86-128 g) and mean body weight of females was 81 g (range 64-95 g). At the end of the study, non-fasted rats were decapitated under CO_2 anaesthesia.

The general health of the test animals was checked daily, and test animals were examined and palpated once a week. Rats were weighed weekly during the first 13 weeks, then every four weeks for the duration of the study. Feed consumption was determined for a period of one week every four weeks during the study. Blood samples were drawn from a tail vein of all surviving animals for haematological examination at 12 and 18 months and at the end of the study. At the end of the study, surviving animals were necropsied; tissues and organs were subjected to gross and microscopic pathology examination.

No compound-related changes were associated with administration of 50 mg/kg bw/day for 24 months; however, body weights and body-weight gains of rats receiving 50, 150, or 500 mg 2-ethyl-1-hexanol/kg bw/day were decreased in a statistically significant dose-dependent manner compared to vehicle control rats. At the end of the study, body weights were about 5%, 11%, and 23% below control values and body weight gains were about 8%, 16%, and 33% below control values, respectively. Feed consumption of male and female rats receiving 500 mg/kg bw/day showed occasional statistically significant decreases compared to both control groups of rats, but no dose-response relationship was observed.

An EH-associated increase in mortality was observed for female mice of the high-dose group only (males: vehicle controls--34%, 50 mg/kg bw/day--46%, 150 mg/kg bw/day--32%, 500 mg/kg bw/day--38%; females: vehicle controls--28%, 50 mg/kg bw/day--28%, 150 mg/kg bw/day--26%, 500 mg/kg bw/day--52%).

For rats receiving 100 mg/kg bw/day, the study reported a) statistically significant reductions in body weight (males: 11%; females: 9%) and body weight gain (males: 16%; females: 12%) compared to vehicle control rats and b) slightly increased numbers of animals with clinical symptoms and incidences of symptoms (frequency/animals) such as poor general condition (100 mg/kg bw/day: males--69/15; vehicle control: males--62/12), labored breathing (100 mg/kg bw/day: males--4/1, females--30/5; vehicle control: males--2/1, females--9/3), piloerection (100 mg/kg bw/day: males--17/1; vehicle control: males--0/0), and genital regions smeared with urine (100 mg/kg bw/day: females--31/4; vehicle controls: females--0/0). Feed consumption of male and female rats receiving 150 mg/kg bw/day showed occasional statistically significant decreases compared to both control groups of rats, but no dose-response relationship was observed.

The following treatment-related changes were observed in rats dosed with 500 mg/kg bw/day 2-ethyl-1-hexanol for 24 months: a) statistically significant reductions in body weight gain for males (33%) and females (31%); b) increased incidences of male and female rats with clinical symptoms (frequency/animals) such as poor general condition (500 mg/kg bw/day: males--200/14, females--248/21;

vehicle control: males--62/12, females--34/8), labored breathing (500 mg/kg bw/day: males--41/4, females--75/12; vehicle control: males--2/1, females--9/3), piloerection (500 mg/kg bw/day: males--67/2, females--21/5; vehicle control: males--0/0, females--2/1), and/or genital region smeared with urine (500 mg/kg bw/day: males--13/1, females--502/21; vehicle control: males--0/0, females--44/6); and c) statistically significant increased mortality in dosed females as reflected in the number of animals that died or were sacrificed in a moribund condition during the study (52%) compared with vehicle control females (28%).

Male rats dosed with 500 mg/kg bw/day had slightly increased anisocytosis, predominantly microcytosis at 12 months, but not at 18 nor 24 months, compared to vehicle control males. No malignant tumours were detected in high-dose animals that died before scheduled termination and the sum of primary tumours, benign tumours and malignant tumours was remarkably lower in the high-dose group compared to both control groups of rats. Thus, 2-ethyl-1-hexanol was not oncogenic in the rat under conditions of this assay (BASF, 1992a).

In a satellite study to the BASF carcinogenicity study in rats cited above as BASF 1992a, EH was administered by gavage (vehicle: distilled water containing 5 mg Polyoxyl 35 castor oil per 100 ml) to two groups of male and female Fischer 344 rats at 500 mg/kg bw/day. A control group of 10 males and 10 females was gavaged with the vehicle only for 18 months; a second (non-recovery) group of 10 males and 10 females was gavaged with EH for 18 months, 5 days/week; a third (recovery) group of 50 males and 50 females was gavaged with EH for 18 months, 5 days/week, then gavaged with the vehicle only for 6 months, 5 days/week. Rats were killed at the end of the treatment periods--18 months for groups one and two; 24 months for group three--and subjected to gross pathological assessment. The general health of the test animals was checked daily, and animals were examined and palpated once a week. Body weights were determined once a week during the first 13 weeks of the study, then once every four weeks. Feed consumption was determined one week in every four weeks throughout the study. Microscopic examination of tissues and organs was performed only on rats that died during the study.

Administration of 500 mg/kg bw/day EH to male and female rats for 18 months caused slightly increased mortality in females (control--20%, non-recovery--40%, recovery--34% during the first 18 months) and decreased feed consumption in males (maximum decrease of approximately 12%). For the non-recovery rats and recovery rats during treatment with EH, body weight gain was significantly decreased (at 18 months, males: control--298.7±19.6 g, non-recovery--215.4±21.3 g, recovery--211.2±22.4 g; females: control--149.9±19.8 g, non-recovery--128.7±21.7 g, recovery--128.5±18.3 g); following the 6 month recovery period, body weight gains of males and females that had been gavaged with EH for 18 weeks had partially recovered but were still significantly decreased compared to controls (males: control--266.5±30.7 g, recovery--216.1±23.0 g; females: control--177.5±27.0 g, recovery--150.6±21.5 g).

The following changes were observed in rats that had been gavaged with 500 mg/kg bw/day EH for 18 months compared to control rats: 1) a greater number of animals and/or a higher incidence of clinical symptoms such as poor general condition, labored breathing, and genital region smeared with urine in males and females; 2) statistically significant decreases in the absolute weights of brain (males and females) and stomach (males); 3) statistically significant decreases in organ-to-body weight ratios of brain (males and females), liver (males and females), kidneys (males and females), stomach (males and females), and testes (BASF, 1992c).

2.2.4   Reproduction studies

The response of mixed cultures of Sertoli and germ cells prepared from Sprague-Dawley rat testes to model testicular toxicants was studied.   After incubation of the cultures with 2×10^{-4} M EH for 24 hrs, no increase was observed in the normal rate of germ cell detachment from Sertoli cells into the culture medium (Gray and Beamand 1984).

Effects of EH on rat testes were examined *in vivo* and *in vitro*.   No testicular damage was observed in male Sprague-Dawley rats given oral doses of 2.7 mmol EH/kg bw/day for 5 days and incubation with EH (0-1 000 μM for 24 or 48 hours) did not enhance detachment of germ cells from primary mixed cultures of rat Sertoli and germ cells (Sjoberg *et al.*, 1986).

EH did not increase lactate and pyruvate concentrations in the medium of *in vitro* cultures of rat Sertoli cells.   Such increases are considered to be sensitive indicators of altered Sertoli cells function associated with Sertoli-cell toxicants (Williams & Foster 1988).

2.2.5   Special studies on developmental toxicity and teratogenicity

2.2.5.1   Mice

Pregnant CD-1 mice were gavaged on gestation days 6-13 with 1525 mg/kg bw/day EH in corn oil; control mice were gavaged with corn oil; dams were allowed to litter.   Administration of EH caused statistically significant (p < 0.05) decreased maternal body weight gain (control: 7.0 ± 2.5 g; EH: 3.9 ± 3.2 g), decreased number of viable litters (control: 33/34; EH: 11/20), decreased liveborn per litter (control: 9.9 ± 2.4; EH: 6.8 ± 3.4), decreased percentage survival of pups (control: 98.2 ± 8.8; EH: 73.4 ± 32.2), and decreased birth weight (control: 1.6 ± 0.1 g/pup; EH: 1.4 ± 0.2 g/pup) and weight gain for pups (control: 0.6 ± 0.1 g/pup; EH: 0.3 ± 0.2 g/pup) (Hardin *et al.*, 1987).

2.2.5.2   Rats

Pregnant Wistar rats were administered undiluted di(2-ethylhexyl) phthalate (DEHP; 12.5 or 25 mmol/kg bw), EH (6.25 or 12.5 mmol/kg bw, approximately equivalent to 800 and 1600 mg/kg bw), or 2-ethylhexanoic acid (EA; 6.25 or 12.5 mmol/kg bw) by gavage on day 12 of gestation.   Control rats were not gavaged (untreated controls). Caffeine (150 mg/kg) was dissolved in water and injected i.p. in some pregnant rats of each group. Rats were killed on day 20 of gestation; following Caesarean section, implantation sites were determined *in situ* and the number of dead or resorbed fetuses was determined. Live fetuses were removed and examined; internal and external soft tissue and skeletal malformations were recorded. At least seven litters for each experimental condition were analyzed.

Administration of each test compound resulted in statistically significant, dose-related increases in malformed live fetuses (DEHP: 12.5 mmol/kg bw [7 litters]--4.5±4.5%, 25 mmol/kg bw [7 litters]--20.8±7.3%; EH: 6.25 mmol/kg bw [7 litters]--2.0±1.3%, 12.5 mmol/kg bw [7 litters]--22.2±14.7%; EA: 6.25 mmol/kg bw [7 litters]--0.8±0.8%; 12.5 mmol/kg bw [10 litters]--67.8±10.9%) compared to controls (no malformed live fetuses in 7 litters). Defects in fetuses following treatment with EH included hydronephrosis (7.8% of live fetuses), tail defects (4.9% of live fetuses), limb defects (9.7% of live fetuses), and other defects (1.0% of live fetuses). For each test compound, caffeine was reported to potentiate (increase) the percent of malformed live fetuses. However, administration of test compounds did not significantly affect the percentage of dead and resorbed fetuses compared to controls. No maternal effects associated with the test compounds were reported. These results are consistent with the hypothesis that the proximal teratogen for DEHP is EA, the metabolic product of EH (Ritter *et al.*, 1986 and 1987).

The developmental toxicity of dermally applied EH was studied in Fischer 344 rats; results of a dose range-finding study for the developmental toxicity study were also included. In the dose range-finding study 0, 420, 840, 1680, or 2520 mg/kg bw/day EH (undiluted) was applied to the clipped dorsal skin of pregnant F344 rats (8 rats/group); a positive dermal control group (2-methoxyethanol) and a sham-treated (deionized water) dermal control group were included in the study. In the developmental toxicity study, 0, 252, 840, or 2520 mg/kg bw/day EH (undiluted) was applied to the clipped dorsal skin of pregnant F344 rats (25/group); a positive dermal control group (2-methoxyethanol) and a sham-treated (deionized water) dermal control group also were included in this study.

Body weights were recorded on gestation days 0, 6, 9, 12, 15, and 21; feed consumption was estimated for 3-day intervals from gestation days 0-21. Skin irritation was measured before and after each 6-hr application period. Surviving females were killed on gestation day 21; uterine and liver weights (both studies) and weights of spleen, adrenals, kidneys, and thymus (developmental toxicity study) were recorded. Corpora lutea and uterine implantation sites were counted; ovaries, cervices, vaginas, and abdominal and thoracic cavities were examined grossly. All live and dead fetuses and resorption sites were noted. Live fetuses were sexed, weighed, and examined for external, visceral, and skeletal malformations and variations.

All pregnant females treated with EH survived. Clinical findings for EH-treated pregnant rats were limited to body weight changes, skin irritation, and nasal and ocular effects. Decreased body weight gain was observed in the dose range-finding study for gestation days 6-15 at doses of 1 680 (10.1±7.1 g) and 2 520 mg/kg bw/day EH (10.7±4.8 g) compared to sham-treated control rats (18.9±6.4 g). In the main study, weight gain was statistically significantly decreased for gestation days 6-9 at 2 520 mg/kg bw/day EH (0.1±2.4 g) compared to sham-treated controls (3.3±1.2 g), and was somewhat, but not statistically significantly, decreased at 840 mg/kg bw/day EH. No significant changes in feed consumption were reported at any treatment level of EH in either study throughout gestation (data not given). EH-related irritation effects at the treatment site were identified as mild, and included exfoliation, encrustation and erythema for all treatment groups in both studies; oedema was not observed.

Gestational effects were observed for neither study at any dose of EH applied dermally. Also, dermal administration of EH was not associated with external, visceral, or skeletal malformations. Dermally applied EH does not produce developmental or teratogenic effects when administered at doses associated with demonstrable maternal toxicity (Tyl *et al.*, 1992).

Groups of approximately 15 pregnant Sprague-Dawley rats were exposed for 7 hrs/day to air saturated with EH vapor (approximately 850 mg/m^3 EH) throughout gestation (Nelson *et al.*, 1988). Dams were weighed daily during the first week of exposure, then weekly. Dams were killed on gestation day 20; fetuses were removed, sexed, weighted and examined for external, visceral and skeletal defects. EH reduced maternal feed intake but did not produce significant maternal toxicity (data not provided). Inhalation of EH under conditions of this experiment was not associated with increased malformations (Nelson *et al.*, 1988).

2.2.6   Special studies on genotoxicity

The results of genotoxicity assays on EH are summarized in Table 2. All reports except Seed (1982) were of negative results for *in vitro* assays; results were negative for several *in vivo* assays, including a dominant lethal assay, a chromosomal aberration assay, and a mutagenicity assay on rat urinary metabolites of EH.

Table 2: Results of genotoxicity assays on EH

Test	Test Subject	EH Conc.	Result	Reference
Ames test[1]	*S. typhimurium* TA98 TA100 TA1535 TA1537 TA1538	0-1.0 μL/plate	neg.	Kirby *et al.*, 1983
Ames test[1]	*S. typhimurium* TA98 TA100 TA1535 TA1537	0-220 μg/plate	neg.	Zeiger *et al.*, 1985
Ames test[1]	*S. typhimurium* TA98 TA100 TA1535 TA1537 TA1538 TA2637	0-2 000 μg/plate	neg.[3]	Agarwal *et al.*, 1985

Test	Test Subject	EH Conc.	Result	Reference
Ames test[1]	*S. typhimurium* TA98 TA100 TA1537 TA1535 TA1538	0-1.8 µl/plate	neg.	Litton Bionetics Inc., 1982a
Ames test[1]	*S. typhimurium* TA98 TA100 TA1535 TA1537 TA1538	urine from rats gavaged with 1 g/kg bw/day EH for 15 day	neg.	DiVincenzo *et al.*, 1983
In vitro cell transformation assay[1]	BALB/3T3 cells	0-0.162 µg/ml	neg.[4]	Litton Bionetics Inc., 1982b
8-Azaguanine resistance assay[2]	*S. typhimurium* TA100	0-1.5 mM	pos.[5]	Seed, 1982
Mouse micronucleus test	B6C3F₁ mouse bone marrow cells	456 mg/kg bw/day i.p. for 1 or 2 day	neg.[6]	Litton Bionetics Inc., 1982c
mouse lymphoma assay[1]	L5178Y/TK[+/-] mouse lymphoma cells	0.01-0.24 µL/mL	neg.	Kirby *et al.*, 1983
Rec-assay	*Bacillus subtilis*	500 µg/disk	neg.	Tomita *et al.*, 1982
CHO mutation assay	Chinese hamster ovary (CHO) cells	1.5-2.8 mM	neg.	Phillips *et al.*, 1982
Unscheduled DNA synthesis assay	Primary rat hepatocytes	Not given	neg.	Hodgson *et al.*, 1982
In vivo dominant lethal assay	ICR/SIM mice	250, 500, 1 000 mg/kg bw/day for 5 day	neg.	Rushbrook *et al.*, 1982
In vivo chromosomal aberration assay	F344 rat bone marrow cells	.02, .07, .21 g/kg bw/day for 5 day	neg.	Putnam *et al.*, 1983

(1)   Both with and without metabolic activation
(2)   Without metabolic activation
(3)   Moderate cytotoxicity reported in most cultures
(4)   Negative from 0-225 µl/ml without metabolic activation; negative from 0-0.162 µl/ml with rat hepatocytes for metabolic activation
(5)   Small dose-related increase (maximum increase was approximately 3.5 times background) in mutation frequency accompanied by decreased survival (cytotoxicity)
(6)   Negative with and without activation with S9 and with and without ß-glucuronidase/arylsulfatase

2.2.7   Observations in humans

Hollenbach and coworkers (1972) reported that laboratory workers exposed to EH (among other substances) reported headaches, dizziness, fatigue and gastrointestinal disorders; also that exposed workers had slightly decreased blood pressure during the day.

3.   COMMENTS

In rats, orally administered 2-ethyl-1-hexanol is absorbed and rapidly eliminated within 28 hours, mainly in urine and faeces. The major urinary metabolite is 2-ethylhexanoic acid. In mice, rats and monkeys, the compound is oxidized by ß-, ω-, and ω-1-oxidation to various metabolites, including 2-ethylhexanoic acid, ethylhexanedioic acid, and 5-hydroxyethylhexanoic acid. Glucuronic acid conjugates are formed in all three species.

The Committee concluded that the available data do not indicate that 2-ethyl-1-hexanol is genotoxic. With a single exception, in which a positive result occurred in the presence of significantly decreased cell survival (cytotoxicity), the results of both *in vivo* and *in vitro* genotoxicity tests were negative.

Although teratogenic effects were reported in the offspring of mice administered 1 500 mg 2-ethyl-1-hexanol/kg bw/day by gavage on days 6-13 of gestation, these effects occurred in the presence of severe maternal toxicity. The body weight gain of treated females was approximately 40% less than that of untreated controls. In rats, administration of 1600 mg/kg bw 2-ethyl-1-hexanol by gavage (but not 800 mg/kg bw) on day 12 of gestation was associated with a statistically significant increase in the number of malformed live fetuses (malformations included hydronephrosis, tail defects and limb defects). Maternal toxicity was not reported in this study.

The results of several short-term toxicity studies suggested that 2-ethyl-1-hexanol administered orally to rats and mice at doses greater than approximately 350 mg/kg bw/day induces liver peroxisome proliferation and/or marker enzymes for peroxisome proliferation. However, the results of carcinogenicity studies did not indicate that long-term oral administration of 2-ethyl-1-hexanol leads to induction of liver tumours in mice or rats.

The results of long-term oral carcinogenicity studies indicated that 2-ethyl-1-hexanol is not carcinogenic in rats (24 months) or mice (18 months). The incidence of hepatocellular carcinomas at 750 mg/kg bw/day in female mice was slightly higher than in historical controls, however this effect was considered to be incidental and unrelated to the administration of 2-ethyl-1-hexanol. The increase was statistically significant when compared with the incidence in vehicle control females but not when compared with the incidence in control females given distilled water by gavage. In these studies, the 750 mg/kg bw/day dose of the compound produced a number of statistically significant, non-carcinogenic adverse effects, but these effects were not observed at 50 or 200 mg/kg bw/day in mice or at 50 mg/kg bw/day in rats.

4.   EVALUATION

On the basis of a NOEL of 50 mg/kg bw/day from the long-term study in rats and using a safety factor of 100, the Committee established an ADI of 0-0.5 mg/kg bw for 2-ethyl-1-hexanol.

5.   REFERENCES

AGARWAL, D.K , LAWRENCE, W.H., NUNEZ, L.J. & AUTIAN, J. (1985). Mutagenicity evaluation of phthalic acid esters and metabolites in *Salmonella typhimurium* cultures. *J. Toxicol. Environ. Health* **16**, 61-69.

ALBRO, P.W. (1975). The metabolism of 2-ethylhexanol in rats. *Xenobiotica* **5(10)**, 625-636.

BARBER, E.D., TEETSEL, N.M., KOLBERG, K.F. & GUEST, D. (1992). A comparative study of the rats of *in vitro* percutaneous absorption of eight chemicals using rat and human skin. *Fundam. Appl. Toxicol.* **19**, 493-497.

BASF (1992a). Report on the study of the oncogenic potential of 2-ethylhexanol in rats after administration by gavage (aqueous emulsion) for 24 months. Department of Toxicology of BASF Aktiengesellschaft, Ludwigshafen/Rhein, Germany. Submitted to WHO by the Flavor and Extract Manufacturers' Association of the United States, Washington, DC, USA.

BASF (1991b). Report on the study of the oncogenic potential of 2-ethylhexanol in mice after administration by gavage (aqueous emulsion) for 18 months. Department of Toxicology of BASF Aktiengesellschaft, Ludwigshafen/Rhein, Germany. Submitted to WHO by the Flavor and Extract Manufacturers' Association of the United States, Washington, DC, USA.

BASF (1991c) Report on the study of the oncogenic potential of 2-ethylhexanol in rats after administration by gavage (aqueous emulsion) for 24 months; Satellite study (recovery and interim sacrifice groups). Department of Toxicology of BASF Aktiengesellschaft, Ludwigshafen/Rhein, Germany. Submitted to WHO by the Flavor and Extract Manufacturers' Association of the United States, Washington, DC, USA.

BASF (1991d) Report on the study of the oncogenic potential of 2-ethylhexanol in mice after administration by gavage (aqueous emulsion) for 18 months; Satellite study (recovery and interim sacrifice groups). Department of Toxicology of BASF Aktiengesellschaft, Ludwigshafen/Rhein, Germany. Submitted to WHO by the Flavor and Extract Manufacturers' Association of the United States, Washington, DC, USA.

DEISINGER, P.J., BOATMAN, R.J. & GUEST, D (1992). Pharmacokinetic studies with 2-ethylhexanol in the female Fischer 344 rat. Eastman Kodak Company, Rochester, N.Y. Submitted to WHO by the Flavor and Extract Manufacturers' Association of the United States, Washington, DC, USA.

DIVINCENZO, G.D., HAMILTON, M.L., MUELLER, K.R., DONISH, W.H. & BARBER, E.D. (1985). Bacterial mutagenicity testing of urine from rats dosed with 2-ethylhexanol derived plasticizers. *Toxicology* **34**, 247-259.

FEMA. (1993). 2-Ethylhexanol. Flavor and Extract Manufacturers' Association of the United States, Washington, DC, USA.

FURIA, T.E. & BELLANCA. (EDS.) (1975). Fenaroli's handbook of flavor ingredients, Second edition, CRC Press, Cleveland, OH.

GRAY, T.J.B., BEAMAND, J.A., LAKE, B.G., FOSTER, J.R. & GANGOLLI, S.D. (1982). Peroxisome proliferation in cultured rat hepatocytes produced by clofibrate and phthalate ester metabolites. *Toxicol. Lett.* **10**, 273-279.

GRAY, T.J.B. & BEAMAND, J.A. (1984). Effect of some phthalate esters and other testicular toxins on primary cultures of testicular cells. *Fd. Chem. Toxic.* **22(2)**, 123-131.

HARDIN, B.D., SCHULER, R.L., BURG, J.R., BOOTH, G.M., HAZELDEN, K.P., MACKENZIE, K.M., PICCIRILLO, V.J. & SMITH, K.N. (1987). Evaluation of 60 chemicals in a preliminary developmental toxicity tests. *Terat. Carcin. Mutagen.* **7**, 29-48.

HODGSON, J.R. (1987). Results of peroxisome induction studies on tri(2-ethylhexyl)trimellitate and 2-ethylhexanol. *Toxicol. Ind. Health* **3(2)**, 49-60.

HODGSON, J.R., MYHR, B.C., MᶜKEON, M. & BRUSICK, D.J. (1982). Evaluation of di-(2-ethylhexyl)phthalate and its major metabolites in the primary rat hepatocyte unscheduled DNA synthesis assay. *Environ. Mutagen.* **4(3)**, 388 (abstract only).

HOLLENBACH, K., SCHMIDT, P. & STREMMEL, D. (1972). Tierexperimentelle Untersuchungen zur Blutdrukwirksamkeit von Thioglykolsaureisoocytylester. Thioglykolsaure und 2-Anthylhexanol. *Z. ges Hyg.* **18**, 481.

KEITH, Y., CORNU, M.C., CANNING, P.M., FOSTER, J., LHUGUENOT, J.C. & ELCOMBE, C.R. (1992). Peroxisome proliferation due to di(2-ethylhexyl)adipate, 2-ethylhexanol and 2-ethylhexanoic acid. *Arch. Toxicol.* **66(5)**, 321-326.

KIRBY, P.E., PIZZARELLO, R.F., LAWLOR, T.E., HAWORTH, S.R. & HODGSON, J.R. (1983). Evaluation of di-(2-ethylhexyl)phthalate and its major metabolites in the Ames test and L5178Y mouse lymphoma mutagenicity assay. *Environ. Mutagen.* **5**, 657-663.

KNAAK, J.B., KOZBELT, S.J. & SULLIVAN, L.J. (1966). Metabolism of 2-ethylhexyl sulfate by the rat and rabbit. *Toxicol. Appl. Pharmacol.* **8**, 369.

LAKE, B.G., GANGOLLI, S.D., GRASSO, P., & LLOYD, A.G. (1975). Studies on the hepatic effects of orally administered di-(2-ethylhexyl)phthalate in the rat. *Toxicol. Appl. Pharmacol.* **32**, 355-367.

LIANG, D., KELLER, B.J., MISRA, U.K. & THURMAN, R.G. (1991) Oxygen tension is a major determinant of hepatotoxicity due to 2-ethylhexanol in isolated tissue cylinders from periportal and pericentral regions of the liver lobule from phenobarbital-treated rats. *Tox. Appl. Pharmacol.* **107**, 344-349.

LITTON BIONETICS, INC. (1982a). Mutagenicity evaluation of 2-ethyl hexanol (2-EH) in the Ames *Salmonella*/microsome plate test. Final report; LBI project no. 20988; July 1982. Litton Bionetics, Inc., Kensington, MD, 20895 USA. Submitted to WHO by the Flavor and Extract Manufacturers' Association of the United States, Washington, DC, USA.

LITTON BIONETICS, INC. (1982b). Evaluation of 2-ethylhexanol in the in vitro transformation of BALB/3T3 cells assay. Final report; LBI project no. 20992; September 1992. Litton Bionetics, Inc., Kensington, MD, 20895, USA. Submitted to WHO by the Flavor and Extract Manufacturers' Association of the United States, Washington, DC, USA.

LITTON BIONETICS, INC. (1982c). Mutagenicity evaluation of 2-ethylhexanol (2-EH) in the mouse micronucleus test. Final report; LBI project no. 20996; September 1982. Litton Bionetics, Inc., Kensington, MD, 20895 USA. Submitted to WHO by the Flavor and Extract Manufacturers' Association of the United States, Washington, DC, USA.

MASHKINA, O.N. (1966). Toxicology of 2-ethylhexanal and 2-ethyl-hexanol. *Mater. Konf. Fiziol. Biokhim. Farmakol. Uchast. Prakt. Vrachei Ufa., USSR*, 168.

MIDWEST RESEARCH INSTITUTE. Metabolism and disposition of di-2-ethylhexanol adipate. Final report; MRI project no. 7550-B; October 18, 1984. Midwest Research Institute, Kansas City, MO 64110 USA. Submitted to WHO by the Flavor and Extract Manufacturers' Association of the United States, Washington, DC, USA.

MOODY, D.E. & REDDY, J.K. (1978). Hepatic peroxisome (microbody) proliferation in rats fed plasticizers and related compounds. *Toxicol. Appl. Pharmacol.* **45**, 497-504.

NELSON, B.K., BRIGHTWELL, W.S., KHAN, A., HOBERMAN, A.M. & KRIEG, Jr., E.F. (1988). Teratological evaluation of 1-pentanol, 1-hexanol, and 2-ethyl-1-hexanol administered by inhalation to rats. *Teratology* **37(5)**, 480.

NIOSH (1976). Registry of Toxic Effects of Chemical Substances. ed. by H.E. Christensen and E.J. Fairchild. Entry #MP03500, p. 586. National Institute for Occupational Safety and Health, Washington, DC, USA.

NRC. (1972). National Research Council/National Academy of Sciences. Committee on Food Protection. A comprehensive survey of industry on the use of food chemicals generally recognized as safe (GRAS). NTIS Accession No. PB 221-949. National Technical Information Service, Springfield, VA, USA.

NRC. (1989). 1987 Poundage and technical effects update of substances added to food. National Research Council/National Academy of Sciences, Washington, DC. Prepared for the U.S. Food and Drug Administration, Washington, DC, USA.

NTP. (1991). Final report on the developmental toxicity of 2-ethylhexanol (CAS No. 104-76-7) in CD-1 Swiss mice. PB91-185900 National Toxicology Program, Research Triangle Park, NC, USA.

PHILLIPS, B.J., JAMES, T.E.B. & GANGOLLI, S.D. (1982). Genotoxicity studies of di(2-ethylhexyl)phthalate and its metabolites in CHO cells. *Mut. Res.* **102**, 297-304.

PUTNAM, D.L., MOORE, W.A., SCHECHTMAN, L.M. & HODGSON, J.R. (1983). Cytogenic evaluation of di-(2-ethylhexyl)phthalate and its major metabolites in Fischer 344 rats. *Environ. Mutagen.* **5**, 227-231.

RHODES, C., SOAMES, T., STONARD, M.D., SIMPSON, M.G., VERNALL, A.J. & ELCOMBE, C.R. (1984). The absence of testicular atrophy and *in vivo* and *in vitro* effects on hepatocyte morphology and peroxisomal enzyme activities in male rats following administration of several alkanols. *Toxicol. Lett.* **21**, 103-109.

RITTER, E.J., SCOTT, W.J., FRADKIN, R. & RITTER, J.M. (1986). Computer analysis of rat teratology data following administration of phthalates and their metabolites. *Teratology* **33(3)**, 93C.

RITTER, E.J., SCOTT, W.J., RANDALL, J.L. & RITTER, J.M. (1987). Teratogenicity of di(2-ethylhexyl) phthalate, 2-ethylhexanol, 2-ethylhexanoic acid, and valproic acid, and potentiation by caffeine. *Teratology* **35**, 41-46.

RUSHBROOK, C.J., JORGENSON, T.A. & HODGSON, J.R. (1982). Dominant lethal study of di-(2-ethylhexyl)phthalate and its major metabolites in ICR/SIM mice. *Environ. Mutagen.* **4**(3), 387 (abstract).

SCALA, R.A. & BURTIS, E.G. (1973). Acute toxicity of a homologous series of branched-chain primary alcohols. *Am. Indust. Hygiene Assoc. J.* **34**(11), 493-499

SCHMIDT, P., GOHLKE, R., & ROTHE, R. (1973), Zur toxizitat einiger C8-aldehyd und -alkohol. *Z. Gesamte Hyg.* **19**(7):485-90

SEED, J.L. (1982). Mutagenic activity of phthalate esters in bacterial liquid suspension assays. *Environ. Health Perspect.* **45**, 111-114.

SETH, P.K. (1982). Hepatic effects of phthalate esters. *Environ. Health Perspect.* **45**, 27-34.

SJÖBERG, P., BONDESSON, U., GRAY, T.J.B. & PLÖN, L. (1986). Effects of di-(2-ethylhexyl) phthalate and five of its metabolites on rat testis in vivo and in vitro. *Acta Pharmacol. Toxicol.* **58**, 225-233.

SMYTH, H.F., Jr., CARPENTER, C.P., WEIL, C.S., POZZANI, U.C., STRIEGEL, J.A. & NYCUM, J.S. (1969). Range-finding toxicity data. List VII. *Am. Indust. Hygiene Assoc. J.* **30**(5), 470-476.

STOFBERG, J. & GRUNDSCHOBER, F. (1987). Consumption ratio and food predominance of flavoring materials. *Perfum. Flavor.* **12**, 27-68.

TOMITA, I., NAKAMURA, Y., AOKI, N. & INUI, N. (1982). Mutagenic/carcinogenic potential of DEHP and MEHP. *Environ. Health Perspect.* **45**, 119-125

TREON, J.F. (1963). Alcohols. In: Patty's Industrial Hygiene and Toxicology, Second Edition, Volume 2, Patty, F.A. (ed.). Interscience Publishers, New York, USA.

TYL, R.W., FISHER, L.C., KUBENA, M.F., VRBANIC, M.A., GINGELL, R., GUEST, D., HODGSON, J.R., MURPHY, S.R., TYLER, T.R. & ASTILL, B.D. (1992). The developmental toxicity of 2-ethylhexanol applied dermally to pregnant Fischer 344 rats. *Fund. Appl. Toxicol.* **19**(2), 176-185.

WILLIAMS, J. & FOSTER, P.M.D. (1988). The production of lactate and pyruvate as sensitive indices of altered rat Sertoli cell function in vitro following the addition of various testicular toxicants. *Tox. Appl. Pharmacol.* **94**, 160-170.

ZEIGER, E., HAWORTH, S., MORTELMANS, K. & SPECK, W. (1985). Mutagenicity testing of di(2-ethylhexyl)phthalate and related chemicals in Salmonella. *Environ. Mutagen.* **7**, 213-232.

α-METHYLBENZYL ALCOHOL

First draft prepared by
Ms E. Vavasour, Toxicological Evaluation Division
Bureau of Chemical Safety, Food Directorate
Health and Welfare Canada
Ottawa, Ontario, Canada

1   EXPLANATION

α-Methylbenzyl alcohol has not previously been evaluated by the Committee. This substance is used as a flavouring agent in foods and beverages; it also occurs naturally in a variety of foods at levels of up to 1.3 ppm (Maarse and Visscher 1991).

2   BIOLOGICAL DATA

2.1   Biochemical aspects

2.1.1   Absorption, distribution, and excretion

Following a single oral dose of 460 mg/kg bw in rabbits, α-methylbenzyl alcohol was rapidly excreted in the urine.   Within 24 hours, 82% of the dose was retrieved as urinary metabolites (Smith et al. 1954).

2.1.2   Biotransformation

Metabolites in the urine of rabbits following a single oral dose of 460 mg/kg bw α-methylbenzyl alcohol were α-methylbenzyl alcohol glucuronide (50%), hippuric acid (30%) and mandelic acid (1-2%) (Smith et al. 1954). These results in the rabbit were cited in a 1959 review, with the observation that both optical forms of the alcohol behaved similarly with respect to biotransformation (Williams, 1959).

Hopkins et al. (1972) reported that a small proportion of a dose of α-methylbenzyl alcohol in rats was excreted in the urine as acetophenone.

Rats displayed substrate stereoselectivity in the metabolism of racemic mixtures of α-methylbenzyl alcohol. The R(+) isomer was largely excreted as the glucuronide while the S(-) isomer underwent further oxidative metabolism (Testa and Jenner 1976).

2.2   Toxicological studies

2.2.1   Acute studies

The results of acute toxicity studies with α-methylbenzyl alcohol are summarized in Table 1.

Table 1. Acute toxicity studies with α-methylbenzyl alcohol

Animal	Route	LD_{50} (mg/kg bw)	Reference
Mouse	Oral	1 250[1]	Dieter 1990
Rat	Oral	400	Smyth & Carpenter 1944
Rat	Oral	1 250[1]	Dieter 1990

[1]Value is a LD_{low}

2.2.2   Short-term toxicity studies

2.2.2.1 Mice

Groups of male and female B6C3F$_1$ mice (4 or 5/sex/group), 6-8 weeks old, received 0, 125, 250, 500, 1 000, or 2 000 mg/kg bw/dy α-methylbenzyl alcohol in corn oil by gavage, 5 days a week over 16 days (12 doses). The animals were observed twice daily and weighed on day 1, after one week and at the end of the study. All animals were necropsied. Histological examinations were performed on two males and two females in the 500 mg/kg bw/dy dose group and on one male and one female in the control group. In the 1 000 and 2 000 mg/kg bw/dy groups, 16/18 mice died within 3 days. No treatment-related histopathological lesions were observed in the 500 mg/kg bw/dy group (Dieter 1990).

In a 13-week study, α-methylbenzyl alcohol was administered by gavage in corn oil to six groups of B6C3F$_1$ mice (10/sex/group) at dose levels of 0, 47, 94, 188, 375 or 750 mg/kg bw/dy for 5 days/week. Animals were observed twice daily and body weights recorded once weekly. A necropsy was performed on each animal and the liver weights were recorded. Histopathological examinations were performed on all animals in the vehicle control groups, all animals dying on test and on all male and female mice in the 750 mg/kg bw/dy group. No deaths occurred which were related to the effects of the test material. At the two top dose levels, mice exhibited laboured breathing, ataxia and lethargy for up to 30 minutes after dosing. Body weights were not affected by administration of the test material. Absolute and relative liver weights were significantly elevated from controls in both male and female groups receiving 187.5 mg/kg bw, but no dose-response relationship was evident. No treatment-related histopathological lesions were observed in the 750 mg/kg bw/dy dose group (Dieter 1990).

2.2.2.2 **Rats**

Groups of male and female F344/N rats (5/sex/group), 6-7 weeks old, received 0, 125, 250, 500, 1 000, or 2 000 mg/kg bw/dy α-methylbenzyl alcohol in corn oil by gavage, 5 days a week over 16 days (12 doses). The animals were observed twice daily and weighed on day 1, after one week and at the end of the study. All animals were necropsied. Histological examinations were performed on two males and two females in the 1 000 mg/kg bw/dy dose group and on one male and one female in the control group. In the 2 000 mg/kg bw/dy group, 2/5 male and 4/5 female rats died before the end of the study. Laboured breathing and lethargy were noted in one rat of each sex immediately after dosing in this group. The body weights of male and female rats in the top three dose groups were lower than those of the respective vehicle controls. In the highest dose group, body weight decrements from controls were 21% and 15%, respectively, for males and females. Haemorrhage in the gastrointestinal tract was observed in one female and two male rats in this group. No treatment-related histopathological lesions were observed in the two male and two female rats in the 1 000 mg/kg bw/dy group (Dieter 1990).

α-Methylbenzyl alcohol in corn oil was administered by gavage to six groups of F344/N rats (10/sex/group) at dose levels of 0, 93, 187, 375, 750, or 1 500 mg/kg bw, 5 days/week for 13 weeks. Animals were observed twice daily and body weights recorded once weekly. A necropsy was performed on each animal. The livers were weighed at this time. Histopathological examinations were performed on all animals in the vehicle control groups, all animals dying on test and on all male and female rats in the 1 500 mg/kg bw/dy group. Histopathological examination of the spleen was carried out in male rats in the 375 mg/kg bw/dy group and in male and female rats in the 750 mg/kg bw/dy group. In the 1 500 mg/kg bw/dy dose group, 1/10 male and 3/10 females died as a result of treatment with the test material. Body weights of male rats in the 1 500 mg/kg bw/dy groups were significantly decreased at the end of the study compared with vehicle controls. Throughout the study, rats receiving 750 or 1 500 mg/kg bw/dy exhibited ataxia, rapid breathing and lethargy for up to 30 minutes after dosing. Relative liver weights were significantly elevated in all the treated female groups and in the 3 top male dose groups. The absolute liver weights were also elevated in comparison with the controls in these groups, with statistical significance in all but one of the treated female groups (187 mg/kg bw) and none of the male groups. No pathological changes of the liver were noted during histopathological examination of the high-dose group. A minimal-to-mild increase in brown pigment, characteristic of haemosiderin, was noted in the macrophages of the spleen in 10/10 of the male rats receiving 750 mg/kg bw, 9/10 receiving 1 500 mg/kg bw. and in none receiving 375 mg/kg bw. In the female rats, a similar pigment was seen in 6/10 receiving 1 500 mg/kg bw. and none receiving 750 mg/kg bw/dy (Dieter 1990).

2.2.3   Long-term toxicity/carcinogenicity studies

2.2.3.1 Mice

A carcinogenicity study was conducted with B6C3F$_1$ mice in which groups of 49 or 50 mice of each sex were administered 0, 375 or 750 mg/kg bw/dy of α-methylbenzyl alcohol in corn oil by gavage, 5 days/week, for 103 weeks. Mice were observed twice daily. Body weights were recorded weekly for the first 12 weeks and once a month for the rest of the study. Necropsy was performed on all animals at termination and those dying on test. Histopathological examination of 33 tissues and organs was conducted in all mice from all groups.

There was a greater than 10% reduction in body weight gain in the high-dose males and females, but administration of α-methylbenzyl alcohol had no effect on survival. There were no increases which were attributable to administration of the test material in neoplastic or nonneoplastic lesions of the kidney or any of the other tissues. The NOEL for this study was 375 mg/kg bw/day based on the reduction in body weight gain at the next higher dose (Dieter 1990).

2.2.3.2 Rats

Male and female F344/N rats, 50/sex/group, received 0, 375 or 750 mg/kg bw/dy α-methylbenzyl alcohol in corn oil by gavage 5 days/week for 103 weeks. Rats were observed twice daily. Body weights were recorded weekly for the first 12 weeks and once a month for the rest of the study. Necropsy was performed on all animals at termination and those dying on test. Histopathological examination of 36 tissues and organs was conducted in all rats from all groups.

There was a greater than 10% reduction in body weight gains in both treated male groups and the high-dose females. Survival of rats in these groups was also significantly reduced. At study termination, male rat survival was 35/50, 8/50 and 1/50 for the control low-dose and high-dose groups, respectively; for the female rats, survival was 34/50, 26/50 and 11/50, respectively. A cluster of accidental deaths in both groups of treated males and in the high-dose females during weeks 48 to 53 were considered to have been gavage-related even though the animals had not been handled differently from the other groups and no other predisposing factors could be found.

Chronic progressive nephropathy was a common age-related finding in both male and female rats. Treatment with either dose of α-methylbenzyl alcohol resulted in an increased severity of this lesion in the male, but not the female rats and also contributed to lowered survival in these groups. A statistically significant increase was noted in the combined incidence of adenomas and adenocarcinomas of the kidney in male rats at both doses (control, 1/49; low-dose, 13/41; high-dose, 14/28 [the denominator represents the number of animals alive at week 81 when the first kidney tumour was observed]). In fact, of these neoplasms, only one adenocarcinoma was detected and it was found in a low-dose animal. Because renal tubular cell neoplasms are often late-appearing, and were not visible macroscopically at necropsy, multiple sections of the kidney were used to evaluate the incidence of these lesions. The incidence of tubular cell hyperplasia in the male rats was 1/49, 7/41 and 6/28 for the control, low-dose and high-dose animals, respectively. There was no indication that the renal toxicity was mediated through α_{2u}-globulin, since no compound-related increases in hyaline droplet formation were observed in the short-term studies described above (data not presented). [However, immunohistochemical analysis for detection of α_{2u}-globulin is a more sensitive technique to preclude this as a mechanism for the genesis of these neoplasms.] Parathyroid hyperplasia, calcification of the heart and glandular stomach, and fibrous osteodystrophy of the bone were observed at markedly increased incidences in the low-dose male rats. These changes were believed to be secondary to a mineral imbalance caused by renal toxicity. The incidence of hyperplasia of the transitional epithelium overlying the renal pelvis also was significantly increased in the low-dose male rats (control - 3/50; low dose - 20/50; high dose - 4/50; females: 1/50, 0/49, 0/50). Transitional cell papillomas of the urinary bladder were observed in 1/47 high-dose male rats and 2/48 high-dose female rats and in none of the other groups. The historical incidence for this lesion in both sexes of F344/N rats is 0.2%. The incidences of epithelial hyperplasia of the urinary bladder did not show an increase in the treated rats (male: control - 3/48; low dose - 4/46; high dose - 1/47; female: 0/49; 1/47; 0/48).

The incidence of several other lesions was increased in treated groups compared with controls: in males (centrilobular necrosis of the liver, inflammation of the forestomach, suppurative inflammation of the nasal cavity, acute inflammation of the salivary glands); or in both sexes (congestion of the lung, haemorrhage and foreign material in the lung). A no-effect level was not observed in this study since reduced survival and body weight gain and an increased incidence of kidney adenomas were noted in the male rats at both doses administered in this study (Dieter 1990).

2.2.4 Reproduction Studies

No information available

2.2.5 Special studies on teratogenicity

α-Methylbenzyl alcohol was applied dermally to the skin of pregnant Sprague-Dawley rats at doses of 0, 0.14, 0.43 and 1.40 ml/kg bw/dy on days 6-15 of gestation. With a specific gravity of 1.01, these doses were equivalent within 1% to the same doses in g/kg bw. At the high dose, the test material exhibited an increased incidence of embryolethality, growth retardation and malformations (anophthalmia, microphthalmia, ventricular septal defects, defects and irregularities affecting the thorax, kinky tail, defects of the thoracic ribs and occurrence of cervical ribs) as well as maternal toxicity. The NOEL in this study was 0.43 g/kg bw/dy. Since only summary data from this study were available in preparation of this monograph, it was not possible to determine the independence of the teratogenic and embryotoxic effects from maternal toxicity (USEPA 1976, cited Dieter, 1990).

2.2.6   Special studies on genotoxicity

The results of genotoxicity studies with α-methylbenzyl alcohol are summarized in Table 2.

Table 2. Results of genotoxicity assays on α-methylbenzyl alcohol

Test System	Test Object	Concentration of α-methylbenzyl alcohol	Results	Reference
Ames test[1]	S. typhimurium TA98, TA100, TA1535, TA1537	33-6 666 μg/ml	Negative	Dieter 1990
DNA damage/growth inhibition	E. coli	50 μl/plate	Negative	Fluck et al. 1976
Yeast mutation	S. sake	0.20%	Positive	Kojima et al. 1976
Mammalian cell mutation (trifluoro- thymidine resistance)	Mouse L5178Y/- TK+/- lymphoma cells	62.5-1 200 μg/ml	Positive	Dieter 1990
Chromosomal aberration[1]	Chinese hamster ovary cells	1 000-3 000 μg/ml	Positive (+S9)	Dieter 1990
Sister chromatid exchange[1]	Chinese hamster ovary cells	33.3-1 000 μg/ml	Negative	Dieter 1990

[1]Both in the presence and absence of metabolic activation.

2.3   Observations in humans

Contact sensitization tests using 8% α-methylbenzyl alcohol in petrolatum produced no sensitization reactions in 25 volunteers (Kligman 1966, 1973).

No information was available concerning the effects of ingestion of this flavouring in humans.

3   COMMENTS

Following oral administration this compound is rapidly excreted in the urine.   The principal metabolites have been identified as hippuric acid and the glucuronide conjugate.

The Committee reviewed a series of acute, short-term, and long-term toxicity studies in which α-methylbenzyl alcohol was administered in corn oil by gavage in rats and mice. In addition, the Committee evaluated a dermal teratogenicity study in rats and a battery of *in vitro* genotoxicity tests, which included bacterial and mammalian point mutation and mammalian chromosomal aberration studies.

In the short-term toxicity studies, high rates of mortality were associated with dose levels of 1 000 mg/kg bw/day and above in the mouse and 2 000 mg/kg bw/day in the rat.

An increase in haemosiderin deposits in macrophages of the spleen was noted at 750 mg/kg bw/day in male rats during a 13-week study. This effect was not, however, noted during a 2-year study. A dose-related increase in liver weight that was noted in both male and female rats in the 13-week study could not be assessed in the 2-year study since liver weights were not recorded. However, an increase in the incidence of centrilobular necrosis was observed in male rats at both dose levels (375 and 750 mg/kg bw/day) in the latter study.

In the long-term toxicity studies, the body weight gains were at least 10% higher in untreated controls in male and female mice and in female rats at doses of 750 mg/kg bw/day and in male rats at 375 and 750 mg/kg bw/day. Long-term survival of the rats, but not the mice, was significantly reduced by oral administration of α-methylbenzyl alcohol at 375 or 750 mg/kg bw/day. Exacerbation of age-related nephropathy was noted at both dose levels in male rats. The incidence of renal tubular cell hyperplasia and adenomas was also statistically-significantly increased in these rats than in untreated controls. A NOEL was not observed in this study.

A teratogenicity study in rats in which α-methylbenzyl alcohol was administered dermally showed a range of teratogenic and embryotoxic effects at the highest dose of 1400 mg/kg bw/day. Maternal toxicity was also demonstrated at this dose. Because α-methylbenzyl alcohol was administered dermally, the extent of absorption and metabolism were likely to differ from absorption and metabolism by the oral route, hence comparability of dose levels was uncertain. The NOEL in this study was 430 mg/kg bw/day.

α-Methylbenzyl alcohol was mutagenic in eukaryotic cells (mammalian and yeast), but not in prokaryotic cells (bacteria) and induced chromosomal aberrations in mammalian cells *in vitro*.

The Committee noted that α-methylbenzyl alcohol administered by gavage in corn oil was associated with a higher incidence of renal tubular cell adenomas in male rats than in untreated contols, but not in female rats or in mice, at dose levels at or exceeding the MTD and in the presence of factors that exacerbated a high incidence of age-related chronic progressive nephropathy.

4   EVALUATION

The intake of this compound is extremely low. On the basis of the available evidence, the Committee concluded that the higher incidence of benign neoplasms in the kidney of male rats is not relevant to humans. In view of the limited database, the Committee concluded that the available data could be used to set an ADI by application of a 1 000-fold safety factor to the minimal-effect level of 93 mg/kg bw/day with respect to liver weight increase in the absence of associated pathology in the 13-week study in rats. On this basis, an ADI of 0-0.1 mg/kg bw/day was allocated for α-methylbenzyl alcohol.

5.   REFERENCES

DIETER, M.P. (1990). Toxicology and carcinogenesis studies of α-methylbenzyl alcohol in F344/N rats and B6C3F₁ mice (gavage studies). National Toxicology Program (NTP), Technical Report Series No. 369, NIH Publication No. 89-2824, Department of Health and Human Services, Research Triangle Park, NC 27709, USA.

FLUCK, E.R., POIRIER, L.A. & RUELIUS, H.W. (1976). Evaluation of a DNA polymerase-deficient mutant of *E. coli* for the rapid detection of carcinogens. *Chem. Biol. Interact.*, **15**, 219-231. (Cited Dieter, 1990).

HOPKINS, R.P., BORGE, P.A. & CALLAGHAN, P. (1972). Dehydrogenation of DL-methylphenyl-carbinol in the rat. *Proc. Biochem. Soc.* **127**, 26P-27P.

KLIGMAN, A.M. (1966). The identification of contact allergens by human assay, III. The maximization test. A procedure for screening and rating contact sensitizers. *Journal of Investigative Dermatology*, **47**, 393. (Cited Opdyke, 1974).

KLIGMAN, A.M. (1973). Report to Research Institute for Fragrance Materials. 9 October. (Cited Opdyke, 1974).

KOJIMA, M., KATOHGI, Y. & HATAE, K. (1976). Induction of a respiration-deficient mutant of *Saccharomyces sake* by phenyl propanols and related compounds. *Hakko Kogaku Zasshi (J. Ferment. Technol.)*, **54**, 11-15. (Cited Dieter, 1990).

MAARSE, H. & VISSCHER, C.A. (1991). Volatile Compounds in Food. Qualitative and Quantitative Data. Supplement 2. TNO Biotechnology and Chemistry Institute. Zeist, The Netherlands.

OPDYKE, D.L.J. (1974). Styrallyl alcohol. *Food and Cosmetics Toxicology*, **12** (Suppl.), (Special Issue - Monographs on Fragrance Raw Materials). December 1974.

SMITH, J.N., SMITHIES, R.H. & WILLIAMS, R.T. (1954). The metabolism of alkylbenzenes. Stereochemical aspects of the biological hydroxylation of ethylbenzene to methylphenylcarbinol. *Biochemistry*, **56**, 320-324. (Cited Dieter, 1990).

SMYTH, H.F. & CARPENTER, C.P. (1944). The place of the range finding test in the industrial toxicology laboratory. *J. Ind. Hyg. Toxicol.* **26**, 269-273. (Cited Dieter, 1990).

TESTA, B. & JENNER, P. (1976). Drug Metabolism: Chemical and Biochemical Aspects. New York: Marcel Dekker, Inc., p. 247. (Cited Dieter, 1990).

U.S. Environmental Protection Agency (USEPA) (1976). Organic Compounds Identified in Drinking Water in the United States. USEPA, Cincinnati. (Cited Dieter, 1990).

WILLIAMS, R.T. (1959). Detoxication Mechanisms. The Metabolism and Detoxication of Drugs, Toxic Substances and Other Organic Compounds, 2nd ed., p. 321. Chapman & Hall Ltd., London. (Cited Opdyke, 1974).

FLAVOUR ENHANCERS

DISODIUM 5'-GUANYLATE AND DISODIUM 5'-INOSINATE

First draft prepared by
Dr K. Ekelman and Dr K. C. Raffaele, Additives Evaluation Branch
Division of Health Effects Evaluation
Center for Food Safety and Applied Nutrition
Food and Drug Administration, Washington, DC, USA

1.   EXPLANATION

The disodium salts of 5'-guanylic acid and 5'-inosinic acid were previously evaluated at the eighteenth meeting of the Committee, when an ADI "not specified" was allocated (Annex 1, reference 35). At that time, metabolism, teratogenicity, and acute, short-term and long-term toxicity of the two substances, as well as data on the reproductive toxicity of inosinic acid and its calcium and sodium salts, were reviewed. The present Committee reviewed these compounds together, as many of the new toxicological studies had been performed on mixtures of the two salts. Data from the earlier reviews have been incorporated into this consolidated monograph.

2.   BIOLOGICAL DATA

2.1   Biochemical aspects

2.1.1   Absorption, distribution, and excretion

Disodium 5'-guanylate

Male and pregnant female (day 10 or 18 of gestation) rats were given 25 mg/kg bw of 8-[^{14}C] disodium 5'-guanylate by gavage. Plasma radioactivity reached a maximum 30 minutes after ingestion and decreased abruptly to near zero within 24 hours; t½ was about one hour. Twenty-four hours after exposure, about 84% of total activity appeared in urine, 0.2% in faeces, none in expired air, between 0-0.6% remained in organs; about 12% of total activity remained in organ-free carcass of males and pregnant females (18th day of gestation) 24 hours after treatment. Fetuses contained about 0.01% of activity 24 hours after treatment (Ohara et al., 1973).

Disodium 5'-inosinate

Male and pregnant female (day 10 or 18 of gestation) rats were given by gavage 25 mg/kg bw of 8-^{14}C labelled disodium 5'-inosinate. Radioactivity in plasma reached maximum levels ½ to 2 hours after treatment and slowly decreased to practically zero after 24 hours; t½ was about 5 hours. About 70% of total activity appeared in the urine, 6-7% in faeces, none in expired air, 0-2% in organs, and 8-17% in the organ-free carcass of males and pregnant females (18th day of gestation) 24 hours after treatment. Fetuses contained about 0.77% of total activity 24 hours after treatment (Ohara et al., 1973).

2.1.2   Biotransformation

Disodium 5'-guanylate

The greater portion of disodium 5'-guanylate in the body is derived from *de novo* purine bio-synthesis and the rest is derived from pre-formed dietary purines. Biosynthesized disodium 5'-inosinate is the precursor of disodium 5'-guanylate, to which it is converted by oxidation to xanthosine-5-mono-phosphate and amination. Dietary or endogenous purine bases and ribonucleosides are converted to the 5'-ribonucleotides by phosphorylation.

Disodium 5'-guanylate is dephosphorylated to guanosine, hydrolyzed to guanine, deaminated to xanthine and oxidized to uric acid. In most mammals, uric acid is further oxidized by the liver enzyme urate oxidase to allantoin. Primates, including humans, lack the enzyme, however; for them, uric acid is the main end product of purine metabolism. In humans, ⅔ of uric acid is excreted in the urine; the rest is further broken down in the gut. Digestion of disodium 5'-guanylate appears to take place mainly in the duodenum: the nucleosides are probably absorbed actively, the purines probably diffuse passively across the intestinal wall (Kojima, 1974).

Disodium 5'-inosinate

Disodium 5'-inosinate derives from dephosphorylation of ATP (adenosine-5-triphosphate) to AMP and deamination. Further conversion to hypoxanthine is slow compared to the conversion of ATP to disodium 5'-inosinate. The greater portion of disodium 5'-inosinate in living tissue is derived from *de novo* purine biosynthesis, and less is derived from ingested dietary purines or nucleotides. Disodium 5'-inosinate is the first purine formed in the complex biosynthesis of purine nucleotides (Kojima, 1974).

2.1.3   Effects on enzymes and other biochemical parameters

Groups of five male rats (control group size was 10) were given 0%, 1%, or 4% disodium 5'-guanylate or disodium 5'-inosinate for five or 10 days in a purine-free basal diet. Levels of uric acid in serum and urine were not significantly affected, and most of the ingested disodium 5'-guanylate and disodium 5'-inosinate was rapidly excreted in urine as allantoin. However, liver hypoxanthine-guanine phosphoribosyl transferase and adenine phosphoribosyl transferase activities were increased and the ratio of liver uricase/xanthine oxidase activity was increased, suggesting metabolism of ingested disodium 5'-guanylate and disodium 5'-inosinate by shunt pathways (Hashimoto et al., 1973).

2.2   Toxicological studies

2.2.1   Acute toxicity studies

Disodium 5'-guanylate

Results of acute toxicity studies with disodium 5'-guanylate are summarized in Table 1.

Table 1: Acute toxicity studies with disodium 5'-guanylate

Species	Sex	Route	LD_{50} (mg/kg bw)	Reference
Mouse	M&F	oral	>10 000	Usui et al., 1971
Mouse	M	oral	15 000	Ichimura & Muroi, 1973
Mouse	F	oral	16 300	Ichimura & Muroi, 1973
Mouse	M	s.c.	5 050	Ichimura & Muroi, 1973
Mouse	F	s.c.	5 050	Ichimura & Muroi, 1973
Mouse	M	i.p.	6 800	Ichimura & Muroi, 1973
Mouse	F	i.p.	5 010	Ichimura & Muroi, 1973
Mouse	M	i.v.	3 580	Ichimura & Muroi, 1973
Mouse	F	i.v.	3 950	Ichimura & Muroi, 1973
Mouse	M	i.v.	3800	Shimamoto et al., 1974
Rat	M&F	oral	>10 000	Usui et al., 1971
Rat	M	oral	17 300	Ichimura & Muroi, 1973
Rat	F	oral	17 300	Ichimura & Muroi, 1973
Rat	M	s.c.	3 550	Ichimura & Muroi, 1973
Rat	F	s.c.	3 400	Ichimura & Muroi, 1973
Rat	M	i.p.	4 750	Ichimura & Muroi, 1973
Rat	F	i.p.	3 880	Ichimura & Muroi, 1973
Rat	M	i.v.	2 720	Ichimura & Muroi, 1973
Rat	F	i.v.	2 850	Ichimura & Muroi, 1973

A series of experiments was performed to assess a variety of acute effects of disodium 5'-guanylate. In mice, an i.v. dose of 500 mg/kg bw disodium 5'-guanylate produced abdominal postures, slight respiratory depression and slight depression of avoidance response to mechanical stimuli at 15 min (response had returned to normal at 30 min). There was no muscular relaxation (defined as failure to remain on a 2 mm diameter metal bar for 30 sec, measured at 10 and 30 minutes after dosing) but spontaneous revolutions (during placement in a rotating cage) were decreased (p < .05 vs. control) at one hour and decreased (not statistically significant) at 2 hr. There was no modification of electroshock convulsion after an i.v. dose of 500 mg/kg bw, but there was a dose-dependent decrease of the dose of metrazol required to produce convulsions when infusion of metrazol was started immediately after i.v. injection of 200 or 500 mg/kg bw disodium 5'-guanylate (this decrease was significant only at 500 mg/kg bw). Doses of 125 mg/kg bw and 500 mg/kg bw disodium 5'-guanylate, i.v., also caused prolongation of the time during which there was loss of righting reflex following methylhexabital anaesthesia (methylhexabital was injected i.p. 10 min after dosing; the time of measurement was not stated), but there was no effect on this response at 50 mg/kg bw disodium 5'-guanylate. Oral administration of 500 mg/kg bw disodium 5'-guanylate to mice did not affect their analgesic response to thermal stimuli (measured as pain threshold in seconds [the method was not described but was presumably the latency of paw removal from a hot plate]). Compared to controls, 100 mg/kg bw s.c. disodium 5'-guanylate in mice depressed salivary secretion following stimulation by pilocarpine. Pilocarpine was administered 35 min after disodium 5'-guanylate; secretion was measured for 20 minutes starting immediately after pilocarpine injection. There was no effect of an oral dose of 500 mg/kg bw disodium 5'-guanylate on carrageenin-induced oedema in rats. Administration of 100 mg/kg bw disodium 5'-guanylate s.c. to rats did not affect the secretion of gastric juices but slightly increased their pH and depressed their total acidity. Intragastric administration of 25 mg/kg bw disodium 5'-guanylate had no diuretic effect in rats. Concentrations of disodium 5'-guanylate below 10^{-4}g/ml had no effect on the contractile response of isolated guinea-pig ilium to acetylcholine, histamine, or barium chloride (Shimamoto et al, 1974).

Topical disodium 5'-guanylate (applied to the tongue acutely at a concentration of 0.01% disodium 5'-guanylate with 0.3% MSG) enhanced the electrical response of the chorda tympani to topical MSG in the rat (Sato et al., 1971).

Disodium 5'-guanylate administered i.p. had no marked effect on the conditioned avoidance response of the rat. Parenteral disodium 5'-guanylate produced transient changes in the electroencephalogram (EEG) of rabbits (Hirayama, 1968).

Intravenous disodium 5'-guanylate had no significant effect on the blood pressure, heart-rate, or electrocardiogram (ECG) of the anaesthetized rabbit (Yabo, 1964).

Rapid intracarotid injection of disodium 5'-guanylate increased the cerebral blood flow but did not affect oxygen consumption or glucose uptake in the perfused cat brain (Otsuki et al., 1968).

Anæsthetized cats were exposed to disodium 5'-guanylate via a tube inserted into the femoral vein or a tube inserted into the medial sacral artery. Acute infusions of 10, 25, or 50 mg/kg bw disodium 5'-guanylate caused transient, slight, dose-dependent hypotension that was associated with tachycardia, and increased blood flow to the hind limbs. Intra-arterial infusion of disodium 5'-guanylate at doses greater than 10 mg/kg caused transient increases in blood flow to the hind limbs. There was no change in ECG pattern with either method of dosing.

In isolated guinea-pig atria, doses of disodium 5'-guanylate up to 10^{-5} g/ml did not affect contractile height or atrial rhythm; disodium 5'-guanylate at 10^{-4} g/ml increased the rate and strength of contractions; 10^{-3} g/ml further increased the rate and slightly decreased the strength of contractions (Shimamoto et al., 1974).

Disodium 5'-inosinate

Results of acute toxicity studies with disodium 5'-inosinate are summarized in Table 2.

A series of experiments was performed by Shimamoto and coworkers to assess a variety of acute effects of disodium 5'-inosinate. In mice, i.v. administration of 500 mg/kg bw disodium 5'-inosinate caused behavioural excitement, increased reflex response, no muscular relaxation (measured by the ability to remain on a horizontal metal bar for 30 sec or by the ability to remain on a screen inclined at 60°) and depressed rotating activity (measured as the number of spontaneous rotations during placement in a rotating cage) during the first hour following administration of disodium 5'-inosinate. Administration of 500 mg/kg bw i.v. did not modify electroshock convulsions in mice; however, disodium 5'-inosinate doses of 100 and 500 mg/kg bw decreased the dose of metrazol that produced continuous convulsions. Administration of 50-500 mg disodium 5'-inosinate/kg bw i.v. to mice prolonged loss of the righting reflex after anaesthesia with methylhexabital. Administration of 10-50 mg disodium 5'-inosinate/kg bw i.v. to cats had no effect on blood pressure, heart rate, ECG, or blood flow to the hind limbs. Incubation with medium containing 10^{-5} g/ml disodium 5'-inosinate did not affect the height and rhythm of spontaneous movements of isolated guinea-pig atria; incubation with 10^{-3} g/ml disodium 5'-inosinate, however, depressed contractile height by 16.5% and slightly increased the rate of contractions (Shimamoto et al., 1974).

A 1:4 000 dilution of disodium 5'-inosinate first increased motility and then decreased tone of an immersed, isolated guinea pig uterus (Floessner, 1934).

Topical disodium 5'-inosinate enhanced the electrical response of the chordotympani to topical MSG in rats and cats (Adachi, 1964; Sato et al., 1965).

Table 2:   Acute toxicity studies with disodium 5'-inosinate

Species	Sex	Route	LD$_{50}$ (mg/kg bw)	Reference
Mouse	M&F	oral	>10 000	Usui *et al.*, 1971
Mouse	?	oral	12 000-14 000	Hara *et al.*, 1966
Mouse	M	oral	17 600	Ichimura & Muroi, 1973
Mouse	F	oral	19 800	Ichimura & Muroi, 1973
Mouse	F	oral	>20 000	Merck petition
Mouse	?	s.c.	6 200-7 000	Hara *et al.*, 1966
Mouse	M	s.c.	5 480	Ichimura & Muroi, 1973
Mouse	F	s.c.	5 630	Ichimura & Muroi, 1973
Mouse	?	i.p.	5 400-5 600	Hara *et al.*, 1966
Mouse	M	i.p.	6 300	Ichimura & Muroi, 1973
Mouse	F	i.p.	6 200	Ichimura & Muroi, 1973
Mouse	?	i.v.	3 300-3 900	Hara *et al.*, 1966
Mouse	M	i.v.	3 950	Ichimura & Muroi, 1973
Mouse	F	i.v.	4 600	Ichimura & Muroi, 1974
Mouse	M	i.v.	4 400	Shimamoto *et al.*, 1974
Rat	M&F	oral	>10 000	Usui *et al.*, 1971
Rat	M	oral	17 100	Ichimura & Muroi, 1973
Rat	F	oral	15 900	Ichimura & Muroi, 1973
Rat	M	s.c.	3 900	Ichimura & Muroi, 1973
Rat	F	s.c.	4 340	Ichimura & Muroi, 1973
Rat	M	i.p.	5 400	Ichimura & Muroi, 1973
Rat	F	i.p.	4 850	Ichimura & Muroi, 1973
Rat	M	i.v.	2 730	Ichimura & Muroi, 1973
Rat	F	i.v.	2 870	Ichimura & Muroi, 1973

A 1% solution of disodium 5'-inosinate decreased the mobility of isolated guinea-pig intestine (Hara *et al.*, 1966).

In a series of studies, Shimamoto and coworkers reported that: 1) administration of 50 and 100 mg/kg bw disodium 5'-inosinate s.c. to mice decreased the pilocarpine-induced increase in salivary secretion; 2) administration of 100 mg/kg bw disodium 5'-inosinate s.c. to mice had no effect on charcoal transport in the small intestine; 3) incubation with medium containing 10^{-3} g/ml disodium 5'-inosinate did not affect the contractile response of isolated guinea-pig ileum to acetylcholine, histamine, or barium chloride; 4) oral administration of 500 mg/kg bw disodium 5'-inosinate had no effect on analgesic response to thermal stimuli in mice or carrageenin-induced oedema in rats; 5) administration of 100 mg/kg bw disodium 5'-inosinate s.c. had no effect on gastric juice volume in the rat but slightly increased gastric pH; and 6) rats given 100 mg/kg bw intragastric disodium 5'-inosinate showed no diuresis (Shimamoto et al., 1974).

Disodium 5'-inosinate caused no changes in renal function or renal venous renin after arterial infusion at 50-500 ug/min in anaesthetized, sodium-depleted dogs (Tagawa and Vander, 1970).

Disodium 5'-inosinate injected i.v. in anaesthetized rabbit had no effect on blood pressure or respiration at 5-10 mg/kg bw, but 50 mg/kg bw and above caused a transient decrease in blood pressure and potentiation of respiration (Hara, 1966).

Disodium 5'-inosinate injected i.v. caused hypotension in the rabbit at 0.2 mg/kg bw and in the dog at 0.35 mg/kg bw (Floessner, 1934).

Pharmacological studies on disodium 5'-inosinate showed no effect on the S-A or A-V nodes in the Langendorff preparation of rat heart (Versprille, 1966).

2.2.2   Short-term toxicity studies

2.2.2.1   Rats

Disodium 5'-guanylate

Groups of 10 male rats were given 0%, 0.1%, or 1% disodium 5'-guanylate in their diet daily for three and six months. The authors stated that no significant abnormalities were noted as regards spontaneous behaviour, body weight gain, food intake, haematology, urinalysis, and macroscopic and histological examination. However, data in tables included only a few subjects in each group so the authors' conclusions could not be confirmed (Usui et al., 1971).

Disodium 5'-inosinate

Groups of 10 male rats were fed diets containing either 0, 10, 100 or 1 000 mg/kg bw/dy naturally derived or synthetically prepared disodium 5'-inosinate for 90 days. No adverse effects were noted on weight gain, organ weights, haematological parameters or histopathology (Hara et al., 1966).

Eight male and 8 female Sprague-Dawley rats were fed diets containing 0%, 0.5%, 1.0%, 2.0% or 4.0% disodium 5'-inosinate for 12 weeks followed by levels of 0%, 0.75%, 1.5%, 3.0%, or 6.0% disodium 5'-inosinate during weeks 13-25. No significant abnormalities in any treatment group with regard to behaviour, body weight gain, food intake, haematology or urinalysis were reported. Some animals in higher dosage groups showed renal medullary calcification; relative mean weights of kidney and spleen in the 6% disodium 5'-inosinate groups were significantly increased.

In a second experiment, 6 male and 6 female Sprague-Dawley rats were given 0%, 1%, 4%, or 8% disodium 5'-inosinate in the diet for 52 weeks. The only adverse effects noted were slight depression of body weight gain in the groups fed 8% disodium 5'-inosinate. Increased renal calcifications was seen in the 4% and 8% females; this was probably related to urine osmolarity. The 8% males and 2% and 8% females showed more severe nephrosis than rats in other groups (Yonetani *et al.*, 1973).

Groups of 10 male rats were given 0%, 0.1%, or 1% of disodium 5'-inosinate in their diet daily for three and six months. Average daily intake of disodium 5'-inosinate was reported to be 45.8 mg/kg bw/dy for the 0.1% group and 496.5 mg/kg bw/dy for the 1% group. Tables in the report included data on only a few animals in each group and did not always indicate the number of animals for which mean values were calculated. The authors stated that no significant abnormalities were noted in spontaneous behaviour, body weight gain, food intake, haematology, urinalysis, or macroscopic and histological examination. However, absolute lung weight was decreased in both disodium 5'-inosinate-fed groups when compared to the control group (mean lung weight at six months: 1239 for controls; 869 for 0.1% disodium 5'-inosinate group; 879 for 1% disodium 5'-inosinate group [units not reported]). Although the authors attributed this change to the presence of pneumonitis leading to increased lung weight, which was most pronounced in control rats, this reviewer was unable to discern any relationship between degree of pneumonitis and lung weight (Usui *et al.*, 1971). The authors stated that some animals were excluded from the final tabulation of results due to pulmonary infection, but the numbers excluded from each group were not provided.

Disodium 5'-guanylate + disodium 5'-inosinate

Male rats (group size unspecified, but apparently 10 at the beginning of the study) were given 0.2, 0.4, 0.8, or 2% of a 50:50 mixture of disodium 5'-guanylate and disodium 5'-inosinate (50:50 mix) in the diet for 6 months. Three rats in each group died during the course of the study due to pulmonary infection. Mean ribotide intake was 30.8 mg/day for the 0.2% group, 63 mg/day for the 0.4% group, 123.5 mg/day for the 0.8% group, and 308.6 mg/day for the 2% group. There were no changes in body weight, haemoglobin, erythrocyte, leucocyte, or haematocrit (blood parameters measured for 5 rats/group only) for rats in any dose group compared to control rats. There were some scattered statistically significant changes in organ weights, which did not appear dose-related; there was a trend toward an increase in kidney weight with dose, but this was not statistically significant. The Committee did not consider the statistics to be reliable, since some statistical findings reported were anomalous.

An additional study reported by the same group included administration of 0.8% and 4% 50:50 mix for 3 months; although some results from the 3-month study were discussed in the report on the 6-month study, data from the 3-month study were not reported separately (Usui *et al.*, 1971).

2.2.2.2 Dogs

Disodium 5'-inosinate

One male and one female beagle were fed diets containing 0%, 3.6-3.9% or 8% disodium 5'-inosinate for four to six weeks without any adverse effect (Noel *et al.*, 1971).

Four male and four female beagles were fed diets containing 0, 0.5, 1 or 2 g/kg disodium 5'-inosinate for two years. No significant changes were reported in body weight gain, feed consumption or ophthalmoscopy. Haematology, biochemistry and urinalysis were normal. Dogs fed 2 g/kg bw/day disodium 5'-inosinate had significantly increased allantoin levels in the serum but these were not dose-related. Histopathological examination showed no significant abnormalities (Rivett *et al.*, 1973).

Disodium 5'-guanylate + disodium 5'-inosinate

Preliminary studies were conducted using groups of 1 male and 1 female beagle dog/dose, with feeding of 50:50 mix in the diet at levels of 0, 2, 5, or 10% for four weeks (6 weeks at the 10% level). Weight gain was slightly decreased in the 10% group during the 3-6 week period. All *post mortem* findings, including organ weights and histological examinations, were normal for all groups (no data were presented for the preliminary study).

Beagle dogs, 4 animals/sex/group (4 months of age at the start of the study) were fed diets containing 0, 0.1 (mean daily intake 30-40 mg/kg bw), 1.0 (mean daily intake 26-48 mg/kg bw), or 2.0% (mean daily intake 51-93 mg/kg bw) 50:50 mix for 2 years. Clinical signs and feed intake were recorded daily; water consumption was checked at monthly intervals. Ophthalmoscopic examinations, urinalyses, haematological examinations, and blood biochemistry studies, including the determination of serum electrolytes, allantoin and uric acid, were conducted before dosing and at 1, 2, 4, 6, 9, 12, 15, 18, 21, and 24 months after initiation of treatment. Serum allantoin and uric acid levels were raised, sometimes in a dose-related manner, at several time points during the study: serum allantoin (mg/100 ml) was raised at 8 weeks in all dosed groups (control=2.11; 0.1%=2.42; 1%=2.58; 2%=2.67), at 16 weeks in the .1% and 1% groups (control=2.03; 0.1%=2.67; 1%=3.23), and at 92 weeks in all groups (control=1.82; 0.1%=2.43; 1%=3.04; 2%=2.90); serum uric acid (mg/100 ml) was raised at 26 weeks in the 1% and 2% groups (control=0.70; 1%=0.96; 2%=1.19), and at week 103 in the 1% group (control=0.51; 1%=1.00). No other findings related to intake of test substance were noted (Worden *et al.*, 1975).

2.2.3 Long-term toxicity/carcinogenicity studies

2.2.3.1 Rats

Disodium 5'-inosinate

Fourteen male and 14 female Sprague-Dawley rats were fed diets containing 0%, 1%, 2%, 4%, or 8% disodium 5'-inosinate for 95 weeks. No significant changes were seen in behaviour, body weight gain, feed intake, haematology, blood chemistry, urinalysis, histopathology or mortality (Yonetani *et al.*, 1973).

Disodium 5'-guanylate + disodium 5'-inosinate

Male and female rats (group size unspecified, but it may have been 10 animals/sex/group) were fed 50:50 mix at 0%, 1% or 2% of the diet for 24 months. Average daily intakes were 427 and 864 mg/kg bw/day for males and 528 and 1026 mg/kg bw/day for females on the 1% and 2% diets, respectively. The authors noted no differences in body weight, food utilization, food intake, mortality, or general health among the treatment groups. Due to the small number of animals/sex/group (10), the pathology findings are difficult to interpret. No increase in tumours associated with consumption of diets containing a 50:50 mixture of disodium 5'-guanylate and disodium 5'-inosinate was reported. There may have been a small increase in testicular atrophy in male rats (3/9 in both 50:50 mix-fed groups, 1/9 in control) and an increase in adrenal enlargement in high-dose female rats (6/10 in females fed 2% a 50:50 mixture of disodium 5'-guanylate and disodium 5'-inosinate, 2/10 in females fed 1% a 50:50 mixture of disodium 5'-guanylate and disodium 5'-inosinate, 2/10 in control females). No effect of 50:50 mix ingestion on tumour incidence, tumour type, or pathological lesions of various organs in rats was seen under conditions of this study (Usui *et al.*, 1971).

2.2.4 Reproduction studies

2.2.4.1 Rats

Disodium 5'-inosinate

In a three-generation reproduction study, groups of ten male and 20 female rats were fed diets containing 0%, 0.5%, 1%, or 2% disodium 5'-inosinate. Animals were fed experimental or control diets for 60 days before mating. No effects on mating performance, pregnancy rate, or duration of gestation were noted. Body weight gain in disodium 5'-inosinate-fed rats was larger than in controls in all generations. Litter size, pup weight, pup mortality and incidence of abnormalities were unaffected by treatment. The authors reported that organ weight analysis, histopathology and skeletal staining of F_{3B} litters revealed no consistent pattern of adverse effects related to disodium 5'-inosinate consumption (Palmer et al., 1973).

Disodium 5'-guanylate + disodium 5'-inosinate

Rats were fed diets containing 0, 0.1, 1.0, or 2.0% 50:50 mix for 3 generations (20 female and 10 male rats per generation). Two litters were produced per generation and the parent group for the next generation was selected from the second litter. The parent group was apparently not randomly chosen, but pups were chosen from as many litters as possible and selected so that pup weights were as close as possible to the mean pup weight at weaning. In parent animals, mortality, bodyweight change, feed consumption, mating performance, pregnancy rate, and gestation period were assessed. All offspring were examined for external abnormalities within 12 hours of birth. At 21 days of age, all pups from the first litter of each generation and surplus pups from the second litter were killed and examined internally and externally for evidence of abnormality. Ten males and 10 females from the third generation (control and 2% 50:50 mix groups only) were subjected to detailed histological examination of the pancreas, urinary bladder, a long bone, stomach, small and large intestines, and bone marrow smears. Brain, liver, heart, pituitary, spleen, thyroid, kidneys, thymus, adrenals, lungs, and gonads were weighed. An additional 10 males and 10 females from the third generation of each exposure group underwent skeletal examination.

The author concluded that there was no evidence of any treatment-related effect at any dose level (few data were included in the article). However, there was a tendency for the litter size to be larger for 50:50 mix-fed rats than for control rats for the first litters and smaller than controls for the second litters. Similarly, pup mortality tended to be lower than controls in the first litters of 50:50 mix-fed rats and higher than controls in the second litters. These tendencies reached statistical significance for the 1.0% treatment group in the second and third generations, but were not dose-related.

The author reported a trend toward increased skeletal variants with increasing dose of 50:50 mix (variants included bipartite thoracic centrum, seven sternebra, and extra ribs); however, only 10 animals of each sex were examined, so the relevance of these findings is unclear (controls: 20% of males and 20% of females exhibited some skeletal variations; 0.1% 50:50 mix group: 10% of males and 30% of females exhibited skeletal variations; 1% 50:50 mix group: 50% of males and 30% of females exhibited skeletal variations; 2% 50:50 mix group: 80% of males and 40% of females exhibited skeletal variations). The author concluded that the findings in this study had no toxicological significance (Palmer, 1975).

2.2.5   Special studies on embryotoxicity/teratogenicity

2.2.5.1   Mice

Disodium 5'-guanylate

Pregnant female mice were treated with 0, 750 or 1 000 mg/kg bw guanosine, injected i.p. on day 10 or day 13 of gestation. Mice were sacrificed on day 19 of gestation, and examined for number of implantation sites and signs of fetal death *in situ*. Live fetuses were removed, weighed, and examined for external deformities and skeletal malformations. Control values were: body weight - 1.40 g, dead offspring - 6.5%; skeletal malformations - 0%; external malformations - 0.5%; subcutaneous haematoma - 0%. Fetuses from mothers injected on day 10 showed a decrease in mean body weight (mean=1.32 g) and an increase in percent live offspring with skeletal malformation (7.7%) at 750 mg/kg bw; there was an increase in percent of dead offspring (26.2%), decrease in mean body weight (mean=1.34 g), and an increase in percent live offspring with skeletal malformation (14.2%) at 1 000 mg/kg bw. Injection on day 13 caused an increase in percent dead offspring (21.3%) and decrease in mean body weight (mean=1.33 g) at 750 mg/kg bw; there was an increase in percent dead offspring (23.1%), decrease in mean body weight (mean=1.35 g), and increase in percent live offspring with external malformation (7.8%) and subcutaneous haematoma (5.3%) after injection of 1 000 mg/kg bw (Fujii *et al.*, 1972).

Disodium 5'-inosinate

Pregnant female mice were treated with 0, 250, 500 or 1 000 mg/kg bw inosine, injected i.p. on day 10 or 500 or 1 000 mg/kg bw injected i.p. on day 13 of gestation. Mice were sacrificed on day 19 of gestation, and examined for number of implantation sites and signs of fetal death *in situ*. Live fetuses were removed, weighed, and examined for external deformities and skeletal malformations. Control values were: body weight - 1.40, percent dead offspring - 6.5; percent skeletal malformations - 0; percent external malformations - 0.5; percent subcutaneous haematoma - 0. Fetuses from mothers injected on day 10 showed an increase in percent of dead offspring (16.5%), decrease in mean body weight (mean=1.35), and an increase in percent live offspring with skeletal malformation (14.0%) at doses of 1 000 mg/kg bw; decrease in mean body weight (mean=1.33) and an increase in percent live offspring with skeletal malformation (15.3%) at 500 mg/kg bw; decrease in mean body weight (mean=1.35) and an increase in percent live offspring with skeletal malformation (12.4%) at 250 mg/kg bw. Injection on day 13 caused an increase in dead offspring (24.6%) and decrease in mean body weight (mean=1.31) at 1 000 mg/kg bw; increase in dead offspring (12.4%) and decrease in mean body weight (mean=1.37) at 500 mg/kg bw, with no increase in skeletal malformations at either dose (Fujii et al., 1972).

Disodium 5'-guanylate + disodium 5'-inosinate

Groups of 14 pregnant mice were given 0 or 2 000 mg/kg bw/dy 50:50 mix orally via gastric tube from days 8-13 of pregnancy. Fetuses were removed by Caesarean section on day 19. Parameters measured were: number of embryonal implantations and fetal deaths, weight, sex differentiation, gross external and visceral malformations, and skeletal malformations; the authors reported no effects of treatment on any measured parameters (Kaziwara *et al.*, 1971).

2.2.5.2 Rats

Disodium 5'-guanylate

Groups of 9 pregnant rats were given 0 or 100 mg/kg bw/dy disodium 5'-guanylate orally via gastric tube on days 9-15 of pregnancy. Fetuses were removed by Caesarean section on day 21. Parameters measured were: number of embryo implantations and fetal deaths, weight, sex differentiation, gross external and visceral malformations, and skeletal malformations; the authors reported no effects of treatment on any measured parameters. The authors reported no effects of treatment on any measured parameters (Kaziwara *et al.*, 1971).

Disodium 5'-guanylate + disodium 5'-inosinate

A group of 9 pregnant rats were given 2 000 mg/kg bw/dy 50:50 mix orally via gastric tube from days 9-15 of pregnancy. Fetuses were removed by Caesarean section on day 21. Parameters were measured as above. There was a change in the sex ratio of the fetuses (M:F ratio was 1.11 in control litters, 0.64 in treated litters); the significance of this change was not commented on by the authors. No other changes were found in any measured parameters (Kaziwara *et al.*, 1971).

2.2.5.3 Rabbits

Disodium 5'-guanylate

Pregnant rabbits were fed either a normal diet (12 animals) or diets containing 0.2 g disodium 5'-guanylate/kg bw/dy or 2.0 g disodium 5'-guanylate/kg bw/dy from days 6-18 of gestation (9-10 animals/group). All except four dams in each group were sacrificed on day 29; remaining dams were allowed to litter spontaneously and their pups were observed until 30 days of age. No adverse effects on body weight were noted; rabbits fed diets containing 2 g/kg bw/dy had reduced feed consumption. Implantation numbers did not differ from controls but mortality of fetuses in the 2 g/kg bw/dy group was lower than in controls. All disodium 5'-guanylate-treated groups showed some delay in ossification, but no treatment-specific skeletal abnormalities. There were no effects on number of delivered fetuses, and survival rate of the 0.2 g/kg group was greater than controls at weaning. Mean pup body weights were reported to be normal and no significant malformations were observed in pups of either dose group (Jojima et al., 1973).

Disodium 5'-inosinate

Groups of 13-18 pregnant female Japanese white rabbits received 0, 200 or 2 000 mg/kg bw/dy disodium 5'-inosinate in their diet during days 6-18 of gestation. Four to five females of each group were allowed to deliver spontaneously and pups were observed to day 30. All other dams were killed on day 29 of gestation. The authors reported that no significant effects were observed on implantation sites, number of live or dead fetuses, body weights of live fetuses nor external abnormalities. The mortality of fetuses in the 0.2 g/kg bw/dy group was lower than that of other groups. All disodium 5'-inosinate-treated groups showed some delay in ossification but no specific skeletal abnormalities were found that appeared to be due to disodium 5'-inosinate. The authors concluded that daily administration of 2 000 mg/kg bw disodium 5'-inosinate had no adverse effect on pup development (Jojima et al., 1973).

2.2.5.4 Chickens

Disodium 5'-guanylate

Chick embryos were injected with guanosine into the yolk sac at 4 days, with doses ranging from 2-12 mg/egg. Of 65 embryos injected, 49 remained alive at 10 days and 45 remained alive at 18 days. 6 embryos showed abnormalities at 11-18 days (12%). The approximate LD_{50} for guanosine in this system was estimated to be 8 mg/egg. Guanosine was neither highly toxic nor teratogenic in this system (Karnofsky et al., 1961).

2.2.5.5 Monkeys

Disodium 5'-guanylate + disodium 5'-inosinate

Pregnant Cynomolgus monkeys were given 0 (2 monkeys), 500 mg/kg bw/dy 50:50 mix (2 monkeys) or 1 000 mg/kg bw/dy 50:50 mix (3 monkeys) orally via gastric tube from day 21 to day 30 of pregnancy. Fetuses were removed by Caesarean section on day 100. Measured parameters were weight, sex differentiation, gross external and visceral malformations and skeletal malformations. All treated females were reported to show some effects of treatment: monkeys receiving 500 mg/kg bw/dy 50:50 mix evacuated soft faeces for 4 or 9 days during treatment; all monkeys receiving 1 000 mg/kg bw/dy 50:50 mix exhibited diarrhoea, one of the three exhibited profuse diarrhoea and vaginal bleeding so that administration was stopped after the 6th day of treatment. Body weight gain of treated animals was similar to that of control animals, except for one animal receiving 500 mg/kg bw/dy who showed no weight gain during the study. The authors reported that one fetus from a treated monkey (500 mg/kg bw) had a hypertrophic spleen which manifested blood stagnation upon histological examination. No gross visceral nor skeletal malformations were observed in treated or control fetuses. A cervical rib was present in 1 control fetus, 2 fetuses from females treated with 500 mg/kg bw/dy and 1 fetus from a female treated with 1 000 mg/kg bw/dy (Kaziwara *et al.*, 1971).

2.2.6   Special studies on genotoxicity

Sodium 5' guanylate, sodium 5' inosinate, and a 50:50 mix were tested for genotoxicity in the *Salmonella*/microsome test (with and without metabolic activation) and chromosomal aberration test *in vitro* using a Chinese hamster fibroblast cell line (without metabolic activation). All substances were negative in the *Salmonella*/microsome test. Results of the chromosomal aberration test were positive for all substances. For disodium 5'-guanylate, the D_{20} (dose at which structural aberrations were detected in 20% of the metaphases observed) was .024 mg/ml and the TR (frequency of cells with exchange type aberrations per unit dose (mg/ml)) was 576. For disodium 5'-inosinate, the D_{20} (dose at which structural aberrations were detected in 20% of the metaphases observed) was 15.2 mg/ml, the TR (frequency of cells with exchange type aberrations per unit dose (mg/ml)) was 0.8. For 50:50 mix, the D_{20} was 1.99 mg/ml and the TR was 4.75 (Ishidate *et al.*, 1984).

2.3   Observations in humans

Disodium 5'-inosinate

Three healthy volunteers were given 0, 1, 1.5, 2, and 2.5 g disodium 5'-inosinate for seven consecutive days (diets had equal amounts of purines). Serum uric acid and urinary uric acid excretion doubled without signs of ill effects. The author reported that uric acid is the major endpoint of disodium 5'-inosinate metabolism in humans; ⅔ of uric acid appears in the urine, with the remainder excreted via the gut, where it was further degraded. (Kojima, 1974).

Disodium 5'-guanylate + disodium 5'-inosinate

Three healthy men were fed 0, 250, 500, 1 000, 2 000, or 4 000 mg/day of a mixture of 50% disodium 5'-inosinate and 50% disodium 5'-guanylate. Equal divided doses were given with three daily meals. Doses were given in an escalating pattern, from 250 to 4 000 mg/day, with 5 days at each dose; uric acid levels in serum and urine were measured before dosing and on the final two days at each dose. Uric acid levels in serum and urine were not significantly increased at doses up to 1 000 mg/day, but doses of 2 000 and 4 000 mg/day caused significant increases in both measures ($p < .005$). The authors stated that the measured values at 2 000 mg/day (serum uric acid: 6.9 mg/100 ml; urinary uric acid: 0.82 g/day) were increased above baseline (serum uric acid: 6.3 mg/100 ml; urinary uric acid: 0.6 g/day) but were within the normal range of these values; however values at 4

000 mg/day (serum uric acid: 8.6 mg/100 ml; urinary acid 1.1 g/day) were elevated above the normal range (Mitoma *et al.*, 1972). (The normal ranges were not given in this article, but Kojima [1974] reported that normal serum urate levels were 5 ± 1 mg/100 ml in 969 normal men and mean urinary uric acid was 8.1 mg/kg bw/24 h in normal men.).

3.   COMMENTS

Disodium 5'-guanylate and disodium 5'-inosinate are widely distributed in all animal and plant tissues.   Their role in purine metabolism as well as their breakdown to uric acid and to allantoin (in most mammals, but not humans) is well documented.   Data presented at the 18th meeting as well as new data on the metabolism, reproductive effects, genotoxicity, and short-term and long-term toxicity of guanylate and inosinate were evaluated at the present meeting.   No evidence of carcinogenicity, teratogenicity, or adverse effects on reproduction has been observed.

Changes in dietary purine intake over the past decade resulting from the use of guanylate and inosinate as flavour enhancers are no greater than those due to variability in the consumption of the major dietary contributors of purines. Naturally occurring nucleotides in the diet (calculated to be up to 2 g/person/day) greatly exceeds their intake resulting from use as flavour enhancers (approximately 4 mg/person/day).

4.   EVALUATION

The Committee concluded that, on the basis of the available data, the combined total daily intake of disodium 5'-guanylate and disodium 5'-inosinate is not of toxicological significance, and re-confirmed the ADI "not specified" that was previously established.   Because exposure to these substances from their use as flavour enhancers is low compared with daily intake of naturally occurring nucleotides in the diet, the Committee found no reason to recommend that foods to which these substances have been added should be labelled on the basis of safety, and withdrew its previous recommendation for labelling.

5.   REFERENCES

ADACHI, A. (1964). *J. Physiol. Soc. Jap.* **26**, 347.

FLOESSNER, I. (1934). The physiological activity of nucleic acids and their derivatives. *Arch. Exptl. Path. Pharmakol.* **174**, 245-254.

FUJII, T., & NISHIMURA, H. (1972). Comparison of teratogenic action of substances related to purine metabolism in mouse embryos. *Japan. J. Pharmacol.* **22**, 201-206.

HARA, S., HORIBE, M., KASAHARA, T., KIKULA, K., SATOH, S., TOKISAKI, K., & YAKAZU, K. (1966). Pharmacological investigations with regards to a toxicity and general pharmacological action of sodium 5'-inosinate, especially comparisons between natural and synthetic products. *J. Tokyo Med. Coll.* **24**, 553-587.

HASHIMOTO, S. *et al.* (1973). Report from Life Sciences Laboratories, Ajinomoto Co., Tokyo, Japan.

HIRAYAMA, H. (1968). *Folia Pharmacol. Jap.* **64**, 279.

ICHIMURA, J. & MUROI, K. (1973). Report from Life Sciences Laboratories, Ajinomoto Co., Tokyo, Japan.

ISHIDATE, Jr., J., SOFUNI, T., YOSHIKAWA, K., HAYASHI, M., NOHMI, T., SAWADA, M., & MATSUOKA, A. (1984). Primary mutagenicity screening of food additives currently used in Japan. *Fd. Chem. Toxicol.* **8**, 623-636.

JOJIMA, M. *et al.* (1973). Report from Life Sciences Laboratories, Ajinomoto Co., Tokyo, Japan.

KARNOFSKY, D.A. & LACON, C.R. (1961). Effects of physiological purines on the development of the chick embryo. *Biochem. Pharmacol.* **7**, 154-8.

KAZIWARA, K., MIZUTANI, J. & IHARA, T. (1971). On the fetotoxicity of disodium 5'-ribonucleotide in the mouse, rat and monkey. *J. Takeda Res. Lab.* **30**, 314-321.

KOJIMA, K. (1974). Safety evaluation of disodium 5'-inosinate, disodium 5'-guanylate and disodium 5'-ribonucleotide. *Toxicology* **2**, 185-206.

MITOMA, C., STONE, H., & DAVIS, P. (1972). Effects of feeding purine containing flavor enhancer (ST-1) on Uric acid levels in man. Unpublished report from Stanford Research Institute, Menlo Park, California 94025, USA. Submitted to WHO by the U.S. Food and Drug Administration.

NOEL, P.R.B. *et al.* (1971). Personal communication, HRC.

OHARA, V., MATSUZAWA, Y. & TAKEDA, J. (1973). Report from Life Sciences Laboratories, Ajinomoto Co., Tokyo, Japan.

OTSUKI, S. *et al.* (1968). *Med. and Biol.* **76**, 107.

PALMER, A.K., BATHAN, P. & NEWMAN, A.J. (1973). Unpublished data.

PALMER, A.K., LOVELL, M.R., SPICER, E.J.F., & WORDEN, A.N. (1975). The effect of disodium 5'-ribonucleotide on reproductive function over three generations in the rat. *Toxicology* **3**, 333-340.

RIVETT, K.F. *et al.* (1973). Unpublished data of HRC.

SATO, M., OGAWA, H., & YAMASHITA, S. (1971). Comparison of potentiating effect on gustatory response by disodium 2-methyl mercapto-5'-inosinate with that by 5'=disodium 5'-inosinate. *Jap. J. Physiol.* **21**, 669-697.

SHIMAMOTO, K., AOMORI, T., MIKODA, T., FUKUDA, A., ISHII, M., WATANABE, K., JIMPU, T., & ARAMAKI, Y. (1974). Pharmacological studies on disodium 5'-Inosinate, disodium 5'-guanylate and disodium 5'-ribonucleotide. *J. Takeda Res. Lab.* **33**, 24-37.

TAGAWA, H., & VANDER, A. (1970). Effects of adenosine compounds on renal function and renin secretion in dogs. *Circ. Res.* **26**, 327-338.

USUI, T., OGIWARA, S., KAZIWARA, A., & SHIMAMOTO, K. (1971). Oral toxicity studies of disodium 5'-ribonucleotide in the rat. *J. Takeda Res. Lab.* **30**, 614-635.

VERSPRILLE, A. (1966). *Arch. Ges. Physiol.* **291**, 261-267.

WORDEN, A.N., RIVETT, K.F., EDWARDS, D.B., STREET, A.E., & NEWMAN, A.J. (1975). Long-term feeding study on disodium 5'-ribonucleotide in dogs. *Toxicology* **3**, 341-347.

YABO, S. (1964). *Folia Pharmacol. Japon.* **60**, 194.

YONETANI, S. *et al.* (1973). Unpublished data.

FOOD COLOURS

CAROTENES FROM NATURAL SOURCES (ALGAL AND VEGETABLE)

First draft prepared by
Dr G.J.A. Speijers
National Institute of Public Health
and Environmental Protection
Laboratory for Toxicology, Bilthoven, The Netherlands

1.   EXPLANATION

Carotenes from natural sources were reviewed at the eighteenth, thirty-first and thirty-fifth meetings of the Committee (Annex 1, references 35, 77 and 88). At its thirty-first meeting, the Committee noted that, while there was a substantial toxicological database relating to carotenes and an ADI had been established for synthetic ß-carotene, the same ADI was not applicable to natural carotenes as they did not comply with the specifications for ß-carotene.

At the thirty-fifth meeting, the Committee concluded that there was insufficient evidence to indicate that data relating to one species of *Dunaliella* algae could be applied to others and that the specifications of the test materials were so different from one another that the results of the toxicity tests could not be generalized. There were insufficient data to evaluate any of these materials for the purpose of establishing an ADI. The Committee concluded that carotene isolated from algal sources would be acceptable for food additive use if it was of sufficient purity to meet the specifications for synthetic ß-carotene. Acceptance of algal biomass or crude extracts of carotene from algal sources for use as food additives would be contingent on the provision of evidence of the safety of such materials.

At its thirty-fifth meeting, the Committee considered limited short-term toxicological studies on material stated to have been prepared from three different algal species designated *Dunaliella bardawil, D. salina and D. kona* (Annex 1, reference 88). At its present meeting, the Committee was informed that *Dunaliella bardawil, D. kona and D. salina* were identical, and that, according to current nomenclature, the species used commercially was *Dunaliella salina*. Some of the preparations produced from this species were dehydrated powders prepared by lyophilization or spray-drying and others were vegetable oil extracts.[1] With respect to the carotene preparations derived from extraction of vegetables, mainly carrots, alfalfa or vegetable oil, the Committee at the thirty-first meeting (Annex 1, reference 77) felt that the need for toxicity tests may be obviated if detailed analytical data were supplied to confirm that natural toxicants occurring at low levels in food/feed stuffsare not concentrated in the extract and that levels of use would not materially exceed the levels of exposure that would result from normal use.

As no toxicological monograph has been prepared previously by the Committee on carotenes from natural sources, data that have been reviewed at previous meetings are incorporated in the present monograph along with the new data that have become available. Because this monograph covers the data on both algal and vegetable carotene preparations, a modified form of the general monograph format has been used, summarizing in order biological data on spray dried concentrated, lyophilized or dehydrated preparations of *Dunaliella*, then data on vegetable oil extracts of *Dunaliella*, then data on carotene extracts from carrots, grass alfalfa and vegetable oil.

ALGAL CAROTENE PREPARATIONS
SPRAY DRIED CONCENTRATED, LYOPHILIZED OR DEHYDRATED
PREPARATIONS OF *DUNALIELLA SALINA*
(syn *DUNALIELLA BARDAWIL* and *DUNALIELLA KONA*)

2. **BIOLOGICAL DATA**

2.1 **Biochemical aspects**

2.1.1 **Absorption, distribution and excretion.**

Male weanling CD rats were fed *ad libitum* a retinol-deficient diet. After 60 days, the retinol content of the livers was 4-5 μg. Depleted rats were allocated to 9 groups of 6 animals, housed individually, and fed a retinol-deficient diet supplemented as follows: Group 1, retinol at 7.5 mg/kg diet; Groups 2-4, all-*trans* β-carotene at 12, 29 or 48 mg/kg diet respectively; Groups 5-7, lyophilized *Dunaliella* contributing 29, 58 or 112 mg β-carotene/kg diet respectively; Group 8, maize oil extract of *Dunaliella* providing 16 mg β-carotene/kg diet; and Group 9, no supplementation. After seven days repletion, livers were taken for analysis for retinol, retinol isomers and β-carotene. The liver analyses revealed a comparable content of retinol related to dose of carotene, irrespective of source whether synthetic, algal biomass or algal oil extract. Rats fed the algae or the algal extract-supplemented diets accumulated 9-*cis* retinol in addition to the all-*trans* isomer. Rats fed synthetic β-carotene, lyophilized algae or algal oil had a liver retinol:β-

---

[1] Although the Committee acccepts that this report does not cover different *Dunaliella* species, the studies are summarized with original names mentioned in the reports or publications submitted.

carotene ratio of about 3:1. Rats fed algae or algal oil accumulated 9-*cis* β-carotene and all-*trans* β-carotene in the liver in a ratio similar to that present in the algae. It was concluded that dried *Dunaliella bardawil* or an oil extract of the alga can serve as a dietary natural β-carotene source which can satisfy the total requirement of retinol in rats (Ben-Amotz *et al.* 1988). [Note: this study is again cited below in discussion of absorption of oil-extracted algal carotene]

A 45-day-feeding study with 21-day old Sprague-Dawley rats was performed to compare the bioavailability of four sources of β-carotene; Spray dried *Dunaliella salina* (0.61 % β-carotene), β-carotene oil extract of *Dunaliella salina* (24.83 % β-carotene), oleoresin of carrots (11.5 % β-carotene) and synthetic β-carotene (100 %). The diet with *Dunaliella salina* powder (59 g/kg diet) was corrected for the amount of sucrose. The diets were made equal in the percentage of β-carotene, and the control diet contained 0.036 % β-carotene.

The rats on the *Dunaliella salina* diets grew more rapidly. Gross macroscopy at autopsy revealed no alterations in the rats.

The bioavailability of *Dunaliella salina* as a source of β-carotene and oil extract of β-carotene from *Dunaliella salina* was higher than that of β-carotene from oleoresin of carrots or synthetic β-carotene. These results may be due to the presence of the extra lipids in both the dried *Dunaliella salina* which contains 8.6 % lipid and the oil extract of *Dunaliella salina*. These results lead to the recommendation that dried *Dunaliella salina*, when used as a source of ß-carotene, should be consumed in oil to increase ß-carotene bioavailability. This is because activity of carotene dioxygenase, the enzyme responsible for the conversion of β-carotene to vitamin A, is increased in the presence of oil (Ghazi et al., 1992).

In one experiment, groups of 1-day-old white Leghorn chicks received a retinol-deficient semi-purified diet or a similar diet supplemented with 8.04 mg retinol/kg diet, or 30 mg synthetic β-carotene/kg diet or lyophilized *D. bardawil* at 1 g algae/kg diet. The algal powder contained 30 g β-carotene and 200 g NaCl/kg and provided 30 mg β-carotene/kg diet. In a second experiment, four similar groups were used except that the lyophilized algal powder was replaced with a similar concentration of drum-dried algae. The drum-dried algal powder contained 34 g β-carotene, 260 g NaCl, 180 g glycerol, 5.5 g chlorophyll, 210 g protein, 170 g carbohydrate and 120 g lipid/kg (34 mg β-carotene/kg diet). A third experiment utilized three groups of 15 one-day-old chicks which received retinol-deficient diet alone, or supplemented with lyophilized *D. bardawil* at 0.58 g/kg diet, or with drum dried algae at 1 g/kg diet. In each experiment, the chicks were assessed visually and weighed daily for 5 weeks and at termination serum and liver were analysed for retinol, β-carotene and lutein.

After an initial lag, the chicks grew equally well on diets containing retinol, β-carotene or algae in all experiments. Serum and liver concentrations of retinol were normal in all cases except for the chicks receiving retinol-deficient diets without supplements. The serum of chicks fed the algal-supplemented diets contained lutein but no β-carotene although the ratio of ß-carotene to lutein in the algae exceeded 15:1.

In a separate experiment, two groups of 3 egg-laying hens received a control diet containing 150 g maize meal/kg or the same diet supplemented with 4 g lyophilized *D. bardawil*/kg. The algal preparation contained 50 g β-carotene and 300 g NaCl/kg (200 mg β-carotene/kg diet). Eggs from these hens showed an enhanced yolk colour attributable to lutein; no ß-carotene was present in the egg yolk (Ben-Amotz 1986).

2.1.2   Biotransformation

No information available.

2.1.3   Effects on enzymes and other biochemical parameters

No information available.

2.2   Toxicological studies

2.2.1   Acute toxicity studies

2.2.1.1 Mice

Acute toxicity of *Dunaliella bardawil* spray dried powder was established in an LD_{50} test with mice. A single dose of 2.5, 5.0 or 10.0 g *Dunaliella bardawil*/kg diluted with CMC-Na solution was administered by oral intubation. The observation period was 14 days, and mortality, general symptoms, body weights and gross necropsy examination were recorded. The LD_{50} value was greater than 10 g *Dunaliella bardawil*/kg for both male and female mice (Aruga, 1987).

2.2.1.2 Rats

Male Sprague-Dawley rats were given dried *Dunaliella* by gavage at a dose of 5 g/kg bw and observed for the subsequent 14 days. There were neither mortalities nor overt signs of toxicity and all the rats gained weight during the observation period (Lock 1985).

2.2.2   Short-term toxicity studies

2.2.2.1 Mice

In the search for an antioxidative-anticarcinogenic substance, the effects of repeated ingestion (no dose level given) of spray dried *Dunaliella bardawil* on mammary growth and endocrine parameters were examined in mice. In an additional group the mice received also the vitamin A-deficient synthetic standard diet supplemented with synthetic all-trans β-carotene, whereas the control animals received the normal synthetic diet adequate in vitamin A. The concentration of β-

carotene in both test diets was 0.55 mg/kg. The ingestion of the *Dunaliella bardawil*-containing diet between 20 and 120 days of age showed no deleterious side-effects on mammary gland and uterine growth nor mammatrophic hormone secretion, these results were similar to previously-observed results in aged and mammary tumour-bearing mice. Puberty and body growth were accelerated by *Dunaliella bardawil* compared to the synthetic all-trans β-carotene (Nagasawa *et al.*, 1989).

2.2.2.2 Rats

Two groups of 10 male and 10 female weanling Sprague-Dawley rats, caged individually, were given powdered diets containing 0 or 10% algal β-carotene powder for 12 weeks. Body weight gain and food intake were recorded at intervals up to and at termination when the animals were autopsied. Weights of heart, lungs, liver, kidneys, spleen, gonads and adrenals were determined at autopsy and blood was collected for determination of serum glucose, ASAT, ALAT, alkaline phosphatase, uric acid, BUN, triglycerides and cholesterol. One male rat in the treated group died during the study from "non-specific problems" not related to treatment.

Significant differences were observed in neither food intake nor body weight gain between treated and untreated animals of either sex and there were no treatment-related differences in organ weights. Except for one treated male which displayed elevated ASAT and ALAT levels, no significant differences were observed in any of the clinical biochemical parameters between treated and untreated animals of either sex. No histopathological examination was performed (Majnarich 1988).

In a 28-day toxicity study spray dried *Dunaliella bardawil* powder was orally administered to rats (5/group/sex) at dosages of 0.5 and 2.5 g *Dunaliella bardawil*/kg bw/dy. The control animals (only) received 0.5 % aqueous solution of sodium CMC, which was used as the vehicle for the preparation of the test article suspension. Toxicological parameters recorded included food consumption, body weight gain, urinalysis, ophthalmoscopy, haematology, serum biochemistry, organ weights and histopathological examination.

In the males of the 2.5 g *Dunaliella bardawil*/kg bw/dy group a significant increase in the relative weight of the kidneys was noticed. Except slight changes in the thymus and the kidneys in a few animals of the 2.5 g *Dunaliella bardawil*/kg bw/dy group, no histopathological changes were reported. Although the effects were observed mainly in the kidneys, it was suggested by the authors that the dosage of 2.5 g *Dunaliella bardawil*/kg bw/dy was a NOEL (Furahashi, 1989).

2.2.3   Long-term toxicity/carcinogenicity studies

No information available.

2.2.4   **Reproduction studies**

The safety of the alga *Dunaliella bardawil* for food use was evaluated in a multigeneration study with rats. Four generations were raised on diets containing 0, 50 and 100 g/kg of dehydrated *D. bardawil*. The caloric value of the diets with the *Dunaliella bardawil* preparations was adapted by lowering the amount of starch. Each experimental group comprised 10 males and 20 females. Starting with an F_0-generation 3 other generations (F_1 - F_3) were raised. The rats of the F_0-generation were kept on the different diets for 1 year and 5 male and 5 female rats were studied for general toxicological effects. No significant differences were observed between the rats consuming algae and the controls, of any generation, in general appearance, behaviour, growth, reproductive performance or gross pathology. The only effect of *D. bardawil* powder observed was a significantly increased relative kidney weights. The blood chemistry and haematology of the first-generation animals, after 1 year on the diets, showed no appreciable differences between the experimental and control animals. The only differences in histopathology observed were a decrease in some chronic inflammations, a slightly higher frequency of metaplasia of the renal pelvis epithelium with ectopic nephrocalcinosis in the renal papillae and an increased frequency of focal bronchopneumonia in rats fed 10 g algae/kg feed when compared with the controls. The latter effect may be attributed to the powdery nature of the algal diet. Although at dose levels effect were recorded on the kidneys and which were not explained, the authors concluded that this multigeneration feeding study may be indicative of the safety of *D. bardawil* for human consumption (Mokady *et al.*, 1989).

2.2.5   **Special studies on genotoxicity**

A mutagenicity study (Ames test) in *Salmonella typhimurium* TA 98, TA 100, TA 1535 and TA 1537 and *Escherichia coli* WP2 uvrA both with and without activation by a liver microsomal S-9 mix was performed at dose levels of 312.5, 625, 1 250, 2 500 and 5 000 μg *Dunaliella bardawil* paste/plate. *Dunaliella bardawil* was not mutagenic in any strain (Aruga, 1988).

2.3   **Observations in humans**

Nine subjects were maintained on a low-carotene diet for two weeks and serum carotene levels were then determined. For the next ten days the volunteers took a daily dose of the powdered algal preparation providing 75 000 IU β-carotene (approx 135 mg) in capsule form. Serum carotene was measured on days 7 and 10 of treatment. There was considerable interindividual variation in response to the same dose of carotenes, both in absolute values and in the treatment-dependent increase in serum concentration of carotene. In six of the subjects the serum level of carotene continued to rise between the seventh and tenth day of the study while in three others there was a slight fall in this period. One subject with normal serum carotene levels at the outset showed virtually no response to treatment. No adverse effects due to ingestion of the algal preparation were reported (Cyanotech, 1988).

ALGAL CAROTENE PREPARATIONS
VEGETABLE OIL EXTRACT OF *DUNALIELLA SALINA*
(syn *DUNALIELLA BARDAWIL* and *DUNALIELLA KONA*)

2.   BIOLOGICAL DATA

2.1   Biochemical aspects

2.1.1 Absorption, distribution and excretion.

In an experiment fully described in section 2.1.1 describing results with spray dried concentrated, lyophilized or dehydrated preparations of *Dunaliella*, male weanling CD rats were fed a retinol-deficient diet *ad libitum*. After depletion, rats were allocated to groups and fed a retinol-deficient diet supplemented with one of: retinol; all-*trans* β-carotene; lyophilized *Dunaliella*; maize oil extract of *Dunaliella*; and no supplementation. After seven days repletion, livers were taken for analysis of retinol, retinol isomers and β-carotene. The liver analysis revealed a comparable content of retinol related to dose of carotene, irrespective of source i.e. synthetic, algal biomass or algal oil extract. It was concluded that dried *Dunaliella bardawil* or an oil extract of the alga can serve as a dietary natural β-carotene source which can satisfy the total requirement of retinol in rats (Ben-Amotz *et al.* 1988).

2.1.2 Biotransformation

No information available.

2.1.3 Effects on enzymes and other biochemical parameters

No information available.

2.2   Toxicological studies

2.2.1 Acute toxicity studies

No information available.

2.2.2 Short-term toxicity studies

No information available.

2.2.3   Long-term toxicity/carcinogenicity studies

No information available.

2.2.4   **Reproduction studies**

No information available.

2.2.5   **Special studies on genotoxicity**

The commercial, carotene-rich corn oil extract of *Dunaliella salina* was inactive in an *in vitro* primary hepatocyte unscheduled DNA synthesis assay (Cifone 1987).

The extract was negative in an assay of forward mutation at the HGPRT locus in cultured Chinese hamster ovary cells, with or without metabolic activation with rat liver S9 fraction. A dose-related cytotoxicity was noted at concentrations above 2.0 μl/ml without S9 and above 10.0 μl/ml in the presence of S9 (Young 1987).

The material was not mutagenic in the *Salmonella*/microsome assay (Ames test) with *Salmonella typhimurium* strains TA-1535, TA-1537, TA-1538, TA-98 and TA-100 with or without metabolic activation (Jagannath 1987).

In an *in vivo* mouse micronucleus assay using adult ICR mice, the commercial carotene extract did not induce a significant increase in micronuclei in bone marrow polychromatic erythrocytes (Ivett 1987).

2.3   **Observations in humans**

After a depletion period of 10 days on a low-carotene diet, 12 male and 20 female healthy adults were randomly assigned to one of five treatment groups. Two groups received capsules of carotene obtained by vegetable oil extraction of *Dunaliella salina* providing β-carotene at levels of 8 or 24 mg and α-carotene at levels of 1.1 or 3.2 mg respectively. Two further groups received carrots (69.1 or 207.3 g respectively) that provided a similar amount of β-carotene to the *Dunaliella salina* extract groups; the corresponding amounts of α-carotene were 6.3 and 18.9 mg respectively. A fifth group received placebo capsules. The subjects received the treatment for seven days and then underwent another depletion phase of 7 days.
Treatment with carotene capsules or carrots led to an expected increase in serum α- and β-carotenes, with the higher dose treatments being less efficient per mg carotene consumed. The encapsulated algal carotenes were more efficient at raising serum values per mg fed, consistent with other reports that carotenes are better absorbed from oily solution than a vegetable matrix (Jensen *et al.* 1985).

In a study on the bioavailability of cis- and trans-β-carotenes, 16 healthy adults, who had been on a low-carotene diet for ten days, were fed either β-carotene extracted from *Dunaliella salina* alga, containing approximately equal amounts of all-trans-β-carotene and 9-mono-cis-β-carotene, or β-carotene in the form of fresh carrots containing predominantly trans-β-carotene, or avocado oil-placebo capsules. Subjects were randomly divided into three groups: they consumed daily in a single dose either 3 β-carotene capsules (24 mg β-carotene), 207.3 g carrots (24 mg β-carotene); or 3 β-carotene free placebo capsules for seven days. HPLC determinations of serum trans-cis β-carotene ratios showed trans β-carotene to be the predominate serum isomer before and during all treatments. Serum trans-β-carotene concentrations were significantly increased in the β-carotene capsules and carrot groups. Cis-β-carotene concentrations were increased in the carrot and placebo groups. However, the serum isomer increments for those taking β-carotene capsules and carrots strongly favoured trans-β-carotene over cis-β-carotene. These data demonstrate a predominant absorption of intact trans-β-carotene over intact cis-β-carotene into human serum even when approximately equivalent amounts of these isomers were ingested. This selective absorption of intact β-carotene isomers might be a factor in their biopotency in humans (Jensen et al., 1987).

CAROTENE EXTRACTS FROM VEGETABLES
(Carrots, alfalfa and vegetable oil)

2.   BIOLOGICAL DATA

2.1   Biochemical aspects

No information available.

2.2   Toxicological studies

No information available.

2.3   Observations in humans

The acute effects of consuming α- and β-carotene from carrots on serum α-carotene and β-carotene levels were investigated in 17 adult subjects (18-58 years of age). After a 10-day low-carotene diet, the subjects were randomized into three groups based on day 6 β-carotene levels. On day 11, fasting baseline blood was drawn. Either 3 carrots, 1 carrot or 3 placebo capsules were then consumed following a low-carotene breakfast. Blood was drawn 1, 2, 3, 4, 5, 7 and 24 hours post-treatment and α- and β-carotene levels were determined by HPLC. Treatment of 3 carrots yielded significantly greater peak α- and β-carotene levels in serum at 5 hours post-treatment than did treatments with 1 carrot or 3 placebos. These results suggest the best condition for drawing blood samples to assess the serum carotene status of adults is at fasting state and that significant alterations in serum can occur within 5 hours of a carotene rich meal (Jensen et al., 1986).

3.   COMMENTS

Few new toxicological data have become available since the previous review by the Committee (Annex 1, reference 88). There were no data from long-term toxicity or teratogenicity studies, although a multigeneration study on dehydrated *Dunaliella bardawil* (= *salina*) in rats did not reveal any adverse effects on reproductive performance or gross fetal morphology. However, a NOEL was not identified in this study, as animals of the F_0-generation maintained on diets containing 5% and 10% algal carotene for one year showed renal pathological changes. In addition, there was focal bronchopneumonia at the higher level. Although the renal changes (metaplastic changes in the pelvic epithelium and nephrocalcinosis) might have been due to nutritional imbalance, this was not clearly established. The focal bronchopneumonia observed in the lung at the higher dose level may have been associated with inhalation of powdered diets, although both low-dose and control rats also received powdered diets without showing similar effects. The Committee considered that the available short-term toxicity studies inadequate for establishing an ADI because of the small numbers of animals tested, lack of or inadequate histopathological examination, or inadequate reporting.

There were virtually no systematic toxicological studies available on the oil-extract of alga. Available data on the dried material could not be extrapolated to the oil extract since the specifications are quite different and lipophilic materials may have been concentrated during the oil extraction process.

4.   EVALUATION

The Committee considered the data inadequate to establish an ADI for the dehydrated algal carotene preparations or for the vegetable oil extracts of *Dunaliella salina*. There is no history of use of *Dunaliella* algae as food.

No relevant toxicological data on vegetable extracts were available. However, the Committee concluded that there was no objection to the use of vegetable extracts as colouring agents, provided that the level of use did not exceed the level normally present in vegetables. Implicit in this conclusion is that the extracts should not be made toxic by virtue of the concentration of toxic compounds (including toxicants naturally occurring in the vegetables) nor by the generation of reaction products or residues of a nature or in such amounts as to be toxicologically significant

5.   REFERENCES

ARUGA, F. (1987). Acute oral toxicity study on *Dunaliella bardawil* spray dried powder in mice. Nihon Bioresearch Center Inc. Hashima, Gifu, Japan, as submitted to WHO by Nikken Sohonsha Corporation, Hashim-City, Japan.

ARUGA, F. (1988). Mutagenicity test of *Dunaliella bardawil* paste with *Salmonella typhimurium* and *Escherichia coli*. Nihon Bioresearch Center Inc. Hashima, Gifu, Japan, as submitted to WHO by Nikken Sohonsha Corporation, Hashim-City, Japan.

BEN-AMOTZ, A., EDELSTEIN, S. & AVRON, M. (1986) Use of the ß-carotene rich alga *Dunaliella bardawil* as a source of retinol. *Brit. Poultry Sci.*, **27**, 613-619

BEN-AMOTZ, A., MOKADY, S. & AVRON, M. (1988) The ß-carotene-rich alga *Dunaliella bardawil* as a source of retinol in a rat diet. *Brit. J. Nutr.*, **59**, 442-449.

CIFONE, M.A. (1987) Mutagenicity test on EK 87-0048 B-CAT in the rat primary hepatocyte unscheduled DNA synthesis assay. Unpublished report of Hazleton Laboratories America Inc. Submitted to WHO by Eastman Kodak Co., Rochester, NY, USA.

CYANOTECH (1988) Ten-day Konatene (TM) feeding study: effects on serum beta-carotene levels. Unpublished summary report submitted to WHO by Cyanotech Corporation, Woodinville, Washington, USA.

FURUHASHI, T (1989) Twenty-eight-day oral subacute toxicity study on *Dunaliella bardawil*. Nihon Bioresearch Center Inc., Hashima, Gifu, Japan, as submitted to WHO by Nikken Sohonsha Corporation, Hashima-City, Japan.

GHAZI, A., DE LUMEN, B. & OSWALD, W.J. (1992). Comparative bioavailability of beta-carotene from *Dunaliella salina*, *Dunaliella salina* extract, carrot extract and synthetic beta-carotene. Report submitted to WHO by Microbio Resources, Inc., San Diego, CA USA.

IVETT, J.L. (1987) Mutagenicity test on EK 87-0047, corn oil control and EK 87-0048, B-CAT in the *in vivo* mouse micronucleus assay. Unpublished report of Hazleton Laboratories America Inc. submitted to WHO by Eastman Kodak Co., Rochester, NY, USA.

JAGANNATH, D.R. (1987) Mutagenicity test on EK 87-0048 B-CAT in the Ames Salmonella/microsome reverse mutation assay. Unpublished report of Hazleton Laboratories America Inc. submitted to WHO by Eastman Kodak Co., Rochester, NY, USA.

JENSEN, C.D., PATTISON, T.S., SPILLER, G.A., WHITTAM, J.H. & SCALA, J. (1985) Repletion and depletion of serum alpha and beta carotene in humans with carrots and an algae-derived supplement. *Acta Vitaminol. Enzymol.*, **7**, 189-198.

JENSEN, C.D., SPILLER, G.A., PATTISON, T.S., WHITTAM, J.H. & SCALA, J. (1986). Acute effects of dietary carotenes on serum alpha and beta carotene in humans. *Nutr. Rep. Int.*, **33**, 117-122.

JENSEN, C.D., HOWES, T.W., SPILLER, G.A., PATTISON, T.S., WHITTAM, J.H. & SCALA, J. (1987). Observations on the effects of ingesting *cis*- and *trans*-beta-carotene isomers on human serum concentrations. *Nutr. Rep. Int.*, **35**, 413-422.

LOCK, S. (1985) Fourteen days oral rat testing using dried *Dunaliella* cells, BioMed No. 4476. Unpublished summary report of Biomed Research Laboratories Inc. submitted to WHO by Cyanotech Corporation, Woodinville, Washington, USA.

MAJNARICH, J.J. (1988) Subchronic oral toxicity (12 week) study of algal beta carotene fed to male and female Sprague-Dawley rats. Unpublished report of Biomed Research Laboratories Inc. submitted to WHO by Cyanotech Corporation, Woodinville, Washington, USA.

MOKADY, S., ABRAMOVICI, A. & COGAN, U. (1989) The safety evaluation of *Dunaliella bardawil* as a potential food supplement. *Fd. Chem. Toxic.*, **27**, 221-226.

NAGASAWA, H., FUJII, Y., YAMAMOTO, K., KONOSHI, R. & BEN-AMOTZ, A. (1989). No deleterious side-effects on mammary growth and endocrine parameters of chronic ingestion of beta-carotene-rich alga *Dunaliella bardawil* in virgin mice in comparison with synthetic all-*trans* beta-carotene. *The Cancer Journal*, **2**, 391-394.

YOUNG, R.R. (1987) Mutagenicity test on EK 87-0048 B-CAT in the CHO/HGPRT forward mutation assay. Unpublished report of Hazleton Laboratories America Inc. submitted to WHO by Eastman Kodak Co., Rochester, NY, USA.

SWEETENING AGENTS

MALTITOL AND MALTITOL SYRUP

First draft prepared by
Dr J.L. Herrman
International Programme on Chemical Safety
World Health Organization
Geneva, Switzerland

1.   EXPLANATION

Hydrogenated glucose syrups were evaluated at the twenty-fourth, twenty-seventh, and twenty-ninth meetings of the Committee (Annex 1, references 53, 62, and 70). A temporary ADI was allocated at the twenty-seventh meeting, with the requirement that the results of a lifetime feeding study be submitted. At the twenty-ninth meeting the Committee concluded that the previously-requested lifetime feeding study was not necessary because hydrogenated glucose syrups are fully metabolized to natural body constituents. An ADI "not specified" was allocated, which applied to hydrogenated glucose syrups that met the established specifications.
At the thirty-third meeting (Annex 1, reference 83) the specifications for hydrogenated glucose syrups were revised and retitled "maltitol syrup". The Committee confirmed that the ADI "not specified" previously allocated to hydrogenated glucose syrups applied to maltitol syrup meeting the revised specifications. In addition, an ADI "not specified" was allocated to maltitol, which was specified as having a minimum 98% purity.
A combined long-term toxicity/carcinogenicity study in rats using a commercial product has now been completed, which is summarized in this monograph addendum.

2.   BIOLOGICAL DATA

2.1   Biochemical aspects

No new information.

2.2   Toxicological studies

2.2.3   Long-term toxicity/carcinogenicity study

2.2.3.1 Rats

In a combined long-term toxicity/carcinogenicity study a commercial preparation containing approximately 87% maltitol was fed to Crl:CD(SD)BR male and female rats at doses equal to 0, 0.5, 1.5, or 4.5 g/kg bw/day. [The highest dose corresponded to an average of about 10% of the commercial product in the diet.] Rats were maintained on these diets for 52 weeks in the long-term study (20 animals/sex/group) or for 106 weeks in the carcinogenicity study (50 animals/sex/group), after which they were killed.

In both experiments animals were examined daily for signs of ill health or behavioral changes.   Food consumption and body weights were recorded immediately prior to the start of administration of the test compound, at weekly intervals for the first 12 weeks, and then every 4 weeks until the end of the experiment. Animals were inspected twice daily for mortality, and those found dead or sacrificed "in extremis", as well as those killed at the end of the study, were subjected to complete necropsies and organs were removed, weighed, and histologically examined.   Caecum and colon diameters were measured in the long-term study.

Ten animals/sex/group were subjected to ophthalmoscopic examination prior to the start of treatment and at weeks 13, 26, and 52 in the long-term study. Haematological examinations, blood chemistry tests, and urinalyses were performed on 10 animals/sex/group at weeks 14, 26, and 51 in this study.

Results of the long-term toxicity study

No animals in the mid- or high-dose groups died.   Three animals in the control group and four in the low-dose group died, most of which were caused by accidents; none of these deaths was related to treatment.   No treatment-related clinical signs were noted.   Treatment had no effect on body weight.   Sporadic differences in food consumption were noted in males, with no apparent trend. Mean food consumption was significantly less in high-dose females at 12 and 52 weeks than in the other groups.   No treatment-related eye abnormalities were observed. Sporadic differences were observed in haematological parameters but, except for a decrease in leukocytes in mid-dose females, none of these differences were observed at all observation times.   Occasional significant differences were observed in blood chemistry and urinalysis parameters, but none of these differences were major and most of them were not dose-related.   No treatment-related effects were observed after gross or histopathological examination.   A significant increase in the caecum diameter of high-dose males was observed, which was due to higher values in 3 out of 20 rats.   A trend toward a decrease in caecum diameter was observed in low- and high-dose females when compared to controls.   The NOEL in this study was the highest dose tested, 4.5 g commercial product/kg bw/day (Conz & Fumero, 1989).

Results of the carcinogenicity study

Mortality was not affected by treatment. No treatment-related clinical signs were noted. Body weights of all treated males and of high-dose females were comparable to those of animals in their respective control groups. Mean body weights of low- and mid-dose females were slightly lower than those of controls, which reached statistical significance only occasionally, including weeks 100 and 104. Food intake was not affected by treatment. No gross pathological treatment-related changes were observed in any organs, including the intestine and caecum. Occasional masses or nodules of the adrenal glands were observed, but they were not dose-related and the highest frequencies were within the control incidences observed in 2-year carcinogenicity studies in rats of the same strain performed in the same laboratory.

Histopathological changes related to treatment were observed in the adrenal gland. The findings are summarized in Table 1. Both benign and malignant phaeochromocytomas, when considered either separately or together, occurred with higher incidence in both males and females in the high-dose group when compared with the control group. In addition, slight to moderate medullary hyperplasia occurred at an increased frequency in all treated groups when compared to controls. The trend test showed a significant increase in females, with a significant difference between high-dose females and the control group.

Table 1. Histopathological changes observed in the adrenal gland in the carcinogenicity study in rats

Sex/	M				F			
Dose Level[1]	0	0.5	1.5	4.5	0	0.5	1.5	4.5
Phaeochromocytoma								
Benign	8	4	10	20	2	2	4	10
Malignant	6	12	4	10	2	2	2	4
Total	14	16	14	30	4	4	6	14
Medullary hyperplasia	24	32	38	32	14	22	24	34

[1]50 adrenal glands/sex/group were examined except for the mid-dose males, in which 49 were examined.

An increased incidence of mammary gland adenocarcinomas was observed in females: 4/50 (8.0%), 2/43 (4.6%), 8/50 (18.6%, P=0.054), and 10/50 (20.0%, P=0.044) in the controls and low-, mid-, and high-dose animals, respectively. Although the trend was significant (P=0.013), the incidences at the two highest doses were barely significantly different than the controls. Increased incidences of mammary gland adenomas or fibroadenomas were not observed. The incidences of mammary gland adenocarcinomas were within the historical control incidences of mammary gland adenocarcinomas in female rats in the same laboratory in 7 studies carried out between 1978 and 1989, which have ranged from 0 to 22% (Conz & Maraschin, 1992).

3.   COMMENTS

At its present meeting, the Committee reviewed a recently completed combined long-term toxicity/carcinogenicity study, in which a commercial preparation containing approximately 87% maltitol was administered in the diet of Sprague-Dawley rats at levels equal to 0, 0.5, 1.5, or 4.5 g/kg bw/day for either 52 weeks (toxicity study) or 106 weeks (carcinogenicity study). No adverse effects were observed in the toxicity study. In the carcinogenicity study, histopathological changes related to treatment were observed in the adrenal gland, which included increased incidences of both benign and malignant phaeochromocytomas in male and female rats in the high-dose group and an increased frequency of slight to moderate adrenal medullary hyperplasia in all treated groups. A slightly increased incidence of mammary gland adenocarcinomas was observed in female rats at the 1.5 and 4.5 g/kg bw/day doses, however the incidence was within the range reported in the historical control. Increased incidences of mammary gland adenomas or fibroadenomas were not observed, and the combined incidences of mammary gland adenocarcinomas and adenomas were not increased. For these reasons, the Committee did not consider the increase in mammary gland adenocarcinomas to be related to treatment.

4.   EVALUATION

Previous Committees have taken cognisance of adrenal medullary lesions in rats associated with high intake levels of poorly-absorbed polyols when allocating ADIs to them (Annex 1, reference 62). In line with earlier conclusions regarding the significance of these lesions, the Committee confirmed the ADI "not specified" for maltitol and maltitol syrup that meet the specifications established at the present meeting. The Committee recommended that the information database on adrenal medullary hyperplasia and phaeochromocytomas associated with polyols and other poorly-absorbed carbohydrates be reviewed and that mechanisms of the appearance of these lesions and their toxicological significance be assessed at a future meeting.

5.   REFERENCES

CONZ, A. & FUMERO, S. (1989). Combined chronic toxicity/carcinogenicity study in Sprague Dawley Crl:CD(SD)BR rats treated with the test article MALBIT® (crystal powder) administered at the dosages of 0, 0.5, 1.5, and 4.5 g/kg/day in the diet: chronic toxicity study. Unpublished report from RBM, Istituto di Richerche Biomediche, Ivrea, Italy. Submitted to WHO by Cerestar Research & Development, Vilvoorde, Belgium.

CONZ, A. & MARASCHIN, R. (1992). Combined chronic toxicity/carcinogenicity study in Sprague Dawley Crl:CD(SD)BR rats treated with the test article MALBIT® (crystal powder) administered at the dosages of 0, 0.5, 1.5, and 4.5 g/kg/day in the diet: carcinogenicity study. Unpublished report from RBM, Istituto di Richerche Biomediche, Ivrea, Italy. Submitted to WHO by Cerestar Research & Development, Vilvoorde, Belgium.

SACCHARIN AND ITS SALTS

First draft prepared by
Ms E. Vavasour
Toxicological Evaluation Division
Bureau of Chemical Safety, Food Directorate
Health and Welfare Canada
Ottawa, Ontario, Canada

1   EXPLANATION

Saccharin was evaluated by the Committee at its eleventh, eighteenth,
twenty-first, twenty-fourth, twenty-sixth and twenty-eighth meetings (Annex 1,
references 14, 35, 44, 53, 59, and 66). At the twenty-first meeting, the Committee
changed the previously unconditional ADI of 5 mg/kg bw to a temporary ADI of
0-2.5 mg/kg bw and withdrew the conditional ADI of 0-15 mg/kg bw for dietetic
purposes only. This decision was based primarily on results of animal studies which
indicated that excessive and long-term ingestion of saccharin might represent a
carcinogenic hazard. At the twenty-fourth and twenty-sixth meetings, the temporary
ADI of 0-2.5 mg/kg bw was extended pending the completion of ongoing
investigations, including a long-term feeding study in rats and a large-scale
epidemiological study. At the twenty-eighth meeting, the results of a 2-generation
feeding study in rats and epidemiological data were reviewed and the temporary
ADI was again extended, pending the evaluation of further data on bladder
histopathology from the 2-generation study and information to elucidate the
mechanism by which the compound produced bladder tumours. These data, along
with recent epidemiological studies, were reviewed at the present meeting, and are
summarized in this monograph addendum.

2   BIOLOGICAL DATA

2.1   Biochemical aspects

2.1.1   Absorption, distribution, and excretion

The disposition of saccharin has been discussed in the previous monograph
and monograph addendum. In addition, a good review of these aspects of saccharin

is presented in Renwick (1985). The main features of saccharin disposition are presented here.

The disposition of saccharin is influenced by its acidic properties. With a pK_a of 2.2, saccharin exists predominantly in the un-ionized form in acidic media from which it is more readily absorbed. It is nearly completely ionized at physiological pH (in body fluids). Saccharin is more completely absorbed from the stomachs of species with low pH (guinea pig - pH 1.4; rabbit - pH 1.9) than from those with a higher pH (rat - pH 4.2) (Ball 1973; Minegishi et al. 1972). In the higher pH of the intestines, it is slowly absorbed, and rapidly eliminated in the urine. Following administration of a single oral dose of saccharin in rats and humans, peak plasma levels of saccharin were rapidly achieved (Sweatman and Renwick 1980; Sweatman et al. 1981). However, clearance of saccharin from the plasma was prolonged. Intravenous administration results in rapid elimination of saccharin in the rat and human. Consequently, prolonged plasma clearance following oral administration was attributed to slow and incomplete absorption from the intestines. The presence of food in the gut was associated with a reduced initial peak plasma concentration in animals (Matthews et al. 1973; Sweatman and Renwick 1980) and in man (Sweatman et al. 1981).

The extent of faecal excretion has been used as an indicator of unabsorbed saccharin following an oral dose. On the basis of results from studies of i.v. administration, only a very small percentage of absorbed saccharin appears in the faeces. Measurement of the extent of faecal excretion of orally administered saccharin indicated that gastrointestinal absorption was incomplete and variable in the rat, with the percentage of the administered dose recovered in the faeces ranging from 3-39% (Renwick 1985). For the most part, higher doses were associated with higher faecal concentrations of saccharin. In humans, 1-8% was recovered in the faeces following doses of 2 g/person (Sweatman et al. 1981).

Urinary excretion has also been used as a measure of gastrointestinal absorption since it is the main route of excretion for absorbed saccharin and since saccharin does not undergo detectable biotransformation. In rat feeding studies in which saccharin and its salts were incorporated into commercial rat chow at levels of 5 or 7.5%, approximately equal amounts of ingested saccharin were excreted in the urine and faeces (Anderson et al. 1987b; Fisher et al. 1989). By contrast, the administration of the same level of sodium saccharin in a semi-purified diet (AIN-76A) resulted in the urinary excretion of 10-20 times more saccharin compared with the faeces, indicating that absorption from the GI tract had been more extensive (Fisher et al. 1989).

The gastrointestinal absorption of orally-administered saccharin in man was 85% based on urinary excretion and area under plasma concentration-time curves (Sweatman et al. 1981). Almost 80% of the daily dose was recovered in the urine of human volunteers receiving 1 g of saccharin (as the sodium salt)/day for 4 weeks (Roberts and Renwick 1985).

Saccharin was found to bind reversibly to plasma proteins (Renwick 1985). The extent of binding showed a wide range: 3%, 24-35% and 69-86% in the rat and 70-80% in man. Following a single oral dose to adult rats, saccharin was found to be distributed to most organs with the highest concentrations in the organs of elimination (kidney and bladder) followed by the plasma (Matthews *et al.* 1973; Lethco and Wallace 1975; Ball *et al.* 1977; Sweatman and Renwick 1980). The steady-state concentrations of saccharin in adult male rats fed 1-10% saccharin in the diet were consistent with the observations from these single-dose studies. There is no evidence of bioaccumulation of saccharin in any tissue. Placental transfer of saccharin to the fetus has been observed in rats (Ball *et al.* 1977), monkeys (Pitkin *et al.* 1971) and humans (Cohen-Addad *et al.* 1986).

As indicated above, the urine is the principal route of elimination for saccharin after both oral and parenteral dosing. Renal tubular secretion is the major mechanism of elimination in both rats and humans as indicated by the reduction in plasma clearance of saccharin when administered with probenecid, an inhibitor of the renal tubular secretion of anions. Glomerular filtration is not considered to be as important a mechanism due to the high degree of plasma protein binding of saccharin. Renal tubular secretion is a saturable process and plasma concentrations of saccharin greater than 200 μg/ml have been associated with saturation in the rat (Sweatman and Renwick 1980). Dietary levels of saccharin exceeding 5% resulted in accumulation of saccharin in the plasma and tissues due to decreased renal clearance. However, decreased renal clearance was not detected following administration of an oral dose of 2 g in humans which produced a peak plasma concentration of 40 μg/ml (Sweatman *et al.* 1981).

2.1.2   Biotransformation

The consensus of the most recently conducted research in a number of experimental species or humans is that saccharin is not metabolized (Renwick 1985). In addition, radiolabelled saccharin did not bind to the DNA of the liver or bladder of rats *in vivo* (Lutz and Schlatter 1977), indicating that saccharin was not metabolized to an electrophilic compound.

2.1.3   Effects on enzymes and other biochemical parameters

The high concentrations of sodium saccharin in the lumen of the gastrointestinal tract due to dietary administration of sodium saccharin resulted in the decreased activity of a number of digestive enzymes of the pancreas and intestines. Saccharin is an inhibitor of urease and proteases *in vitro* (Lok *et al.* 1982) and feeding saccharin in the diet causes accumulation of protein and tryptophan and its metabolites in the caecum (Sims and Renwick 1985).

Saccharin also led to the inhibition of carbohydrate digestion which resulted in the faecal elimination of polysaccharides. The *in vitro* activities of amylase, sucrase and isomaltase were inhibited by the presence of saccharin (Renwick 1989).

Feeding male rats a diet containing 5% sodium saccharin for 14 days did not result in induction of hepatic cytochrome P-450 (Hasegawa et al. 1984).

The administration of 7.5% sodium saccharin to rats in both 1- and 2-generation feeding studies had no effect on hepatic concentrations of cytochrome P-450, cytochrome b5, cytochrome P-450 reductase, arylhydrocarbon hydroxylase activity or glutathione content per mg protein. Hepatic dimethylnitrosamine-N-demethylase activity was increased in both neonatal and adult male and female rats fed a high dietary concentration of sodium saccharin (Heaton and Renwick 1991a).

Sulfate conjugation of phenol in vivo was reduced in both male and female rats fed a 7.5% sodium saccharin diet in a 2-generation protocol. The maximum effect was detected in neonatal animals at 5 weeks of age. Dietary supplementation with cysteine restored sulfate conjugation, indicating that the effect was caused by poor availability of sulfur-containing amino acids rather than inhibition of the sulfotransferase enzyme (Heaton and Renwick 1991b).

2.2   Toxicological Studies

2.2.1   Long-term toxicity/carcinogenicity studies

There have been no additional 2-generation carcinogenicity studies on saccharin since the IRDC study which was available as unpublished data at the twenty-eighth meeting in 1984. The data for this study have been published (Schoenig et al. 1985). The tumour incidence data for the urinary bladder of F_1 male rats were the same as those reported in the previous monograph addendum (Annex 1, reference 67) with the exception that the incidence of total tumours at 3% sodium saccharin in the diet was 1.7%, not 1.6% as then reported. The no-observed effect level was 1% in the diet, although the application of a threshold dose-response model to the data suggested a threshold close to 3% (Carlborg 1985).

The bladder histology studies have been re-evaluated under blind conditions with the result that higher incidences of papillomas and carcinomas were reported in both the control and lower treatment groups and the apparent increases in transitional cell carcinomas and combined neoplasms in the 3% group were found to be not statistically significant (p=0.25 and 0.41, respectively). The blind reevaluation confirmed that the 1% dietary level of sodium saccharin had no carcinogenic nor proliferative effect on the bladder epithelium (Squire 1985).

Although no new 2-generation study has been reported in rats or other species, studies on promotion of bladder carcinogenicity used control groups in which the animals received 5% sodium, calcium and acid saccharin in the diet

SACCHARIN AND ITS SALTS 109

without treatment with an initiator. After 2 years or 72 weeks, respectively, of feeding with sodium saccharin, the incidence of simple hyperplasia was higher than that in untreated controls. The incidence of papillomas and carcinomas of the bladder was comparable in the sodium-saccharin-treated groups and untreated controls (Hasegawa *et al.* 1985; Cohen *et al.* 1991).

Nodular hyperplasia but no papillomas or carcinomas were detected in the bladder epithelium of male rats given 5% sodium saccharin in the diet for a period of 112 weeks, starting at 7 weeks of age (Hibino *et al.* 1985).

2.2.2 Special studies on promoting activity

The promotion of known bladder carcinogens by high dietary concentrations of sodium saccharin has been detected only in rats (Fukushima *et al.* 1983a). Administration of 5% sodium saccharin in the diet does not increase the incidence of bladder tumours in mice initiated with 2-acetylaminofluorene (Frederick *et al.* 1989).

High dietary concentrations of sodium saccharin (5.0% of the diet or 2.0 g/kg bw/dy from drinking water) promoted the effects of known bladder carcinogens such as methyl-N-nitrosourea (MNU) (Hicks *et al.* 1973), N-[4-(5-nitro-2-furyl)-thiazolyl]formamide (FANFT) (Cohen *et al.* 1979), N-butyl-N-(4-hydroxybutyl)nitrosamine (BBN) (Nakanishi *et al.* 1980b) and 2-acetylaminofluorene (AAF) (Nakanishi *et al.* 1982). Feeding rats with high concentrations of sodium saccharin following an insult such as freeze ulceration causes increases in nodular hyperplasia (Murasaki and Cohen 1983) and in bladder tumours (Hasegawa *et al.* 1985). Promotion of the effect of bladder carcinogens is not sex-specific and has been reported in both male (Cohen *et al.* 1979) and female (Hicks *et al.* 1978) rats. The sex specificity of promoting activity has been studied in male and female F344 rats given BBN as an initiator and up to 5% sodium saccharin as the promoter. Papillomas and carcinomas were not detected, but both sexes showed a similar dose-response for sodium saccharin-related simple hyperplasia and papillary or nodular hyperplasia (Nakanishi *et al.* 1980a).

Administration of a diet containing 5% sodium saccharin to rats increased DNA synthesis in the urinary bladder, but not in liver or forestomach. It did not affect ornithine decarboxylase activity (a molecular marker of tumour promotion) in these organs (Tatematsu *et al.* 1986). An increase in DNA synthesis in the urothelium is produced by a number of promoters of diverse structure (Shibata *et al.* 1989c).

Transitional cell carcinomas of the urinary bladder in rats initiated with FANFT treatment for 4 or 6 weeks followed by long-term treatment with sodium saccharin or other promoters have been analyzed for the presence of H-ras gene activation. There was evidence of increased expression of the *ras* gene product, p21, in transitional cell carcinomas and of H-*ras* gene mutations. The compounds used in the promoting phase had essentially no effect on H-*ras* mutation, and the authors concluded that the effects observed were due to the FANFT initiation phase (Masui *et al.* 1990, 1991).

Proto-oncogenes may contribute to the development of malignancy when their structure or expression is altered, and *ras* gene activation in particular has been demonstrated in 5-17% of human urinary tract tumours (Fujita *et al.* 1984, 1985). Similar activation of the *ras* gene has been demonstrated in animals treated with the bladder carcinogens BBN and FANFT (Jones and Wang 1989; Sawczuk *et al.* 1987). The expression of *ras* p21 has been studied using immunohistochemical techniques in normal urothelium as well as in urothelial lesions in rats from long-term promotion studies using FANFT. Immunoreactivity with *ras* p21 antibody was demonstrated in urinary bladder lesions of more than 50% of rats treated with FANFT alone or FANFT followed by sodium saccharin (0.2 or 5.0% in the diet). Immunoreactivity to *ras* p21 was not observed in rats treated with sodium saccharin alone. More recent studies by the same authors have confirmed the mutational activity of the H-*ras* gene in rat urinary bladders induced by FANFT and the lack of any effect of sodium ascorbate or sodium saccharin on this activation (Masui *et al.* 1990, 1991).

2.2.3   Special studies on genotoxicity

The results of genotoxicity studies with saccharin are summarized in Table 1.

Table 1. Genotoxicity studies with saccharin.

Test System	Test Object	Concentration of saccharin	Results	Reference
Cell mutation/-ouabain resistance	Human RSa cells	10 - 22.5 mg/ml	Positive	Suzuki and Suzuki 1988
In vitro chromosomal aberration	Chinese hamster lung fibroblasts	8 - 16 mg/ml	Positive	Ashby and Ishidate 1986
In vivo chromosomal aberration	ICR/Swiss male mice	0, 0.5, 1.0 and 1.5 g/kg bw/day, p.o. for 24 weeks	Positive	Prasad and Rai 1987
Dominant lethal	ICR/Swiss male and female mice	0, 1 and 2 g/kg bw/12 h x 5, p.o.	Positive	Prasad and Rai 1986
Insect genotoxicity	*Drosophila melanogaster*, meiosis repair deficient	0.5, 5.0 and 50 mg in nutrient media	Negative	Lamm *et al.* 1989

A review by Ashby (1985) presents evidence that the positive results obtained in genotoxicity studies with saccharin, mostly showing clastogenicity, probably do not involve covalent interaction of saccharin with nuclear DNA, but are more probably the result of ionic imbalances at the high concentrations used in the assays. The low systemic toxicity of saccharin to mammals and their constituent cells in culture has allowed the use of exceptionally high dose levels in genotoxicity assays. It was concluded that the structural disturbances of eukaryotic cells *in vitro* and very weak intermittent activity *in vivo* were equivalent to and comparable to the genotoxic profile for sodium chloride.

The different salts of saccharin (at 8-16 mg/ml) showed equal clastogenic activity in Chinese hamster lung cells (Ashby and Ishidate 1986), indicating that both ionic and osmotic changes to the medium may be critical determinants of the observed clastogenic effects. Mutagenicity and/or chromosome aberrations due to sodium chloride at high concentrations have been demonstrated recently using mouse lymphoma cells (Brusick 1986; Moore and Brock 1988) and *Saccharomyces cerevisae* (Parker and von Borstel 1987). Sodium chloride was included as a control in a study on human RSa cells and gave a small non-significant increase at a concentration equivalent to the high concentration of sodium saccharin (0.11M) (Suzuki & Suzuki 1988). However, the results of this study are difficult to interpret because the prolonged exposure to high concentration of sodium ion and chloride ion may have affected Na^+/K^+-ATPase activity, and sodium and chloride channels, thereby altering intracellular sodium concentration and sensitivity to ouabain.

Positive results have also been reported in 2 recent studies in which mice were dosed with solutions prepared by dissolving commercial saccharin tablets in water (no information was given on the salt form, purity or the excipients present). In one study, a dose-related increase in the incidence of chromosomal abnormalities in bone marrow and meiotic cells (not specified) was reported (Prasad and Rai 1987). This finding contrasts with a report that administration of saccharin at 20 g/L (salt not specified) in drinking water for 100 days affected neither bone marrow cells nor dividing spermatocytes (Leonard and Leonard 1979).

The second study using commercial saccharin tablets involved a dominant lethal test. An increased incidence of dead implants was reported in the females mated with saccharin-treated male mice (Prasad and Rai 1986).

A positive dominant lethal test had been reported previously in a study in which mice were treated with a 1.72% solution of sodium saccharin, again prepared by the dissolution of commercial saccharin tablets manufactured in India and administered as drinking water (Sanjeeva Rao and Qureshi 1972).

In contrast to these studies, pure sodium saccharin has been shown to be negative in dominant lethal studies using male mice treated at 5 g/kg/day for 5 days (Machemer and Lorke 1973); using male and female mice treated at 2 g/kg/day for 10 weeks (Lorke and Machemer 1975); and using male mice given either a single intraperitoneal injection (2 g/kg) or 2% saccharin in the drinking water for 100 days (Leonard and Leonard 1979). The positive findings also conflict with the negative data from multi-generation feeding studies in mice (Kroes *et al.* 1977).

2.2.4   Special studies on cell transformation

Malignant transformation of cultured human foreskin fibroblasts occurred when the cells were exposed to a non-toxic concentration of sodium saccharin (50 μg/ml) after being released from the G_1 phase, followed by exposure to either N-ethyl or N-methylnitrosourea. The combination of nitrosourea and saccharin was necessary for the observation of transformation (Milo *et al.* 1988).

Prolonged exposure (up to 89 days) to sodium saccharin (6 or 12 mM; approximately 1-2 mg/ml) caused hyperplastic and other abnormal cellular changes in cultures of bladder epithelial cells from female rats (Knowles *et al.* 1986). A subsequent study (Knowles and Jani 1986) showed that treatment of the culture with N-methylnitrosourea (MNU) resulted in the appearance of preneoplastic epithelial foci and that treatment with sodium saccharin (12 mM) following a low dose of MNU (25 μg/ml) resulted in a very small but apparently significant significant increase in such foci. The incidences of such lesions were 0/896 for MNU alone and 3/1096 for MNU followed by saccharin. The parameters for determining significance were not indicated. No concurrent controls were run for this experiment and the incidence in controls from a different experiment run in the same series was 6/863. In contrast to the foci produced by high doses of MNU alone (250 μg/ml), none of the foci produced by MNU (25 μg/ml) followed by saccharin gave cell lines that were tumorigenic *in vivo*.

The combined effects of sodium saccharin with MNU on *in vitro* explants of female rat bladders were also studied. MNU alone exhibited severe and extensive cytotoxicity to both the urothelium and stroma, while sodium saccharin (0.5% in the medium) as well as sodium cyclamate and cyclophosphamide produced changes in the urothelium consistent only with hyperplasia, demonstrating globular and pleomorphic microvilli. Treatment with a low dose of MNU (100 μg/ml) after exposure to sodium saccharin (0.1 or 0.5% for 28 days) elicited more extensive abnormalities. On the basis of these *in vitro* data, the authors suggested that saccharin may have initiating activity in a multistage process, a conclusion which is at variance with the large body of information on the mechanism of action of saccharin (Norman *et al.*, 1987).

Sodium saccharin (6 mM) did not produce proliferating epithelial foci in bladder explants from female rats but increased the numbers of foci in explants treated with MNU (50 or 100 μg/ml) prior to exposure to saccharin. Cultured cell lines from foci derived from explants treated with MNU alone and MNU + saccharin formed tumours when injected into mice (Nicholson and Jani 1988).

The urothelial transforming activity of sodium saccharin *in vitro* has been studied using epithelial cells derived from male rat bladders and treated with 2-amino-4-(5-nitro-furyl)thiazole (ANFT), a water-soluble metabolite of FANFT. Prolonged treatment with ANFT (1 μg/ml), but not sodium saccharin (25 μg/ml), transformed the cells *in vitro* as evidenced by morphological changes, the ability to grow on plastic, and tumorigenicity when injected into mice. Exposure to sodium saccharin and ANFT produced effects similar to ANFT alone, while urea (0.05%) may have enhanced the effects of ANFT. The absence of "promotion" in this study compared with those presented above may have arisen from the lower concentration of sodium saccharin employed (Mann et al. 1991).

A model of promotion of bladder carcinogenicity has been reported in which male Fischer 344 rats were given the bladder carcinogen BBN (0.05%) for 3 weeks, followed by the possible promoter for 9 weeks. At termination, the urinary bladders were removed, digested with collagenase and DNAase and the number of colonies able to grow on double soft agar was determined. Growth in double soft agar is considered indicative of transformation (Hamburger and Salmon 1977; Colburn et al. 1978). In this test system, 9 weeks of dietary administration of 5% sodium saccharin, 1% D-tryptophan, DL-, D-, or L-leucine and DL- or L-isoleucine all significantly increased the numbers of colonies growing in vitro. Dietary administration of 2% L-tryptophan did not significantly increase the numbers of colonies. Treatment of the rats with BBN for 6 weeks in the absence of a putative promoter resulted in a high yield of colonies (Hashimura et al 1987).

High concentrations of the sodium, potassium and calcium salts of saccharin (100-200 mM; equivalent to 18-36 mg/ml) are toxic to the AY27 line of transformed rat bladder epithelial cells. Comparable toxicity was shown by sodium ascorbate but not by sodium, potassium or calcium chlorides. The authors claim that these observations are of relevance because such high concentrations of sodium and saccharin are present in the urine of rats fed saccharin-containing diets. However, the intra-cellular concentration of the saccharin anion in vivo is much closer to that of plasma which is about 10-fold less than that in urine (Garland et al. 1989a).

2.2.5 Special studies on the effect of saccharin on urine composition and bladder epithelial proliferation

Statistically significant, dose-related changes in urinary parameters (increased Na^+ concentration, increased urine volume and decreased osmolality) have been found to precede and to occur in association with tumour development in the urinary bladder of male rats. A large number of studies have been conducted to establish the effect of factors modifying these non-neoplastic responses on subsequent outcomes of the treatment on the bladder epithelium.

2.2.5.1 Salt form

Feeding different salts of saccharin (sodium, potassium, calcium and acid) for 10 weeks resulted in different effects on [³H]-thymidine labelling in the urinary bladder epithelium (Hasegawa & Cohen 1986). Dietary ingestion of the sodium salt resulted in the highest labelling index (0.6±0.2%), the potassium salt resulted in a weak, but significant, effect (0.2±0.1%), the calcium salt resulted in a questionable and non-significant effect $(0.1 \pm 0.1\%)$, while the acid form $(0.07 \pm 0.04\%)$ gave a result similar to controls $(0.06 \pm 0.04\%)$. In each of these cases, the bladder epithelium was exposed to similar concentrations of the saccharin anion in the urine. Dietary ingestion of the sodium and potassium salts of saccharin were associated with an increased urine volume and slightly higher urine pH (sodium salt only) compared with untreated controls, while a decrease in urine pH and no change in urine volume was found in the calcium and acid saccharin groups.

These findings were essentially confirmed in a subsequent study in which male rats were fed diets containing 200 μmol/g of the different salt forms (equivalent to 5% sodium saccharin) for 10 weeks. Simple hyperplasia of the bladder epithelium was noted in the rats ingesting the sodium and potassium salts, but not in those ingesting the calcium or free acid forms. The effect was independent of the total urinary saccharin or urinary concentration of saccharin (Anderson *et al.* 1988a).

Based on the finding that the sodium, potassium, calcium and acid forms of saccharin differed in the extent to which they produced epithelial proliferation in the bladder of the male rat in the presence of similar concentrations of saccharinate anion, Williamson and coworkers investigated the possibility that differences in the ionic concentration of urine could result in differences in the electronic structure of the saccharin molecule itself. Using nuclear magnetic resonance spectroscopy, the electronic structure of the saccharin molecule was observed in the presence of varying concentrations of hydrogen, potassium, sodium, calcium, magnesium, bicarbonate and urate ions. The presence of these ions at physiological levels did not significantly alter the electronic structure of the saccharin molecule (Williamson *et al.*, 1987).

A recent study has extended these short-term observations to a full initiation-promotion study in which male rats were given 0.2% dietary FANFT for 6 weeks followed by various treatments for 72 weeks. Treatments included doses of sodium saccharin equivalent to the bottom (3%) and middle (5%) of the dose-response as reported in the IRDC 2-generation bioassay (Schoenig *et al.* 1985). Sodium saccharin in Prolab diet produced a dose-related increase in the incidence of bladder carcinoma over that in FANFT-initiated controls. Calcium saccharin also produced a statistically significant increase of bladder carcinomas but equimolar dietary concentrations of acid saccharin did not produce a significant increase in the incidence of bladder tumours.

The observation that co-administration of ammonium chloride (NH_4Cl) with 5% sodium saccharin abolished the promoting activity was of equal or greater significance to the data for the different salt forms of saccharin. The urine pH of animals given sodium saccharin following FANFT initiation was slightly, but significantly higher (by about 0.1 - 0.2 pH units) than that of the corresponding controls, while calcium saccharin caused a slight decrease in urine pH. In contrast, the urine pH of animals given saccharin acid or sodium saccharin + NH_4Cl was 1 pH unit less than that of the corresponding controls. The study also showed that administration of calcium saccharin with sodium chloride or sodium saccharin with calcium carbonate resulted in promoting activity similar to that with sodium saccharin alone. In addition, sodium chloride itself had a significant tumour-promoting effect. The authors concluded that the enhancing factors for promotion of bladder carcinogenesis in the rat by compounds such as sodium saccharin are a high urinary sodium concentration, a high urinary pH (>6.5) and possibly an increase in urine volume (Cohen *et al.* 1991).

A study in which a range of compounds was given to male F344 rats for 16 weeks reported that 5% sodium saccharin caused an approximately 5-fold increase in labelling index. Sodium bicarbonate produced a 10-fold increase and a combination of sodium saccharin and sodium bicarbonate gave an approximately additive effect (Debiec-Rychter and Wang 1990).

2.2.5.2 Anion specificity

High dietary concentrations of the sodium salts of other organic acids ($>1\%$) have also been tested for their ability to enhance DNA synthesis or hyperplasia of the urinary epithelium of the rat or act as promoters of bladder carcinogenesis.

In initiation-promotion models, the sodium salts of the following compounds were found to act as promoters of bladder carcinogenesis in the rat: ascorbate (Fukushima *et al.* 1983b, 1983c, 1984, 1986a and b); Cohen *et al.* 1991b); erythorbate (Fukushima *et al.* 1984); *o*-phenylphenate (Fukushima *et al.* 1983d); citrate (Fukushima *et al.* 1986c); bicarbonate (Fukushima *et al.* 1986a, 1988a). All of these salts increased urine pH and sodium excretion compared with untreated controls. Promotion of bladder carcinogenesis was not caused by the corresponding acids erythorbic acid (Fukushima *et al.* 1987a); *o*-phenylphenol (Fukushima *et al.* 1983d); or nitrilotriacetic acid (Kitahori *et al.* 1988).

Sodium hippurate, which was not a promoter, increased urinary sodium excretion, but did not significantly increase urine pH (Fukushima *et al.* 1983b, 1986b).

One study did not show a promoting effect for sodium citrate or sodium ascorbate in an initiation-promotion protocol despite the expected increase in urinary sodium concentrations and demonstrated increase in urine pH (Inoue *et al.* 1988). The period for promotion in this study was 20 weeks as compared with 32 weeks in the positive studies.

Co-adminstration of ascorbic acid with salts which increased urine pH and elevated urinary sodium concentrations (sodium bicarbonate or potassium bicarbonate but not calcium carbonate or magnesium carbonate), resulted in promoting activity (Fukushima *et al.* 1986a, 1987b, 1988a, 1988b). Administration of the sodium salts of ascorbic acid and nitrilotriacetic acid in conjunction with ammonium chloride (sodium ascorbate and trisodium nitrilotriacetate) resulted in decreased urinary pH and decreased promoting activity (Fukushima *et al.* 1986a; Kitahori *et al.* 1988).

These data showing the importance of urine pH are consistent with the report that co-administration of sodium ascorbate with sodium saccharin enhances bladder tumour promotion in male rats. The co-administration of ascorbic acid with sodium saccharin both lowered the urine pH (by about 1 pH unit) compared with sodium saccharin on its own and abolished the promoting activity (Fukushima *et al.* 1990)]

Similar results were obtained in studies with administration of high doses of organic acids either alone or in combination with other acidifying and alkalinizing salts using increased DNA synthesis and urothelial hyperplasia as the endpoints. Those treatments which caused a marked increase in urinary pH, sodium concentration and urine volume were associated with increased epithelial hyperplasia of the urinary bladder (5% ascorbic acid - Shibata *et al.* 1989b; 6% monosodium glutamate - De Groot *et al.* 1988).

Sodium bicarbonate fed at a level of 0.64% of the diet for 104 weeks study resulted in elevated urinary pH and Na^+ concentration, but did not result in pleomorphic microvilli or a significant increase in bladder tumour incidence (Fukushima *et al.* 1989). These findings suggest that although elevated urinary sodium concentrations and elevated pH are necessary co-factors in bladder tumour promotion, they are not sufficient stimulus for bladder tumour formation in the absence of an initiator.

2.2.5.3 Urine volume

The possible promoting activity arising from an increase in urine volume without a marked change in urine pH or sodium ion concentration has been studied using the diuretics acetazolamide and furosemide. Acetazolamide (0.35%) decreased the urine osmolality and increased fluid intake but lacked promoting activity in one study (Fukushima *et al.* 1983b). However, that study showed limited sensitivity in demonstrating the effects of 5% sodium saccharin and 5% sodium ascorbate.

A more recent initiation-promotion study using acetazolamide (0.35%) has reported significant promoting activity, but these effects were not shown to be independent of a change in pH since acetazolamide also increased the urine pH from 6.7 to 7.4 (Masui *et al.* 1988b).

Furosemide treatment 250 mg/kg, 3 times weekly for 32 weeks) was not a promoter of bladder carcinogenesis in male F344 rats. The dose produced an increase in urine volume, a slight increase in urine pH, but did not increase urinary sodium ion concentration (Shibata *et al.* 1989a). These data suggest that an increase in urine volume in the absence of changes in pH and sodium ion concentration does not result in the promotion of bladder carcinogenicity.

2.2.5.4 Diet and rat strain

Feeding rats 5 or 7.5% sodium saccharin in commercial diets, *i.e.* Prolab and Purina for 4 or 10 weeks resulted in an increased [³H]thymidine labelling index in the bladder epithelium. However, a greatly diminished or negligible increase in labelling index was observed when the same concentrations were incorporated into NIH-07 (a crude cereal-based diet) or AIN-76A (a purified diet) diets. Diet-related differences in urine volumes and urine pH were implicated as being contributory factors since rats fed 7.5% sodium saccharin in the AIN-76A diet had the lowest urine volume and the lowest pH compared with Purina diet. The urinary concentration of saccharin *per se* was highest in the group fed saccharin in the AIN-76A diet (this was the group which showed no increase in labelling index) indicating that the urinary concentration of saccharin is not a critical factor. The F344 strain was more sensitive to saccharin-induced hyperplasia and increases in the [³H]-thymidine labelling index than were Sprague-Dawley rats (Garland *et al.* 1989b).

In a similar study, sodium and calcium saccharin were fed to male F344 rats at 5% in either Prolab 3200 or AIN-76A diets to assess the effects on urinary parameters. The urine volume was actually greater in rats fed the AIN-76A diet containing saccharin than in the corresponding Prolab group and the urinary saccharin concentration was less. The urine pH was about 1.5 units lower in the urine from rats fed with the AIN-76A diets compared with those fed the Prolab diets (Fisher *et al.* 1989).

A full initiation-promotion study with sodium saccharin has shown that dietary levels of 5% do not act as a promoter of bladder carcinogenesis if given to rats in the AIN-76A diet (Okamura *et al.* 1991). This is consistent with an earlier observation with this diet (Imaida and Wang 1986).

The basal diet has been shown to play a similar critical role in the promotion of bladder carcinogenesis by sodium ascorbate (Mori *et al.* 1987). The nature of the basal diet also influences the urinary changes associated with the administration of monosodium glutamate (De Groot *et al.* 1988).

2.2.6 Special studies on the basis of sex/species specificity of carcinogenic effects of saccharin

Crystals and flocculent precipitate have been observed in the urine of rats fed sodium saccharin for four weeks (Cohen *et al.* 1989). Milky flocculent precipitate has also been noted in the urine of rats fed 5% sodium saccharin in a chronic study which was more pronounced in males than in females and was found to contain saccharin and protein (Arnold *et al.* 1980).

In preliminary evaluations, a correlation was demonstrated for individual rats between early appearance of the precipitate, consistent appearance over the course of the study and the subsequent severity of "bladder effects" over a 10-week treatment period (cited Cohen and Garland 1992).

A number of methods have been used to quantify this urinary precipitate. Visual inspection of the filtered urine showed that a white precipitate was frequently noted on the filters from male rats treated with sodium saccharin, but rarely on the filters from control male rats, control and treated female rats and control and treated male and female mice. In addition, precipitate was not noted in the filtered urine of rats treated with acid saccharin. A turbidity assay which measured absorbance of the urine at 620 nm showed that urine turbidity was increased by feeding of sodium saccharin to rats (information on sex not available but presumed to be male), at levels exceeding 3% and with sodium ascorbate at 6.84%. The urine turbidity of rats treated with lower levels of saccharin or with acid saccharin, ascorbic acid, sodium saccharin with ammonium chloride or sodium saccharin in AIN-76A semi-synthetic diet was similar to that in untreated rats (cited in Cohen and Garland 1992).

Gel filtration of the protein component of the urinary precipitate showed it to migrate with low molecular weight proteins including α_{2u}-globulin (Cohen et al. 1990). Binding of saccharin to urinary proteins is minimal at a pH of 5.5, but increases with increasing pH. Treatments which were associated with a urinary pH less than 6.5 did not result in the formation of a urinary precipitate or in the production of proliferative changes in the bladder (cited in Cohen and Garland 1992).

A study was conducted to determine whether α_{2u}-globulin plays a role in the development of bladder lesions in sodium saccharin-treated rats. The effects of sodium saccharin on urinary parameters and bladder morphology were compared in NCI-Black-Reiter (NBR) male rats which do not synthesize α_{2u}-globulin, castrated male F344 rats which have lower α_{2u}-globulin levels, and intact male F344 rats. Scanning electron microscopy and light microscopy showed that 7.5% sodium saccharin in the diet had less of an effect on the bladders with respect to morphological changes (simple and proliferative hyperplasia) of the NBR rats than in the intact F344 rats, and the results from the castrated F344 rats were intermediate between the intact F344 and NBR male rats. The ability of saccharin to bind in vitro to urinary proteins was much less with NBR rat urine than with urine from intact F344 rats. Urine from castrated F344 rats was not tested. Binding was predominantly to proteins of low molecular weight in the F344 rat and equally divided between low and higher MW proteins in the NBR rat. Although urine volume and sodium concentration were elevated, urine pH was actually decreased in sodium saccharin-treated rats as compared with respective controls, but still exceeded values of 6.5. The NBR rats had in general a much greater urine volume, so that urinary concentration of solutes was decreased. Visual inspection indicated that a white precipitate was occasionally present in the urine of untreated rats, in the majority of urine samples collected from sodium saccharin-treated intact and castrated F344 rats and in approximately half of the sodium saccharin-treated NBR rats. The presence of α_{2u}-globulin was detected using Western blot analysis in the urine from intact male F344 rats, very low levels in the urine from female F344 rats and none in the urine from NBR rats. Data for the castrated rats were not available from this study, but levels are reported to be intermediate between those of intact and NBR rats. The results of this experiment demonstrated a relationship between urinary α_{2u}-globulin levels, binding of saccharin to urinary proteins and morphological changes in the bladder (Garland et al. 1992a).

The Committee was not convinced that this evidence showed that α_{2u}-globulin has a role in bladder carcinogenesis.

2.2.7 Special studies on the possible significance of exposure to saccharin through lactation

The physiological changes in young male rats that had been exposed to sodium saccharin from parturition (up to 5% in the diet) have been compared to those detected in animals exposed only from weaning and to controls. The results at 10 weeks after weaning showed that exposure during lactation slightly enhanced the effects of saccharin compared to animals exposed only from weaning. The animals exposed from parturition showed a significantly lower urine osmolality, lower body weight and lower food intake and a non-significant increase in urine mass, bladder mass and bladder hyperplasia compared with those exposed after weaning (Anderson et al. 1988b).

Administration of a diet containing 7.5% sodium saccharin during a 2-generation protocol resulted in anaemia in both dams and pups and a severe reduction in post-natal body weight (35% by day 30). This observation had been made previously in weanling rats from the IRDC long-term study (Schoenig et al. 1985). Saccharin-treated pups, 28-30 days old, showed the typical saccharin-related changes in the gastrointestinal tract (increased caecum weight and moist faeces) and in the urine (increased volume and decreased osmolality, increased Na^+ and decreased K^+ and Ca^{++}). Pups raised on saccharin-containing diets had elevated serum concentrations of cholesterol, triglycerides and Vitamin E, and decreased concentrations of Vitamin A and folate in the serum and liver compared with untreated controls (Garland et al. 1991a).

A subsequent investigation at dietary concentrations of 0, 1, 3 and 7.5% sodium saccharin using a two-generation protocol, investigated these findings in 30-day-old pups in more detail. The effects of sodium saccharin on anaemia, serum folate and Vitamin A were dose-dependent, while the effect on serum concentrations of vitamin E, cholesterol and triglycerides was biphasic, with a decrease at 1% and 3% and an increase at 7.5% in the diet. These effects were mostly reversible by 90 days of age. At 7.5% in the diet, there was a decrease in liver weight which was associated with a decrease in glycogen and an increase in the numbers of lipid vacuoles. The dietary NOEL for sodium saccharin-induced changes in the liver and for anaemia was estimated to be 1% (Garland et al. 1991b).

These nutritional and biochemical effects resemble findings in pups of iron-deficient dams, and further studies were conducted to see whether iron and/or folate supplementation could counteract the effects of 7.5% dietary sodium saccharin in pups up to 30 days old. Iron supplementation reversed some of the biochemical changes, but had no effect on the majority of the urinary changes which are typically observed with high dietary levels of sodium saccharin and implicated with enhancing the epithelial hyperplasia of the bladder. It is likely that the biochemical changes in the neonatal rat described above are a consequence of iron deficiency which is an indirect effect of sodium saccharin treatment and probably independent of urinary and bladder effects (Garland et al. 1992b).

Cohen and his associates have proposed that during the neonatal period newborn rats are uniquely sensitive to the mitogenic effects of saccharin on the urothelium. In this model, the importance of exposure to sodium saccharin during the this period arises from the fact that approximately one third of the total lifetime mitoses of the urothelium occur within the first 3 weeks of life (Cohen and Ellwein 1991). A significant increase in cell proliferation rates due to sodium saccharin administration during the 3 weeks after birth (Masui et al 1988a), coupled with the background probability of spontaneous genomic errors would substantially increase the number of initiated cells (Cohen and Ellwein 1990).

The critical event(s) occurring during the neonatal phase, leading to an increased population of initiated cells, has not been identified.

2.2.8   Special studies on the effects of saccharin on digestion

The caecal enlargement which results from feeding high dietary concentrations of saccharin to rats is accompanied by an increase in the total numbers of micro-organisms (Mallett et al. 1985). Since saccharin has been shown to inhibit the activity of digestive enzymes mediating hydrolysis of complex carbohydrates, as well as that of several proteases and urease (Section 2.1.3), this increase in the numbers of caecal bacteria suggests a large increase in nutrient availability for microorganisms in the lower GI tract.

A study was performed to investigate a possible connection between the saccharin-mediated decrease in hydrolysis of complex carbohydrates and altered urinary parameters (increased urine volume, concomitant bladder mass increase and decreased osmolality) in the male rat. However, when the starch component of the 5% saccharin-containing diet was replaced with an equivalent amount of glucose, the effect on caecal enlargement was the same, leading the authors to conclude that in addition to inhibiting carbohydrate digestion, 5% sodium saccharin in the diet of rats also inhibited intestinal transport of glucose. A diet low in carbohydrates (3% sucrose) resulted in a smaller increase in caecal volume compared with diets containing various forms of carbohydrates at a level of 65%. It abolished the increase in relative urine volume and bladder mass noted in the carbohydrate-fed groups even though low-carbohydrate groups had a comparable increase in water intake. The authors concluded that the responses of urinary parameters in rats ingesting high doses of sodium saccharin were dependent on the effects of sodium saccharin on carbohydrate metabolism and glucose transport from the intestine. However, they did not take into consideration the effects of the high concentrations of cellulose and fat in the low-carbohydrate diet on the absorption of water from the GI tract. They also did not comment on the fact that absorption of ingested saccharin was markedly decreased in rats on the low carbohydrate diet compared with the 65% carbohydrate diets; only 31% of the ingested dose of saccharin was excreted in the urine compared with 67-83% in the carbohydrate diets (Anderson *et al.* 1987a).

Measurement of the caecal contents of the rat has shown that sodium saccharin ingestion increases the total protein content of the caecum (Sims and Renwick 1985) and produces dose-related increases in the urinary excretion of the bacterial amino acid metabolites, indican and *p*-cresol, which are known to have promoting or co-carcinogenic properties (Lawrie *et al.* 1985; Lawrie and Renwick 1987). The toxicological significance of these abnormal metabolic profiles is uncertain.
Comparison of the extent of hyperplasia of the bladder epithelium in rats fed diets containing 5% sodium saccharin and/or 1.5% indole has demonstrated that indole *per se* does not contribute significantly to hyperplasia in the urinary bladder (Anderson *et al.* 1989).

Administration of 1 g/day of sodium saccharin to humans did not alter the urinary excretion of these bacterial amino acid metabolites (Lawrie and Renwick 1987).

A mechanism of action involving enhanced microbial activity in the gut resulting from excess undigested carbohydrates and protein in saccharin-treated rats was not apparent.

2.3   **Observations in humans**

Epidemiology studies on the possible association between saccharin ingestion and bladder cancer in humans covering the period up to 1983 were reviewed. The studies and conclusions included in this review were mentioned in the previous monograph addendum (Annex 1, reference 67), including a meta-analysis of 8 of the studies which concluded that the relative risk associated with ingestion of saccharin and subsequent development of bladder cancer was close to one for males, females or both sexes combined (Morgan and Wong 1985).

Since the review of 1985, there have been additional epidemiology studies published which considered the potential effect of saccharin on the urinary bladder.

A novel study using autopsy specimens reported on the histological changes in sections from the urinary bladder in humans in which the numbers of cell rows and the presence and extent of cells with atypical nuclei were recorded. A total of 6503 sections from 282 patients were examined. No relationship was found between the changes in the bladder epithelium and the use of artificial sweeteners in general (Auerbach and Garfinkel 1989).

Another important study was published by the group which had previously reported a significantly increased saccharin-related risk for males (odds ratio 1.6) but not females (Howe *et al.*, 1977). The more recent case-control study used 826 histologically-verified cases of bladder cancer (compared with 480 men and 152 women in the earlier study). The relative risk for the use of a number of artificial sweeteners, including saccharin, did not suggest an association with bladder cancer in either males or females (Risch *et al.* 1988).

Two studies attempted to identify the principal risk factors for bladder cancer in Spain using 406 patients with bladder cancer (353 males and 53 females) and age-matched controls from the same hospital who did not have any malignant disease. Consumption of wine with "gaseosa", which contains saccharin and cyclamate, was associated with an enhanced risk of bladder cancer in males although there was no association between alcohol ingestion and bladder cancer (after stratification for smoking). The authors did point out, however, that the wine consumed with gaseosa was typically of low quality and contained large amounts of impurities. Consequently, the low quality of the wine was an additional risk factor (Bravo and Del Rey-Calero 1987).

In a related paper, discriminant analysis was applied to the data obtained from the same patients (not presented) in order to identify and rank factors increasing the risk of bladder cancer. Use of artificially-sweetened beverages ranked fourth and use of artificial sweeteners themselves ranked eighth. The number of cigarettes smoked was the most important factor. Saccharin was not specifically mentioned (Bravo *et al.* 1987).

A small case-control study (194 bladder cancer patients and the same number of age- and sex-matched controls) conducted in Turkey reported a statistically significant association ($p < 0.05$) between the use of artificial sweeteners and the development of bladder cancer. The authors did not distinguish between the use of specific sweeteners and only 19 cases and 8 controls reported using these substances. In addition, there was no investigation of the possible influence of confounding factors (Akdas *et al.* 1990).

Two population-based case-control studies in the U.S.A. concluded that there was no link between consumption of artificial sweeteners and bladder cancer. One study was conducted with 173 female patients with bladder cancer and had only two categories of use of artificial sweeteners, that being 100 times or more life-time use of artificially-sweetened beverages or tabletop sweeteners or less than 100 times use (Piper *et al.* 1986).

The second study investigated the potential of increased volume of fluid intake or of specific fluids, including artificially-sweetened beverages, to increase the risk of bladder cancer. No association was found between the volume of intake of artificially-sweetened beverages and bladder cancer (Slattery *et al.* 1988).

A case-control study with 117 patients apparently showed no association between saccharin consumption and bladder cancer (the data were not presented) (Iscovitch *et al.* 1987). Although this study was small compared with some previous investigations, it was of sufficient power to show that cigarette smoking was a major risk factor.

An update of the earlier review of Morgan and Wong (1985) in which most of the above-mentioned studies were analyzed, was provided. In addition, they added two of these studies to the meta-analysis performed previously. The conclusions from this meta-analysis were the same as those in the previous paper: the relative risk from the combined data of 15 studies indicated that there was no association between ingestion of saccharin and development of bladder cancer (Elcock and Morgan 1992).

A study which investigated the correlation between the urinary excretion of the microbial amino acid metabolites indican, *p*-cresol and phenol (which have been shown to be co-carcinogenic or promoters) and bladder cancer was conducted in thirty-two patients with histologically-confirmed carcinoma of the urinary bladder and a similar number of matched controls. There was wide variability between individuals in the excretion of these metabolites, but no difference was detected between the two groups (Renwick *et al.* 1988).

3.   COMMENTS

An independent assessment of the bladder histopathology data from the most recent two-generation feeding study in rats that was reviewed at the twenty-eighth meeting revealed the presence of transitional cell papillomas and carcinomas in the control group. This assessment reduced concern over setting the NOEL at a dose where tumours were observed and it eradicated the statistical significance of the increase in tumour incidence at the 3% dietary level. Application of a dose-response model to the carcinogenicity data suggested a threshold for carcinogenesis close to 3% saccharin in the diet. This is the dietary level at which saturation of renal tubular secretion occurs in the rat and anaemia and other biochemical changes occur in weanling rats. In this study, the absolute and relative weights of the urinary bladder of treated rats were significantly higher than those of controls when sodium saccharin was included in the diet at levels of 3% or higher.

The rat is the only species that has been reported to show an increase in the incidence of bladder tumours at high dietary concentrations of sodium saccharin in a 2-generation study. Apart from mice, studies in other species have not included neonatal exposure to saccharin at levels above the maximum tolerated dose. The Committee concluded from the long-term feeding studies that the dose-related carcinogenic activity of sodium saccharin on the urinary bladder was specific to the male rat and that exposure during the neonatal period was critical for the subsequent development of these tumours in the absence of an initiator or stimulus such as freeze ulceration. The critical events during the neonatal phase that lead to an increase in the population of initiated cells have not been identified.

The Committee considered the genotoxic potential of saccharin on the basis of its physicochemical properties and results from *in vitro* and *in vivo* assays. At physiological pH, saccharin exists almost exclusively as the anion. As such, the parent compound does not resemble an electrophilic chemical carcinogen that would bind to DNA, nor has it been shown to bind to DNA *in vivo*. Because it is not metabolized, it is not converted to an active metabolite. On the other hand, sodium saccharin has exhibited clastogenic activity in a number of *in vivo* and *in vitro* genotoxicity assays. Since high concentrations of sodium saccharin were used in these assays, it has been suggested that the clastogenic activity could be attributable to ionic imbalances at the chromosomal level at high concentrations. The clastogenic activity is also in disagreement with the results of the long-term studies and tumour-initiation promotion studies with sodium saccharin.

The conditions required for the hyperplastic and tumour-promoting activities of high dietary concentrations of saccharin (usually 5% or higher) on the urothelium in the male rat are an increased urinary concentration of sodium ion and an elevated pH. The response does not appear to be specific to saccharin, since high dietary concentrations of other organic anions have been shown to promote bladder carcinogenesis and induce urothelial hyperplasia under the same conditions. The differences in tumour-promoting activities observed between organic acids and their sodium salts were unrelated to the urinary concentration of the parent organic molecule.

The Committee was not convinced that the available evidence implicated α_{2u}-globulin in bladder carcinogenesis. The Committee also noted that a proposed mechanism of action involving enhanced microbial activities in the gut, resulting from excess undigested carbohydrates and protein in rats administered saccharin in the diet had been investigated without any conclusive evidence.

The epidemiological studies on saccharin did not show any evidence that saccharin ingestion increases the incidence of bladder cancer in human populations.

The Committee accepted that, on the basis of data reviewed to date, it would be inappropriate to consider the bladder tumours induced in male rats by sodium saccharin to be relevant to the assessment of a toxicological hazard to humans.

4.   EVALUATION

In re-assessing saccharin, the Committee considered that the 1% dietary level in the most recent 2-generation feeding study in rats, equivalent to 500 mg/kg bw/day, was appropriate for establishing an intake causing no relevant toxicological effects. This was based on the observation that, although dose levels of up to 7.5% sodium saccharin in the diet had no adverse effect on survival, the animals demonstrated a marked disturbance of homoeostasis at levels of 3% and higher. In particular, persistent dose-related decreases in body weight gain in the presence of increased food consumption are indicative of decreased biological performance and were probably related to the inhibitory effects of saccharin on carbohydrate and protein digestion. A no-effect level of 500 mg/kg bw/day was also observed in a long-term toxicity study in monkeys reviewed at the twenty-sixth meeting (Annex 1, reference 60).

The Committee allocated a group ADI of 0-5 mg/kg bw/dy to saccharin and its calcium, potassium, and sodium salts, based on the NOEL of 500 mg/kg bw/day in the 2-generation long-term feeding study in rats and a safety factor of 100.

5.   REFERENCES

AKDAS, A., KIRKALI, Z. & BILIR, N. (1990). Epidemiological case-control study on the etiology of bladder cancer in Turkey. *Eur. Urol.*, **17**, 23-26.

ANDERSON, R.L., FRANCIS, W.R. & LEFEVER, F.R. (1987a). Effects of dietary carbohydrate type and content on the response of male rats to dietary sodium saccharin. *Food Chem. Toxicol.* **25**, 271-275.

ANDERSON, R.L., LEFEVER, F.R. & MAURER, J.K. (1987b). Effect of inherent urine output on the response of male rats to 7.5% dietary sodium saccharin. *Food Chem. Toxicol.*, **23**, 641-643.

ANDERSON, R.L., LEFEVER, F.R. & MAURER, J.K. (1988a). The effect of various saccharin forms on the gastro-intestinal tract, urine and bladder of male rats. *Food Chem. Toxicol.*, **26**, 665-669.

ANDERSON, R.L., LEFEVER, F.R. & MAURER, J.K. (1988b). Comparison of the responses of male rats to dietary sodium saccharin exposure initiated during nursing with responses to exposure initiated at weaning. *Food Chem. Toxicol.*, **26**, 899-907.

ANDERSON, R.L., LEFEVER, F.R, MILLER, N.S. & MAURER, J.K. (1989). Comparison of the bladder response to indole and sodium saccharin ingestion by male rats. *Food Chem. Toxicol.* **27**, 777-779.

ARNOLD, D.L., MOODIE, C.A., GRICE, H.C., CHARBONNEAU, S.M., STAVRIC, B., COLLINS, B.T., MCGUIRE, P.F., ZAWIDZKA, Z.Z. & MUNRO, I.C. (1980). Long-term toxicity of ortho-toluenesulfonamide and sodium saccharin in the rat. *Toxicol. Appl. Pharmacol.*, **52**, 113-152.

ASHBY, J. (1985). The genotoxicity of sodium saccharin and sodium chloride in relation to their cancer promoting properties. *Food Chem. Toxicol.*, **23**, 507-519.

ASHBY, J. & ISHIDATE, M. (1986). Clastogenicity *in vitro* of the Na, K, Ca and mg salts of saccharin; and of magnesium chloride; consideration of significance. *Mutation Res.*, **163**, 63-73.

AUERBACH, O. & GARFINKEL, L. (1989). Histologic changes in the urinary bladder in relation to cigarette smoking and use of artificial sweeteners. *Cancer*, **64**, 983-987.

BALL, L.M. (1973). The metabolism of saccharin and related compounds. Report 4 from the Department of Biochemistry, St. Mary's Hospital Medical School, London, U.K. Unpublished report submitted to WHO. Cited in the 1982 monograph (Annex 1, Ref 59).

BALL, L.M., RENWICK, A.G. & WILLIAMS, R.T. (1977). The fate of [¹⁴C]saccharin in man, rat and rabbit and of 2-sulphamoyl[¹⁴C]benzoic acid in the rat. *Xenobiotica*, **7**, 189-203.

BRAVO, M.P., & DEL REY-CALERO, J. (1987). Bladder cancer and the consumption of alcoholic beverages in Spain. *Eur. J. Epidemiol.*, **3**, 365-369.

BRAVO, M.P., DEL REY-CALERO, J. & CONDE, M. (1987). Risk factors of bladder cancer in Spain. *Neoplasma*, **34**, 633-637.

BRUSICK, D. (1986). Genotoxic effects in cultured mammalian cells produced by low pH treatment conditions and increased ion concentrations. *Environmental Mutagenesis*, **8**, 879-886.

CARLBORG, F.W. (1985). A cancer risk assessment for saccharin. *Food Chem. Toxicol.*, **43**, 464-469.

COHEN, S.M. & ELLWEIN, L.B. (1990). Cell proliferation in carcinogenesis. *Science*, **249**, 1007-1011.

COHEN, S.M. & ELLWEIN, L.B. (1991). Cell proliferation and bladder tumor promotion. Chemically Induced Cell Proliferation: Implications for Risk Assessment, 347-355. Wiley-Liss, Inc.

COHEN, S.M. & GARLAND, E.M. (1992). Summary of recent results of research concerning the carcinogenicity of saccharin. Unpublished report.

COHEN, S.M., ARAI, M., JACOBS, J.B. & FRIEDELL, G.H. (1979). Promoting effect of saccharin and DL-tryptophan in urinary bladder carcinogenesis. *Cancer Res.*, **39**, 1207-1217.

COHEN, S.M., CANO, M., GARLAND, E.M. & EARL, R.A. (1989). Silicate crystals in urine and bladder epithelium of male rats fed sodium saccharin. *Proc. Am. Assoc. Cancer Res.* **30**, 205.

COHEN, S.M., FISHER, M.J., SAKATA, T., CANO, M., SCHOENIG, G.P., CHAPPEL, C.I. & GARLAND, E.M. (1990). Comparative analysis of the proliferative response of the rat urinary bladder to sodium saccharin by light and scanning electron microscopy and autoradiography. *Scanning Microscopy*, **4**, 135-142.

COHEN, S.M., ELLWEIN, L.B., OKAMURA, T., MASUI, T., JOHANSSON, S.L., SMITH, R.A., WEHNER, J.M., KHACHAB, M., CHAPPEL, C.I., SCHOENIG, G.P., EMERSON, J.L. & GARLAND, E.M. (1991). Comparative bladder tumour promoting activity of sodium saccharin, sodium ascorbate, related acids and calcium salts in rats. *Cancer Res.*, **51**, 1766-1777.

COHEN-ADDAD, N., CHATTERJEE, M., BEKERSKY, I. & GLUMENTHAL, H.P. (1986). *In utero* exposure to saccharin: A threat? *Cancer Letters*, **32**, 151-154.

COLBURN, N.H., BRUEGGE, W.F., BATES, J.R., GRAY, R.H., ROSSEN, J.D., KELSEY, W.H. & SHIMADA, T. (1978). Correlation of anchorage-independent growth with tumorigenicity of chemically transformed mouse epidermal cells. *Cancer Research*, **38**, 624-634.

DEBIEC-RYCHTER, M. & WANG, C.Y. (1990). Induction of DNA synthesis by sodium phenobarbital, uracil, and sodium saccharin in urinary bladder of the F344 rat. *Toxicol. Appl. Pharmacol.*, **105**, 345-349.

ELCOCK, M. & MORGAN, R.W. (1992). Update on artificial sweeteners and bladder cancer. Unpublished report.

FISHER, M.J., SAKATA, T., TIBBELS, T.S., SMITH, R.A., PATIL, K., KHACHAB, M., JOHANSSON, S.L. & COHEN, S.M. (1989). Effect of sodium saccharin and calcium saccharin on urinary parameters in rats fed Prolab 3200 or AIN-76 diet. *Food Chem. Toxicol.*, **27**, 1-9.

FREDERICK, C.B., DOOLEY, K.L., KODELL, R.L., SHELDON, W.G. & KADLUBAR, F.F. (1989). The effect of lifetime sodium saccharin dosing on mice initiated with the carcinogen 2-acetylaminofluorene. *Fundam. Appl. Toxicol.*, **12**, 346-357.

FUJITA, J., YOSHIDA, O., YUASA, Y., RHIM, J.S., HATANAKA, M. & AARONSON S.A. (1984). Ha-*ras* oncogenes are activated by somatic alterations in human urinary tract tumours. *Nature*, **309**, 464-466.

FUJITA, J., SRIVASTAVA, S.K., KRAUS, M.H., RHIM, J.S., TRONICK, S.R. & AARONSON, S.A. (1985). Frequency of molecular alterations affecting *ras* protooncogenes in human urinary tract tumors. *Proc. Natl. Acad. Sci.*, **82**, 3849-3853.

FUKUSHIMA, S., ARAI, M., NAKANOWATARI, J., HIBINO, T., OKUDA, M. & ITO, N. (1983a). Differences in susceptibility to sodium saccharin among different strains of rats and other animal species. *Jpn. J. Cancer Res. (Gann)*, **74**, 8-20.

FUKUSHIMA, S., HAGIWARA, A., OGISO, T., SHIBATA, M. & ITO, N. (1983b). Promoting effects of various chemicals in rat urinary bladder carcinogenesis initiated by N-nitroso-*n*-butyl-(4-hydroxybutyl)amine. *Food Chem. Toxicol.*, **21**, 59-68.

FUKUSHIMA, S., IMAIDA, K., SAKATA, T. OKAMURA, T., SHIBATA, M. & ITO, N. (1983c). Promoting effects of sodium-L-ascorbate on two-stage urinary bladder carcinogenesis in rats. *Cancer Res.*, **43**, 4454-4457.

FUKUSHIMA, S., KURATA, Y., SHIBATA, M., IKAWA, E. & ITO, N. (1983d). Promoting effect of sodium *o*-phenylphenate and *o*-phenylphenol on two-stage urinary bladder carcinogenesis in rats. *Jpn. J. Cancer Res. (Gann)*, **74**, 625-632.

FUKUSHIMA, S., KURATA, Y, SHIBATA, M., IKAWA, E. & ITO, N. (1984). Promotion by ascorbic acid, sodium erythorbate and ethoxyquin of neoplastic lesions in rats initiated with N-butyl-N-(4-hydroxybutyl) nitrosamine. *Cancer Letters*, **23**, 29-37.

FUKUSHIMA, S., SHIBATA, M., SHIRAI, T., TAMANO. & ITO, N. (1986a). Roles of urinary sodium ion concentration and pH in promotion by ascorbic acid of urinary bladder carcinogenesis in rats. *Cancer Res.*, **46**, 1623-1626.

FUKUSHIMA, S., SHIBATA, M., KURATA, Y, TAMANO, S. & MASUI, T. (1986b). Changes in the urine and scanning electron microscopically observed appearance of the rat bladder following treatment with tumor promoters. *Jpn. J. Cancer Res.* (Gann), **77**, 1074-1082.

FUKUSHIMA, S., THAMAVIT, W., KURATA, Y. & ITO, N. (1986c). Sodium citrate; a promoter of bladder carcinogenesis. *Jpn. J. Cancer Res.* (Gann)., **77**, 1-4.

FUKUSHIMA, S., OGISO, T., KURATA, Y., SHIBATA, M. & KAKIZOE, T. (1987a). Absence of promotion potential for calcium L-ascorbate, L-ascorbic dipalmitate, L-ascorbic stearate and erythorbic acid on rat urinary bladder carcinogenesis. *Cancer Letters*, **35**, 17-25.

FUKUSHIMA, S., SHIBATA, M., SHIRAI, T., KURATA, Y., TAMANO, S. & IMAIDA, K. (1987b). Promotion by L-ascorbic acid of urinary bladder carcinogenesis in rats under conditions of increased urinary K ion concentration and pH. *Cancer Res.*, **47**, 4821-4824.

FUKUSHIMA, S., IMAIDA, K., SHIBATA, M., TAMANO, S., KURATA, Y. & SHIRAI, T. (1988a). L-Ascorbic acid amplification of second-stage bladder carcinogenesis promotion by NaHCO$_3$. *Cancer Res.*, **48**, 6317-6320.

FUKUSHIMA, S., SHIRAI, T., HIROSE, M. & ITO, N. (1988b). Significance of L-ascorbic acid and urinary electrolytes in promotion of rat bladder carcinogenesis. In Diet, Nutrition and Cancer, edited by Y. Hagashi, *et al.*, pp 159-168. Japan. Sci. Soc. Press/VNU Sci. Press., Utrecht, The Netherlands.

FUKUSHIMA, S., INOUE, T., UWAGAWA, S., SHIBATA, M. & ITO, N. (1989). Co-carcinogenic effects of NaHCO$_3$ or *o*-phenylphenol-induced rat bladder carcinogenesis. *Carcinogenesis*, **10**, 1635-1640.

FUKUSHIMA, S., UWAGAWA, S., SHIRAI, T., HASEGAWA, R. & OGAWA, K. (1990). Synergism by sodium L-ascorbate but inhibition by L-ascorbic acid for sodium saccharin promotion of rat two-stage bladder carcinogenesis. *Cancer Res.*, **50**, 4195-4198.

GARLAND, E.M., PARR, J.M., WILLIAMSON, D.S. & COHEN, S.M. (1989a). *In vitro* cytotoxicity of the sodium, potassium and calcium salts of saccharin, sodium ascorbate, sodium citrate and sodium chloride. *Toxic. in Vitro*, **3**, 201-205.

GARLAND, E.M., SAKATA, T., FISHER, M.J., MASUI, T. & COHEN, S.M. (1989b). Influences of diet and strain on the proliferative effect on the rat urinary bladder induced by sodium saccharin. *Cancer Res.*, **49**, 3789-3794.

GARLAND, E.M., KRAFT, P.L., SHAPIRO, R., KHACHAB, M., PATIL, K., ELLWEIN, L.B. & COHEN, S.M. (1991a). Effects of *in utero* and postnatal sodium saccharin exposure on the nutritional status of the young rat. I. Effects at 30 days post-birth. *Food Chem. Toxicol.*, **29**, 657-667.

GARLAND, E.M., SHAPIRO, R., KRAFT, P.L., MATTSON, B.J., PARR, J.M. & COHEN, S.M. (1991b). Effects of *in utero* and postnatal sodium saccharin exposure on the nutritional status of the young rat. II. Dose response and reversibility. *Food Chem. Toxicol.*, **29**, 669-679.

GARLAND, E.M., ST. JOHN, M., EKLUND, S.H., MATTSON, B.J., JOHNSON, L.S., CANO, M. & COHEN, S.M. (1992a). A comparison of the effects of sodium saccharin in NBR rats and in intact and castrated male F344 rats. Unpublished report.

GARLAND, E.M., SHAPIRO, R., WEHNER, J.M., JOHNSON, L.S., MATTSON, B.J. & COHEN, S.M. (1992b). The effects of dietary iron and folate supplementation on the nutritional and physiological changes produced in weanling rats by sodium saccharin exposure. Unpublished report.

de GROOT, A.P., FERON, V.J. & IMMEL, H.R. (1988). Induction of hyperplasia in the bladder epithelium of rats by a dietary excess of acid or base: implications for toxicity/carcinogenicity testing. *Food Chem. Toxicol.*, **26**, 425-434.

HAMBURGER, A.W. & SALMON, S.E. (1977). Primary bioassay of human tumor stem cells. *Science*, **197**, 461-463.

HASEGAWA, R. & COHEN, S.M. (1986). The effect of different salts of saccharin on the rat urinary bladder. *Cancer Letters*, **30**, 261-268.

HASEGAWA, R., SO, J.M.K., CANO, M., ISSENBERG, P., KLEIN, D.A., WALKER, B.A., JONES, J.W., SCHNELL, R.C., MERRICK, B.A., DAVIES, M.H., MCMILLAN, D.T. & COHEN, S.M. (1984). Bladder freeze ulceration and sodium saccharin feeding in the rat: Examination for urinary nitrosamines, mutagens and bacteria, and effects on hepatic microsomal enzymes. *Fed. Chem. Toxicol.*, **22**, 935-942.

HASEGAWA, R., GREENFIELD, R.E., MURASAKI, G., SUZUKI, T. & COHEN, S.M. (1985). Initiation of urinary bladder carcinogenesis in rats by freeze ulceration with sodium saccharin promotion. *Cancer Res.*, **45**, 1469-1473.

HASHIMURA, T., KANAMARU, H. & YOSHIDA, O. (1987). Soft agar colony formation of bladder cells during carcinogenesis induced by N-butyl-N-(4-hydroxybutyl)nitrosamine and application to detection of bladder cancer promoters. *Jpn. J. Cancer Res.*, **78**, 473-479.

HEATON, G.D. & RENWICK, A.G. (1991a). The effects of high dietary concentrations of saccharin on *in vitro* metabolism of xenobiotics in rats. *Food Chem. Toxicol.*, **29**, 297-303.

HEATON, G.D. & RENWICK, A.G. (1991b). The effects of high dietary concentrations of sodium saccharin on *in vivo* metabolism of xenobiotics in rats. *Food Chem. Toxicol.* **29**, 305-312.

HIBINO, T., HIRASAWA, Y. & ARAI, M. (1985). Morphologic changes in the urinary bladder and stomach after long-term administration of sodium saccharin in F344 rats. *Cancer Letters*, **29**, 255-263.

HICKS, R.M., WAKEFIELD, J. ST. J., & CHOWANIEC, J. (1973). Co-carcinogenic action of saccharin in the chemical induction of bladder cancer. *Nature* (London), **243**, 347-349.

HICKS, R.M. CHOWANIEC, J. & WAKEFIELD, J.S.J. (1978). Experimental induction of bladder tumors by a two-stage system. *Carcinogenesis*, *Vol.2. Mechanisms of Tumor Promotion and Cocarcinogenesis*. Edited by T.J. Slaga, A. Sivak and R.K. Boutwell, Raven Press, New York, pp 475-489.

IMAIDA, K. & WANG, C.Y. (1986). Effect of sodium phenobarbital and sodium saccharin in AIN-76A diet on carcinogenesis initiated with N-[4-(5-nitro-2-furyl)-2-thiazolyl]formamide and N,N-dibutylnitrosamine in male F344 rats. *Cancer Res.*, **46**, 6160-6164.

INOUE, T., IMAIDA, K., SUZUKI, E., OKADA, M. & FUKUSHIMA S. (1988). Combined effects of L-ascorbic acid, citric acid or their sodium salts on tumor induction by N-butyl-N-(4-hydroxybutyl)nitrosamine or N-ethyl-N-(4-hydroxybutyl)nitrosamine in the rat urinary bladder. *Cancer Letters*, **40**, 265-273.

ISCOVICH, J., CASTELLETTO, R., ESTEVE, J., MUNOZ, N., COLANZE, R., CORONEL, A., DEAMEZOLA, I., TASSI, V. & ARSLAN, A. (1987). Tobacco smoking, occupational exposure and bladder cancer in Argentina. *Int. J. Cancer*, **40**, 734-740.

JONES, R. F. & WANG, C.Y. (1989). Activation of Ha-*ras*-1 genes in bladder tumors induced in rats with N-butyl-N-(4-hydroxybutyl)nitrosamine (BBN) or N[4-(5-nitro-2-furyl)-2-thiazolyl]formamide (FANFT). *Proc. Am. Assoc. Cancer.* Res., **30**, 436.

KITAHORI, Y., SHIMOYAMA, T. OHSHIMA, M., MATSUKI, H., HASHIMOTO, H., MINAMI, S., KONISHI, N. & HIASA, Y. (1988). Effects of trisodium nitrilotriacetate monohydrate, nitrilotriacetic acid and ammonium chloride on urinary bladder carcinogenesis in rats pretreated with N-bis(2-hydroxypropyl)nitrosamine. *Cancer Letters*, **43**, 105-110.

KNOWLES, M.A. & JANI, H. (1986). Multistage transformation of cultured rat urothelium : the effects of N-methyl-N-nitrosourea, sodium saccharin, sodium cyclamate and 12-O-tetradecanoylphorbol-13-acetate. *Carcinogenesis*, **7**, 2059-2065.

KNOWLES, M.A., JANI, H. & HICKS, R.M. (1986). Induction of morphological changes in the urothelium of cultured adult rat bladder by sodium saccharin and sodium cyclamate. *Carcinogenesis*, **7**, 767-774.

KROES, B., PETERS, P.W.J., DERKVENS, J.M., VERSCHUUREN, H.O., DE VRIES, T. & VAN ESCH, G.J. (1977). Long term toxicity and reproduction study (including a teratogenicity study) with cyclamate, saccharin and cyclohexylamine. *Toxicology*, **8**, 285-300.

LAMM, L.M., REICHERT, D.F. & LAMM, D.L. (1989). Rapid screening of potential human bladder carcinogens: genotoxicity in meiosis repair deficient *Drosophila melanogaster*. *J. Urol.*, **142**, 1356-1358.

LAWRIE, C.A. & RENWICK, A.G. (1987). The effect of saccharin ingestion on the excretion of microbial amino acid metabolites in rat and man. *Toxicol. Appl. Pharmacol.* **91**, 415-428.

LAWRIE, C.A., RENWICK, A.G. & SIMS, J. (1985). The urinary excretion of bacterial amino-acid metabolites by rats fed saccharin in the diet. *Food Chem. Toxicol.*, **23**, 445-450.

LEONARD, A. & LEONARD, E.D. (1979). Mutagenicity test with saccharin in the male mouse. *J. Environ. Pathol. Toxicol.*, **2**, 1047-1053.

LETHCO, E.J. & WALLACE, W.C. (1975). The metabolism of saccharin in animals. *Toxicology*, **3**, 287-300.

LOK, E., IVERSON, F. & CLAYSON, D.B. (1982). The inhibition of urease and proteases by sodium saccharin. *Cancer Letters*, **16**, 163-169.

LORKE, D. & MACHEMER, L. (1975). Effect of several weeks treatment of male and female mice with saccharin, cyclamate or cyclohexylamine sulfate on fertility and dominant lethal effects. *Hum. Genet.*, **26**, 199. Cited In: Ashby, 1985.

LUTZ, W.K. & SCHLATTER, CH. (1977). Saccharin does not bind to DNA of liver or bladder in the rat. *Chemico-Biol. Interactions.*, **19**, 153.

MACHEMER, L. & LORKE, D. (1973). Dominant lethal test in the mouse for mutagenic effects of saccharine. *Humangenetik*, **19**, 193-198.

MALLETT, A.K., ROWLAND, I.R. & BEARNE, C.A. (1985). Modification of rat caecal microbial biotransformation activities by dietary saccharin. *Toxicology*, **36**, 253-262.

MANN, A.M., MASUI, T., CHLAPOWSKI, F.J., OKAMURA, T., BORGESON, C.D. & COHEN, S.M. (1991). *In vitro* transformation of rat bladder epithelium by 2-amino-4-(5-nitro-2-furyl)thiazole. *Carcinogenesis*, **12**, 417-422.

MASUI, T., SAKATA, T., GARLAND, E.M., ELLWEIN, L.B., JOHANSSON, S.L. & COHEN, S.M. (1988a). Effects of sodium saccharin (NaS) on rat fetal and neonatal urinary bladder. *Proc. Am. Assoc. Cancer Res.*, **29**, Abs. 642.

MASUI, T., SHIRAI, T., IMAIDA, K., UWAGAWA, S. & FUKUSHIMA, S. (1988b). Effects of urinary crystals induced by acetazolamide, uracil and diethylene glycol on urinary bladder carcinogenicity in N-butyl-N-(4-hydroxybutyl)nitrosamine - initiated rats. *Toxicol. Lett.*, **40**, 119-126.

MASUI, T., MANN, A.M., GARLAND, E.M., OKAMURA, T., JOHANSSON, P.L. & COHEN, S.M. (1990). Point mutation in codons 12 and 61 of the Ha-*ras* gene in rat urinary bladder carcinomas induced by N-[4-(5-nitro-2-furyl)-2-thiazolyl]formamide. *Molecular Carcinogenesis*, **3**, 210-215.

MASUI, T., MANN, A.M., MACATEE, T.L., OKAMURA, T, GARLAND, E.M., FUJII, H., PELLING, J.C. & COHEN, S.M. (1991). H-*ras* mutations in rat urinary bladder carcinomas induced by N-[4-(5-nitro-2-furyl)-2-thiazolyl]formamide and sodium saccharin, sodium ascorbate, or related salts. *Cancer Res.*, **51**, 3471-3475.

MATTHEWS, H.B., FIELDS, M. & FISHBEIN, L. (1973). Saccharin: Distribution and excretion of a limited dose in the rat. *J. Agric. Fd. Chem.*, **21**, 916-919. Cited In: Renwick, 1985b.

MILO, G.E., OLDHAM, J.W., NOYES, I., LEHMAN, T.A., KUMARI, L., WEST, R.W., KADLUBAR, F.F. (1988). Cocarcinogenicity of saccharin and N-alkylnitrosoureas in cultured human diploid fibroblasts. *J. of Toxicol. Environ. Health*, **24**, 413-421.

MINEGISHI, K.I., ASAHINA, M. & YAMAHA, T. (1972). The metabolism of saccharin and the related compounds in rats and guinea pigs. *Chem. Pharm. Bull., Tokyo*, **20**, 1351.

MOORE, M.M. & BROCK, K.H. (1988). High concentrations of sodium chloride induce a "positive" response at the TK locus of L5178Y/TK$^{+/-}$ mouse lymphoma cells. *Environ. Mol. Mutagen.*, **12**, 265-268.

MORGAN, R.A. & WONG, O. (1985). A review of epidemiological studies on artificial sweeteners and bladder cancer. *Food Chem. Toxicol.*, **23**, 529-533.

MORI, S., KURATA, Y, TAKEUCHI, Y., TOYAMA, M., MAKINO, S. & FUKUSHIMA, S. (1987). Influences of strain and diet on the promoting effects of sodium L-ascorbate in two-stage urinary bladder carcinogenesis in rats. *Cancer Res.*, **47**, 3492-3495.

MURASAKI, G. & COHEN, S.M. (1983). Effects of sodium saccharin on urinary bladder epithelial regenerative hyperplasia following freeze ulceration. *Cancer Res.*, **43**, 182-187.

NAKANISHI, K., HAGIWARA, A., SHIBATA, M., IMAIDA, K. TATEMATSU, M. & ITO, N. (1980a). Dose response of saccharin in induction of urinary bladder hyperplasias in Fischer 344 rats pretreated with N-butyl-N-(4-hydroxybutyl)nitrosamine. *J. Natl. Cancer Inst.*, **65**, 1005-1010.

NAKANISHI, K., HIROSE, M., OGISO, T., HASEGAWA, R., ARAI, M., & ITO, N. (1980b). Effects of sodium saccharin and caffeine on the urinary bladder of rats treated with N-butyl-N-(4-hydroxybutyl)nitrosamine. *Jpn. J. Cancer Res.* (Gann), **71**, 490-500.

NAKANISHI, K., FUKUSHIMA, S., HAGIWARA, A., TAMANO, S., & ITO, N. (1982). Organ-specific promoting effects of phenobarbital sodium and sodium saccharin in the induction of liver and bladder tumors in male F344 rats. *J. Natl. Cancer Inst.*, **68**, 497-500.

NICHOLSON, L.J. & JANI, H. (1988). Effects of sodium cyclamate and sodium saccharin on focus induction in explant cultures of rat bladder. *Int. J. Cancer*, **42**, 295-298.

NORMAN, J.T., HOWLETT, A.R., SPACEY, G.D. & HODGES, G.M. (1987). Effects of treatment with N-methyl-N-nitrosourea, artificial sweeteners, and cyclosphosphamide on adult rat urinary bladder *in vitro*. *Lab. Invest.*, **57**, 429-438.

OKAMURA, T., GARLAND, E.M., MASUI, T., SAKATA, T., ST. JOHN, M. & COHEN, S.M. (1991). Lack of bladder tumor promoting activity in rats fed sodium saccharin in AIN-76A diet. *Cancer Res.*, **51**, 1778-1782.

PARKER, K.R. & VON BORSTEL, R.C. (1987). Base-substitution and frameshift mutagenesis by sodium chloride and potassium chloride in *Saccharomyces cerevisiae*. *Mutat. Res.*, **189**, 11-14.

PIPER, J.M., MATANOSKI, G.M. & TONASCIA, J. (1986). Bladder cancer in young women. *Am. J. Epidemiol.*, **123**, 1033-1042.

PITKIN, R.M., REYNOLDS, W.A., FILER, L.J. & KLING, T.G. (1971). Placental transmission and fetal distribution of saccharin. *Am. J. Obstet. Gynecol.*, **111**, 280-286. Cited In: IARC, 1980.

PRASAD, O. & RAI, G. (1986). Mutagenicity of saccharin as evidenced by the induction of dominant lethals in albino mice. *Nat. Acad. Sci. Letters*, **9**, 55-58.

PRASAD, O. & RAI, G. (1987). Induction of chromosomal aberrations by prefeeding saccharin in albino mice. *Indian J. Exp. Biol.*, **25**, 124-128.

RENWICK, A.G. (1985). The disposition of saccharin in animals and man - a review. *Food Chem. Toxicol.*, **23**, 429-435.

RENWICK, A.G. (1989). Saccharin: A toxicological evaluation. *Comments Toxicology*, **3**, 289-305.

RENWICK, A.G., THAKRAR, A., LAWRIE, C.A. & GEORGE, C.F. (1988). Microbial amino acid metabolites and bladder cancer, no evidence of promoting activity in man. *Human Toxicol.*, **7**, 267-272.

RISCH, H.A., BURCH, J.D., MILLER, A.B., HILL, G.B., STEELE, R. & HOWE, G.R. (1988). Dietary factors and the incidence of cancer of the urinary bladder. *Am. J. Epidemiol.*, **127**, 1179-1191.

ROBERTS, A. & RENWICK, A.G. (1985). The effect of saccharin on the microbial metabolism of tryptophan in man. *Food Chem. Toxicol.*, **23**, 451-455.

SANJEEVA RAO, M. & QURESHI, A.B. (1972). Induction of dominant lethals in mice by sodium saccharin. *Indian J. Med. Res.*, **60**, 599-603.

SAWCZUK, I.S., WALSH, W., KING, W., OLSSON, C.A. & NGUYEN-HUU, C. (1987). Enhanced expression of Harvey-*ras* oncogene in FANFT-induced transitional cell carcinoma. *Urol. Int.*, **42**, 321-325.

SCHOENIG, G.P., GOLDENTHAL, E.I., GEIL, R.G., FRITH, C.H., RICHTER, W.R. & CARLBORG, F.W. (1985). Evaluation of the dose response and *in utero* exposure to saccharin in the rat. *Food Chem. Toxicol.*, **23**, 475-490.

SHIBATA, M.A., HAGIWARA, A., TAMANO, S., ONO, S. & FUKUSHIMA S. (1989a). Lack of a modifying effect by the diuretic drug furosemide on the development of neoplastic lesions in rat two-stage urinary bladder carcinogenesis. *J. Toxicol. Environ. Health*, **26**, 255-265.

SHIBATA, M.A., TAMANO, S., KURATA, Y., HAGIWARA, A., & FUKUSHIMA, S. (1989b). Participation of urinary Na$^+$, K$^+$, pH and L-ascorbic acid in the proliferative response of the bladder epithelium after the oral administration of various salts and/or ascorbic acid to rats. *Food Chem. Toxicol.*, **27**, 403-413.

SHIBATA, M., YAMADA, M., TANAKA, H., KAGAWA, M. & FUKUSHIMA, S. (1989c). Changes in urine composition, bladder epithelial morphology, and DNA synthesis in male F344 rats in response to ingestion of bladder tumor promoters. *Toxicol. Appl. Pharmacol.*, **99**, 37-49.

SIMS, J. & RENWICK, A.G. (1985). The microbial metabolism of tryptophan in rats fed a diet containing 7.5% saccharin in a two-generation protocol. *Food Chem. Toxicol.*, **23**, 437-444.

SLATTERY, M.L., WEST, D.W. & ROBISON, L.M. (1988). Fluid intake and bladder cancer in Utah. *Int. J. Cancer*, **42**, 17-22.

SQUIRE, R.A. (1985). Histopathological evaluation of rat urinary bladders from the IRDC two-generation bioassay of sodium saccharin. *Food Chem. Toxicol.*, **23**, 491-497.

SUZUKI, H. & SUZUKI, N. (1988). Mutagenicity of saccharin in a human cell strain. *Mutation Res.*, **209**, 13-16.

SWEATMAN, T.W. & RENWICK, A.G. (1980). The tissue distribution and pharmacokinetics of saccharin in the rat. *Toxicol. Appl. Pharmacol.*, **55**, 18-31.

SWEATMAN, T.W., RENWICK, A.G. & BURGESS, C.D. (1981). The pharmacokinetics of saccharin in man. *Xenobiotica*, **11(8)**, 531-540.

TATEMATSU, M., MERA, Y., KOHDA, K., KAWAZOE, Y. & ITO, N. (1986). Ornithine decarboxylase activity and DNA synthesis in rats after long term treatment with butylated hydroxyanisole, sodium saccharin or phenobarbital. *Cancer Lett.*, **33**, 119-124.

WILLIAMSON, D.S., NAGEL, D.L., MARKIN, R.S. & COHEN, S.M. (1987). Effects of pH and ions on the electronic structure of saccharin. *Food Chem. Toxicol.*, **25**, 211-218.

THICKENING AGENTS

KONJAC FLOUR

First draft prepared by
Dr K. B. Ekelman and Dr G. A. Dannan, Additives Evaluation Branch
Division of Health Effects Evaluation
Center for Food Safety and Applied Nutrition
Food and Drug Administration, Washington, DC, USA

1.   EXPLANATION

Konjac flour, commonly referred to as konjac mannan, is a ß-D-(1→4)-linked linear copolymer of glucose and mannose substituted with O-acetate every 9-19 sugar units. Konjac flour is derived from the tubers of *Amorphophallus konjac*. The flour, which constitutes 60-80% of the dried root tuber, is obtained by a dry milling process of thin tuber slices. Carbohydrates (as water-soluble fiber) make up approximately 75% of konjac flour, the remainder being protein (2-8%), fat (<1%), ash (3-5%), and moisture (<15%).

Konjac flour has not been evaluated previously by the Committee. The current evaluation was undertaken because of anticipated new food additive uses of konjac flour as a gelling agent, thickener, emulsifier, and stabilizer in such foods as soup, gravy, mayonnaise, and jam. Nevertheless, there is a long history of use of konjac (containing approximately 4% konjac flour) in traditional Japanese and Chinese foods; the average consumption of konjac flour from these uses is estimated to be 2-3 g/person/day, and occasionally as high as 4 g/person/day. The anticipated maximum consumption of konjac flour from food additive uses is about 3 g/person/day.

Numerous physicochemical studies have been done on konjac. The primary polysaccharide constituent in konjac flour is a high-molecular-weight glucomannan (200 000 to 2 000 000 daltons depending on the strain and place of cultivation) in which D-glucose and D-mannose, in a molar ratio of 1.0:1.6, are linked by ß-1→4 glycosidic bonds. Branching from the C_3 of either hexose is estimated to occur every ten repeating units through 1,3 linkages. Acetyl groups bound every 9-19 units along the glucomannan backbone are thought to contribute to the high solubility characteristic of konjac flour (Nishinari *et al.*, 1992).

Doi and coworkers (1982) reported that the viscosity of konjac flour is greater than that of guar gum, one of the most viscous of the dietary fibers. Ebihara and coworkers (1981) reported that, compared to dietary fibers such as carboxymethylcellulose (CMC) and pectin, the relative viscosity of konjac flour increases extraordinarily as its concentration in water increases. When fiber concentration in water is increased from 1 to 3 g/l, the relative viscosity of pectin increases from 1.8 to 3.2, the relative viscosity of CMC increases from 4.6 to 10.4, and the relative viscosity of konjac flour increases from 5.7 to 171.2 (water was arbitrarily assigned a viscosity of 1.0).

2.   BIOLOGICAL DATA

2.1   Biochemical aspects

Due to the ß-glycosidic linkages between the glucose and mannose building blocks (ß-1→4 linkages in the main chain and ß-1→3 linkages at the branch points) konjac flour is commonly regarded as a non-digestible polysaccharide. Because of its high water solubility, conferred mainly by attached acetyl groups, konjac flour is also classified as a soluble fiber. Following alkali treatment or heating, konjac flour loses acetyl groups and forms a gel. Gelling is thought to result from cross-linking, mainly through hydrogen-bonding between konjac flour moieties that are deficient in acetyl groups (Nishinari et al., 1992).

Since konjac flour's polymeric structure is assumed to render it unavailable for intestinal degradation or absorption, konjac flour is commonly believed to pass through the gastrointestinal tract unaltered. Although no studies have been performed for evaluating the possible degradation or hydrolysis of konjac flour in the intestinal tract, formation of oligo- and mono-saccharides from konjac flour has been observed in the presence of 1N sulfuric acid at 100°C (Japan Food Research Laboratories, 1984).

2.2   Toxicological studies

2.2.1   Acute toxicity studies

Table 1 summarizes the results of acute toxicity studies with konjac flour:

Table 1. Acute toxicity studies with konjac flour

Species	Sex	Route	LD_{50}	Reference
Mouse	M & F	oral[1]	>2800 mg/kg bw	Oketani et al., 1984
Rat	M & F	oral[2]	>5 000 mg/kg bw[3]	Kotkoskie et al., 1992
Rat	M & F	inhalation[2]	>0.0015 mg/l	Kotkoskie et al., 1992
Rabbit	M & F	dermal[2]	>2 000 mg/kg bw	Kotkoskie et al., 1992

(1)   Test substance was identified as konjac mannan.
(2)   Test substance was identified as konjac flour.
(3)   This was the only dose tested.

2.2.2 Short-term toxicity studies

In a study conducted to determine appropriate doses for a subsequent embryotoxicity study, Burger and coworkers (1992) fed diets containing 2% carob gum (controls) or 2% konjac flour (Test substance identified as konjac flour from *Amorphophallus oncophyllus* from Thailand) to two groups of 15 adult female British domestic short-hair cats for eight weeks. Feed consumption and body weight were monitored throughout the study. Although no data were presented, report stated that both diets had digestibility coefficients similar to typical canned cat foods. In addition, body weights of cats fed diets containing 2% konjac flour increased more than body weights of cats fed the control diet during the study. Mean body weight gain in adult female cats during the 8-week period was 59 ± 3 g/wk for controls (2% carob gum) and 86 ± 5 g/wk for konjac flour-fed cats; however, the respective mean feed consumption was 190 ± 8 g/day and 181 ± 12 g/day (Burger *et al.*, 1992).

2.2.3   Long-term toxicity/carcinogenicity studies

No information was available.

2.2.4   Reproduction studies

No information was available.

2.2.5   Special studies on anti-carcinogenic effects

A diet containing refined konjac was evaluated for its effects on the incidence of spontaneous liver tumours in C3H/He mice; these tumours generally occur in 60-70% of one-year-old mice of this strain. At seven weeks of age, groups of 30 male mice were fed either a powdered commercial diet (control group) or the same diet to which 10% konjac flour (identified as konjac mannan) had been added (konjac flour group). At one year of age, all animals were necropsied and the number and size of liver tumour nodules were determined. There was a slight decrease in the number of animals with liver tumours in the konjac flour group (control: 63% of 24 mice; konjac flour: 48% of 23 mice) and a statistically significant decrease ($p < 0.05$) in the mean number of tumour nodules per mouse in the konjac flour group (control: 1.1; konjac flour: 0.5). However, mean tumour size was not altered. Weight gain in the 10% konjac flour diet group was lower ($p < 0.05$) than that in the control diet group throughout the experiment, but there was no change in total feed intake between the control and konjac flour-treated mice. While feed efficiency was decreased in konjac flour-treated mice compared to controls (control: 2.9%; konjac flour: 2.3%), the decrease was not statistically significant. In this study, spontaneous liver tumours in C3H/He mice were inhibited by maintaining the mice on a diet containing 10% konjac flour, although the reviewers note that animals maintained on this diet consumed approximately 10% fewer calories per day than control animals (Mizutani and Mitsuoka, 1982).

In another study by the same authors the effect of a diet containing 5% konjac flour on the incidence of colon tumours induced by 1,2-dimethylhydrazine (DMH) in rats was studied. Five-week old male Fisher 344 rats (20/group) were fed either a commercial diet (414 kcal/100 g) or a similar diet containing 5% konjac flour (identified as konjac mannan, diet had an energy content of393 kcal/100 g). At six weeks of age, and weekly thereafter for a total of 13 weeks, all rats were injected i.p. with 20 mg DMH/kg bw. Feed consumption was measured weekly for 20 weeks (duration of the study was approximately 27 weeks). Rats were necropsied 13 weeks after the last injection of DMH; the intestine (small and large) and other organs (unspecified) were examined grossly and microscopically for numbers and types of tumours. Throughout the study, body weights of konjac flour-fed rats were significantly lower than those of rats fed the control diet; however, there was no significant difference in feed efficiency between konjac flour-fed and control rats. The incidence of DMH-induced colon tumours was significantly lower in the konjac flour-fed group (39%) compared to the control group (75%). The number of colon adenocarcinomas per rat was also significantly lower in konjac flour-fed rats (0.22) than in control rats (0.75). However, the mean diameter of colon tumours was not significantly different in the two groups of rats (konjac flour-fed rats: 5.8 ± 1.3 mm; control rats: 6.9 ± 3.6 mm).

In contrast to the effects reported for colon tumours, dietary konjac flour had no significant effect on the incidence of tumours of the small intestine, all of which were adenocarcinomas in this study (control: 45%; konjac flour: 33%); mean diameters of adenocarcinomas of the small intestine were not significantly different in the two groups (control: 8 ± 4 mm; konjac flour: 6 ± 2 mm). Dietary konjac flour did not appear to have a significant effect on the incidences of ear duct or pancreas tumours in rats in this study (Mizutani and Mitsuoka, 1983).

2.2.6. **Special studies on embryotoxicity**

Pregnant British short-hair domestic cats were fed diets containing 2% carob gum (9 control cats) or 2% konjac flour (6 cats; test substance identified as konjac flour from *Amorphophallus oncophyllus* from Thailand) during gestation. Body weights were recorded weekly until parturition and feed consumption was recorded daily during the week prior to parturition. Actual intake of konjac flour during the week prior to parturition ranged from 0.98 to 3.08 mg/kg bw/day. All pregnant females completed a normal gestation period and that there were no significant differences in body weight changes of females fed control and konjac flour-containing diets. Mean birth weight of kittens born to control cats was statistically significantly lower ($p < 0.01$) than mean birth weight of kittens born to konjac flour-fed cats, but mean litter size for control cats was less than mean litter size for konjac flour-fed cats: A total of 32 kittens (mean birth weight 104 ± 17 g) were born to 9 control cats and 36 kittens (mean birth weight 95 g ± 22 g) were born to 6 konjac flour-fed cats; mean litter size was 3.5 ± 1.6 for controls and 5.1 ± 1.2 for konjac flour-fed cats (mean control litter size for cats in the same colony was reported to be 3.3 ± 1.5). All cats in the study completed lactation and reared their progeny successfully. The study also reported that biochemical and haematological parameters were within normal ranges throughout the study (no data were provided) (Burger *et al.*, 1992).

2.2.7   Special studies on gastrointestinal effects.

There was no change in total faecal microflora count in 30 male C3H/He mice fed a diet containing 10% konjac flour (test substance was identified as konjac mannan) for one year compared to 30 male mice fed a powdered control diet. Of the 11 specific types of microflora that were examined, however, two were significantly changed: the frequency of bifidobacteria increased from 30% in control mice to 100% in konjac flour-fed mice and the log count of enterobacteriaceae increased from 6.0 in control mice to 6.6 in konjac flour-fed mice (Mizutani and Mitsuoka 1982).

Five-week-old male C3H/He mice bearing human flora were either maintained on a control diet or fed a diet containing 10% konjac flour (test substance was identified as konjac mannan, sterilized by γ-radiation from ⁶⁰Co). When the mice were five months old, microflora, enzymes, and putrefactive products were analyzed in faecal samples from animals in the control and konjac flour-fed groups. Total bacterial counts were nearly identical in control and konjac flour-fed mice; however, streptococcus bacteria were significantly reduced in the konjac flour-fed mice. Of the soluble enzymes measured, ß-glucuronidase and nitroreductase activities were significantly reduced in the konjac flour-fed mice (67% and 19% of activities in control mice, respectively) while azoreductase activity was slightly increased (139% of activity in control mice). Several putrefactive metabolites (p-cresol, indole, and skatole) were decreased in konjac flour-fed mice compared to control mice. Dietary konjac flour, through material sequestration and lowering of substrate concentration, might lead to suppression of bacterial enzyme activities and intestinal metabolism without significantly affecting microflora composition (Fujiwara *et al.*, 1991).

Three-month-old Fisher 344 male rats were switched from a basal diet to a similar diet containing 10% konjac flour (test substance was identified as konjac mannan, sterilized by γ-radiation from ⁶⁰Co), to which they were allowed *ad libitum* access for two months. Soluble enzyme activities were measured in fresh faecal samples collected two days before and 19, 29, and 39 days after rats were placed on the 10% konjac flour diet. Putrefactive products were analyzed in fresh faecal samples collected the day before and on days 20, 30, and 40 after rats were placed on the konjac flour diet. Mean faecal ß-glucuronidase activity (n = 13 rats) initially rose, then decreased significantly to approximately one-third of its original level of activity at the end of the experimental period. Two faecal reducing enzyme activities significantly decreased following introduction of the konjac flour diet: nitroreductase activity was decreased approximately 2-fold and azoreductase activity was decreased approximately 5-fold by the end of the study. As well, the gastrointestinal (microflora) metabolites tyrosine and tryptophan were significantly altered in rats that consumed a konjac flour-containing diet for 2 months. The reviewers note that concurrent control animals were not included in this study, and effects attributed to consumption of konjac flour could also be due to factors such as age or changes in the test animals' environment (Fujiwara *et al.*, 1991).

Groups of weanling male Wistar rats (six/group) were fed a basal diet (control group: 67% corn starch, 21% casein, 7% corn oil, 4% salt mix and 1% vitamins) or diets containing 20% konjac flour or 20% cellulose (test diets were prepared by substituting the test substance for an equal weight of corn starch in the basal diet, konjac flour was identified as having been derived from *Amorphophallus konjac*. After eight weeks, total protein, DNA, RNA, and the activity of $(Na+K)ATPase$ were determined in homogenates of caecal and colonic mucosa. Compared to rats fed the basal diet, feed intake of the konjac flour-fed rats was unchanged but feed intake of the cellulose-fed rats was significantly increased (data not shown). After eight weeks, the konjac flour-fed group had a significantly reduced mean body weight (90% of control); wet weights of the caecum and colon in konjac flour-fed rats were significantly increased compared to control rats (approximately 300% and 25%, respectively). In contrast, the average body weight of cellulose-fed rats was not significantly different from control rats, but wet weights of the caecum and colon in cellulose-fed rats were increased by approximately 25% and 60%, respectively. Total mucosal DNA in the caecum and colon of konjac flour-fed rats was significantly increased compared to control rats (263% and 159%, respectively); total mucosal DNA in the caecum and colon of cellulose-fed   was also increased compared to control rats (148% and 187%, respectively). Ratios of mucosal RNA/DNA and protein/DNA in the caecum were significantly increased in konjac flour-fed rats compared to control rats. Caecal and colonic mucosal $(Na+K)ATPase$ activities (expressed per mg protein) were significantly increased in konjac flour- or cellulose-fed rats compared to control rats; konjac flour-fed rats had a greater increase in mucosal ATPase activity in the caecum than in the colon (180% vs. 150%, respectively) while the opposite was true for cellulose-fed rats (150% vs. 219%, respectively). Based on these results, this report suggests that caecal enlargement in rats due to ingestion of konjac flour results from both increased number (hyperplasia) and size (hypertrophy) of mucosal cells, but that colonic enlargement due to ingestion of konjac flour and colonic and caecal enlargement due to ingestion results from hyperplasia only (Konishi *et al.*, 1984).

2.2.8   **Special studies on genotoxicity**

Konjac flour was non-mutagenic in five tester strains (TA98, TA100, TA1535, TA1537, and TA1538) of *Salmonella typhimurium* in the presence or absence of liver microsomal metabolic activation (Kotkoskie *et al.*, 1992).

2.2.9   **Special studies on lipid metabolism**

Venter and coworkers (1990) studied the effect of konjac flour on plasma fibrinogen, serum and liver lipid, glucose tolerance, insulin response, and liver glycogen in baboons fed a "Western" diet. Twelve male baboons (mean weight of 19 ± 3 kg) were fed a "Western" diet (approximately 400 g/day) with or without konjac flour (5%) or sodium propionate (2%) supplements for periods of 9 weeks in a crossover, randomized order with period of stabilization between treatment periods. The "Western" diet consisted of 38.3 g corn meal, 13.4 g beef tallow, 10 g sucrose, and 38.3 g of a commercially prepared dietary supplement containing protein, vitamins, and minerals per 100 g diet (the supplement results in normal growth and excellent health when fed in combination with corn meal to young baboons). Parameters were measured before and 4 and 9 weeks after the beginning of each treatment period. After 9 weeks, serum total cholesterol levels were statistically significantly higher than pretest values in baboons fed the unsupplemented "Western" diet, and that konjac flour supplementation of the "Western" diet prevented this increase. Although serum levels of high-density lipoprotein increased with all "Western" diets, the percentage of total cholesterol as high-density lipoprotein was statistically significantly greater in baboons fed the konjac flour-supplemented diet for 9 weeks compared to other diets. Konjac flour-supplementation also was reported to statistically significantly increase levels of serum triglycerides and circulating free fatty acids after 9 weeks. Finally, liver cholesterol concentration was approximately 30% lower and the area under the glucose tolerance curve was smaller when baboons were fed konjac flour-supplemented diets for 9 weeks. Because similar effects were seen with the sodium propionate-supplemented diet, the effects observed in baboons fed konjac flour-supplemented "Western" diets may be due to colonic production and absorption of propionate from this soluble fiber (Venter *et al.*, 1990).

2.2.10   Special studies on nutrient absorption

Kiriyama and coworkers (1974) studied the effects of chemically pure, water-soluble konjac flour (test article was "purified by the method of Sugiyama" and purity was tested) on transport of bile acids in everted ileal sacs of rats. Small intestines (not including the duodenum) from adult male and female Wistar rats were excised, cut into segments, everted, and tied into sacs; these sacs were used to evaluate the uptake of ^{14}C-labelled cholate or taurocholate *in vitro*. Results of this experiment confirmed that the rat ileum actively transports cholic acid against a concentration gradient. Active transport of cholic or taurocholic acid was significantly inhibited (2-3-fold) when 0.25% konjac flour was added to the media outside of sacs made from the ileum (distal small intestine) but not when 0.25% konjac flour was added to the media outside of sacs made from the jejunum (proximal small intestine). However, there was no inhibition of transport in the presence of 0.05% konjac flour. No inhibition of transport was seen when everted ileal sacs were incubated in a konjac flour-free bile acid medium after the sacs had been pre-immersed in 0.25% konjac flour. This suggests that the binding of konjac flour to the surface of the intestinal mucosa is not strong enough to effectively inhibit the active transport of bile acids. This report suggests that konjac flour does not bind, sequester, or adsorb bile acids since, in a simple dialysis experiment, the equilibrium of bile acids across a cellophane membrane was not altered by the presence of konjac flour on one side of the membrane (Kiriyama *et al.*, 1974).

Because previous studies (Reinhold *et al.*, 1975 and 1976) have shown that plant fibers bind minerals, including calcium, zinc, and iron, thereby rendering them unavailable for intestinal absorption, Oku *et al.* (1982) studied the influence of dietary konjac flour and other nutritionally unavailable carbohydrates on intestinal absorption of calcium. Six male Wistar rats/group (initial body weight, 40-50 g) were fed *ad libitum* a basal diet containing 67% corn starch (control) or the same diet in which 20% cellulose I, 20% cellulose II, 10% konjac flour, 20% konjac flour, or 20% pullulan had been substituted for an equal amount of corn starch (konjac flour was identified as having been derived from *Amorphophallus konjac*). Rats were fed control or experimental diets for 7 or 8 weeks. Each rat was placed in a metabolic cage for three days at the end of the study. Body weights were recorded weekly; feed consumption was determined daily during the last 3 days of the study.

Compared to rats fed the control diet, rats fed diets containing 10% and 20% konjac flour had significantly reduced mean body weights (control: 328 g; 10% konjac flour: 296 g; 20% konjac flour: 258 g). Feed consumption of rats fed diets containing 10% or 20% konjac flour, however, was approximately the same as feed consumption of control rats. Serum levels of calcium and inorganic phosphorus were not statistically significantly altered in animals fed diets containing konjac flour, although serum calcium levels showed a declining trend. In *in vitro* investigation of calcium transport using everted duodenal sacs from treated and control rats, calcium transport was significantly reduced (to 60% of control value) in the 20% konjac flour-fed group only. Calcium binding activity in the supernatant of homogenized duodenal mucosa was also significantly depressed in all groups of rats fed diets containing 20% carbohydrate diets, with the greatest effect associated with consumption of diets containing 20% konjac flour (50% of control binding). Based on these results, consumption of unavailable carbohydrates, including konjac flour, may be associated with decreased function of intestinal epithelial protein(s) essential for transport of calcium. As well, because consumption of konjac flour appeared to be associated with a functionally compromised gastrointestinal mucosal surface, absorption of minerals other than calcium may also be affected (Oku *et al.*, 1982).

2.3   Observations in humans

Several experiments were performed to evaluate the effects of konjac fiber on glucose metabolism in normal and diabetic subjects. After a 12-hour fast, 3.9 g konjac flour (test substances were identified as "powdered glucomannan", viscosities were 100-150 000 cP [konjac flour], 52 000 cP [low-viscosity konjac flour], or 194 800 cP [high-viscosity konjac flour]) was consumed either simultaneously with or 15 min. before a glucose load or test meal (This dose was selected because of reports that Japanese subjects experienced abdominal pain and complications following consumption of 5.2 g or more konjac flour.) Venous blood samples were drawn at 0 (fasting), 30, 60, 90, 120, and 180 min. after glucose or test meal consumption. When meals containing konjac flour were fed to seven non-diabetic subjects, mean serum glucose was significantly below levels for control, non-diabetic subjects at 30, 60, 120, and 180 min. Serum insulin levels were also significantly decreased at 30, 60, and 90 min. in these subjects. Less pronounced effects were observed when konjac flour was administered 15 min. before meals; under these circumstances, serum glucose levels were significantly reduced at 30 and 180 min. only. In a similar experiment involving six non-insulin-dependent diabetics, significant reductions in mean serum glucose levels were observed at 30 and 60 min. following consumption of konjac flour. However, no significant reductions in serum glucose levels were observed when guar gum, another gel-forming fiber consisting of galactose and mannose in a molar ratio of 1:2, was fed to subjects instead of konjac flour.

In a study with nine subjects, low-viscosity konjac flour delayed the increase in serum glucose from 30 min. (seen in subjects fed a meal without konjac flour) to 60 min (when the same subjects were fed an identical meal containing konjac flour). In addition, a high-viscosity konjac flour was more effective in delaying the rise in serum glucose following consumption of a konjac flour-containing meal than the low viscosity konjac flour.

Absorption of xylose was measured following administration of 25 g xylose and 50 g glucose to each of five healthy volunteers. Co-administration of 3.9 g konjac flour caused a significant decrease in the excretion of xylose after two hours and appeared to prolong the time required for absorption of xylose, since total xylose excretion after 6 hours was similar in konjac flour-fed and control subjects (no data presented).

When each of 21 diabetic subjects was fed 7.2 g konjac flour daily for 17 days, mean fasting serum glucose levels were significantly decreased throughout the study. When observed for 90 days after daily feeding of 7.2 g konjac flour for 17 days (no data presented), mean serum cholesterol levels decreased significantly for the first 38 days, then gradually increased; triglyceride and HDL-cholesterol levels, however, were reported not to have been affected (Doi *et al.*, 1982).

Following an overnight fast, seven young men (22-32 years old; $110\pm6\%$ of ideal Japanese body weight) were given a 500 ml solution containing 80 g glucose (controls) or a similar solution containing 80 g glucose and 5 g konjac flour (konjac flour was identified as having been prepared fresh from *Amorphophallus konjac* after prompt inactivation of tuber mannanase I and mannanase II by homogenization with ethanol). One week later, the same experiment was performed, but treatments for each group of subjects were reversed. Plasma glucose and insulin levels were measured in venous blood samples collected from each subject at 0 (fasting sample), 30, 60, 90, 120, and 180 min after consuming control and konjac flour-containing glucose solutions. In control and konjac flour-fed subjects, plasma glucose and insulin levels peaked within 30 min.; however, both parameters were lower (the decrease in serum insulin was statistically significant) when subjects consumed the glucose solution containing konjac flour. At 60, 90, and 120 min. following administration of the konjac flour-containing glucose solution, serum glucose and insulin levels were decreased compared to samples following administration of the control glucose solution, although the decreases were not statistically significant; at 180 min., however, serum glucose and insulin levels were increased in subjects administered the konjac flour-containing glucose solution. Thus, when subjects were challenged with glucose, plasma glucose and insulin levels returned more slowly to fasting levels when konjac flour was co-administered with the glucose. Despite the time course differences in plasma glucose in subjects following administration of a glucose solution or a konjac flour-containing glucose solution, the total areas under the plasma glucose curves for 0-180 min. were identical. However, the total area under the plasma insulin curve was significantly smaller after administration of the konjac flour-containing glucose solution than after administration of the control glucose solution. These results suggest that soluble dietary fibers such as konjac flour have beneficial effects on serum glucose levels and that these effects may be due to delayed stomach emptying and delayed glucose diffusion in the intestinal lumen (Ebihara et al., 1981).

The effects of konjac flour on serum glucose levels were evaluated in 72 type II diabetic subjects (mean age 55, range 39-76) by Huang and coworkers; subjects were grouped as mild, moderate, or severe diabetics. Meals containing 2% refined konjac flour in the form of konjac toast or konjac noodles were consumed by test subjects (average intake was 8.6 g konjac flour/day) for approximately 65 days. Weekly food intakes were recorded three times: before konjac flour-ingestion began and during weeks three and seven of the study. Fasting venous blood samples and 2-hr postprandial blood samples (before and after breakfast, respectively) were drawn once before konjac flour-ingestion began and on days 30 and 65 of the study; the following determinations were made: fasting blood glucose (FBG), 2-hour post-prandial blood glucose (PBG), glycosylated haemoglobin (GHB), total cholesterol (TC), high-density lipoprotein cholesterol (HDL-C), low-density lipoprotein cholesterol (LDL-C), and triglyceride (TG). Compared to levels measured before konjac flour-ingestion began, there were statistically significant reductions in FBG levels on days 30 and 65 and in GHB on day 65. Konjac flour appeared to be particularly beneficial to subjects with higher levels of blood glucose because the extent of konjac flour-associated decreases in FBG and PBG appeared to be directly proportional to the severity of subjects' pre-test levels of FBG and PBG. For instance, mild, moderate, and severe diabetic groups had the following initial vs. final FBG levels: 129.4 ± 10.5 vs. 124.0 ± 26.8; 165.9 ± 10.9 vs. 142.6 ± 35.3; and 227.0 ± 25.3 vs. 171.4 ± 37.4, respectively. Finally, the study reported a positive correlation between konjac flour-associated decreases in FBG and PBG.

In general, food containing konjac flour did not appear to have a significant effect on blood lipids. Several subjects were reported to have experienced weight loss during the study: the mean weight loss of 42/59 subjects at 30 days was 1.8 kg (range 0.2-4.7 kg) and the mean weight loss for 41/51 subjects at 65 days was 2.2 kg (range 0.5-6.0 kg).

In this study, subjects reported the following symptoms associated with consumption of meals containing konjac flour: 69-90% of the subjects reported improved appetite, polyuria at night, thirst, and constipation or soft stool; on the other hand, 40 subjects reported a total of 45 symptoms, such as loose stool, flatulence, diarrhoea, and abdominal pain, sounds, or distension (Huang et al., 1990).

A recent study compared the effects of four non-starch polysaccharides, including konjac flour, on glucose tolerance, insulin secretion, gastric emptying, and gut hormone secretion in 12 healthy male volunteers (mean age = 19.5 years). Subjects were divided into two groups; on three separate occasions (at least one week apart) and following an overnight fast, members of each group were given a test meal (white bread, honey, and orange squash containing 100 g carbohydrate) either with or without 10 g soya-bean cotyledon fiber (SCF) or 5 g konjac flour. Soluble paracetamol (1.5 g dissolved in 150 ml water) was consumed simultaneously with each meal; over the following 180 min., plasma levels of paracetamol were measured as an index of liquid gastric emptying. Plasma concentrations of glucose, insulin, and gastric inhibitory polypeptide (GIP) were measured during the same time period. Konjac flour-supplemented meals had a significant depressive effect on post-prandial insulin levels, where peaks for control and konjac flour-supplemented meals were 96.2 ± 11 and 64.3 ± 2.6 mU/l, respectively. The 0-90 min. incremental area under the insulin curve was significantly reduced following consumption of a konjac flour-supplemented meal (82% of area following consumption of a control meal), although consumption of a meal containing SCF increased this parameter (119% of area following consumption of a control meal). Post-prandial plasma glucose, GIP and paracetamol levels were not affected by consumption of meals containing konjac flour or SCF (Morgan et al., 1990).

Results of this study are consistent with results reported in similar experiments by Ebihara et al. (1981) but were inconsistent with results reported by Doi et al. (1982), which Morgan and coworkers attributed to possible differences in the composition of test meals (not specified in the study by Doi et al., 1982) that may have affected gastric emptying.

Zhang and coworkers studied the effects of consuming konjac flour-supplemented diets (5 g konjac flour/day) for 45 days on human lipid metabolism in elderly subjects with hyperlipidaemia. Subjects were described as having borderline risk levels of serum triglycerides (200-230 mg/dl), hypercholesterolaemia (>230 mg/dl), borderline risk levels of serum triglycerides (130-150 mg/dl), hypertriglyceridaemia (>150 mg/dl), or both hypercholesterolaemia and hypertriglyceridaemia. Subjects were randomly divided into two groups: the konjac flour group (66 subjects) consumed normal Japanese diets supplemented with foods containing konjac flour (3 g/day for the first 2 or 3 days, then 5 g/dy for the rest of the study); the control group (44 subjects) consumed normal Japanese diets without konjac flour supplementation; a recovery group (46 of 66 subjects in the konjac flour group) consumed normal Japanese diets for an additional 45 days.

Venous blood samples were drawn before breakfast before the study began, at the end of the study (45 days) and at the end of the recovery period (an additional 45 days). Konjac flour used in this study was described as "konjac meal...in the form of noodles, breads, cakes, etc., to which it was added, or after it was cooked directly with milk, soya-milk, soup, water, or stuffing."

After consumption of konjac flour for 45 days, subjects had statistically significantly decreased levels of serum total cholesterol, triglycerides, and low-density lipoprotein and statistically significantly increased levels of high-density lipoprotein and apoprotein; however, changes in these parameters in the control group during the study were not significant. In addition, konjac flour subjects had statistically significantly decreased body weight, serum total cholesterol, serum triglycerides, and serum low-density lipoprotein and increased serum high-density lipoprotein compared to control subjects after 45 days. After consumption of konjac foods, 27 subjects had statistically significant decreases in body weight (0.5 to 4.7 kg at 45 days); subjects consuming konjac flour reported decreases in dizziness and headaches (9/66) and chronic constipation (13/66); however, subjects also reported that they excreted more bulk faeces (17/66), experienced diarrhoea (3/66), and had increased hunger (4/66). After the 45-day recovery period, subjects (46 of 66 subjects who had previously consumed konjac flour for 45 days) had statistically significant increases in serum total cholesterol and low-density lipoprotein and a statistically significant decrease in high-density lipoprotein; serum triglyceride levels remained the same. This report concluded that beneficial effects observed in hypercholesterolaemic patients following consumption of 5 g konjac flour/day for 45 days were reversible upon discontinuance of konjac flour in the diet (Zhang *et al.*, 1990).

The efficacy of konjac flour (test substance identified as "glucamannan") for weight loss in overweight osteoarthritic patients was evaluated in a double-blind crossover study. Twenty outpatients (3 men and 17 women; mean age 53 years, range 30-68 years) were divided into two groups. For the first two months of the study, each subject was administered 1.5 g of konjac flour or a placebo before breakfast and dinner; for the following two months, treatments were reversed. Sixteen subjects completed the study; one subject stopped because of abdominal discomfort during the konjac flour-treatment period. Body weight was recorded monthly. Decreases in body weight during konjac flour-phases of the study (first group of subjects: mean body weight decreased from 73.7 to 70.1 kg; second group of subjects: mean body weight decreased from 79.0 to 76.4 kg) were reported to be statistically significant and were attributed to konjac flour administration. Study stated that subjects experienced no changes in blood pressure, heart rate, or clinical chemistry, but no data were provided (Biancardi *et al.*, 1989).

The effect of konjac flour on weight loss and blood levels of total cholesterol, total triglycerides, and low-density lipoprotein was investigated in a double-blind study of obese women for 8 weeks. Twenty obese women (weights were at least 20% over ideal body weights) were randomly assigned to two groups (10/group) so that weight and height distributions for each group were similar. The konjac flour group took two capsules of a supplement containing 500 mg "purified glucomannan" three times a day (with 8 oz water), one hour before each meal, for 8 weeks; control subjects took a similar capsule containing 500 mg starch under the same conditions. At the beginning of the study and at 4 and 8 weeks, subjects were weighed and blood samples were drawn. There were statistically significant decreases in weight, serum cholesterol and serum low-density lipoproteins in the konjac flour group compared to the control group at weeks 4 and 8. A statistically significant decrease in serum triglycerides occurred at four weeks, but the decrease was not statistically significant at 8 weeks. This study suggests that konjac flour can be used for weight reduction and serum cholesterol reduction in obese patients (Walsh *et al.*, 1984).

The efficacy of konjac flour was studied in 93 patients with chronic constipation; 78 patients completed the study. In this non-controlled, open study, patients were treated with 1 g konjac flour/day for one month, followed by 1 g konjac flour every other day for one month. Statistically significant improvements were seen in several measures of bowel function (number of days per week with bowel movements and number of enemas given) that lasted until the end of the second month. Konjac flour was well accepted by patients and without significant side effects; in addition, konjac flour reduced (by approximately 50%) the number of patients reporting abdominal disturbances by the end of the study (Passaretti *et al.*, 1991).

The influence of dietary konjac flour (test substance identified as konjac mannan) on absorption of vitamins E (tocopherol acetate) and B_{12} (mecobalamin) was evaluated in six normal volunteers (aged 20-61) and five maturity-onset diabetic patients (aged 57-81) by Doi and coworkers. Control meals containing vitamins E and B_{12} (500 mg and 3 000 μg, respectively) were consumed by each subject; test meals to which 3.9 g konjac flour had been added were consumed by subjects on an alternate day. Vitamin levels in serum were determined immediately before and 1, 3, 5, 8, 12, and 24 hr after consumption of both meals. In normal subjects, the peak serum level of vitamin B_{12} was shifted from 3 hr to 12 hr when the meal was supplemented with konjac flour; however, no shift was seen in the 5-8 hr peak time observed in diabetics when konjac flour was added to the meal. Total absorption of vitamin B_{12} during 24 hr did not appear to be changed by addition of konjac flour to the test meal. Intestinal absorption of vitamin B_{12} was not disturbed by konjac flour.

Addition of konjac flour to the test meal appeared to significantly lower serum levels of vitamin E, especially in normal subjects (by 16-30% at most time points). The results suggested that viscous forms of dietary fibers, such as konjac flour, may form a barrier around some (fat-insoluble) substances (including glucose, essential electrolytes and cations, and possibly vitamin B_{12}), thereby delaying their absorption rather than causing malabsorption. On the other hand, because konjac flour consumption may interfere with the absorption of bile acids, the absorption of the fat-soluble vitamin E, a process which is dependent on the presence of conjugated bile acids, may also be impaired by konjac flour consumption (Doi *et al.*, 1983).

The effect of konjac flour (identified as glucomannan in the form of konjac flour) on intestinal absorption of glibenclamide, a sulfonylurea-type hypoglycaemic drug, was evaluated in nine healthy male volunteers, aged from 21 to 47 years. All subjects participated, on two consecutive days, in both the control and test phases of the experiment. Plasma concentrations of the drug were followed for six hours after subjects received the drug (2.5 g) alone (control phase) or with 3.9 g konjac flour (test phase); in both phases, subjects ate breakfast immediately after receiving the drug. Compared to plasma drug levels during the control phase, subjects in the test phase had lower drug levels at 30 min. and this tendency continued for most subjects until at least 180 minutes. In the control phase, mean plasma levels of glibenclamide peaked rapidly at 60 min. and declined more slowly; when konjac flour was administered with the drug, however, there was no apparent peak in serum drug level. Co-administration of konjac flour with glibenclamide appeared to increase inter-individual variation in plasma drug levels. This study also demonstrates that dietary intake of konjac flour can influence the pharmacokinetics of co-administered oral drugs (Shima *et al.*, 1983).

When dry, non-expanded konjac flour was marketed as a dieting aid, 7 case reports of oesophageal obstruction caused by swelling of these tablets were made. The case reports were reviewed in 1986: all patients were women taking the konjac flour tablets for weight loss; obstruction was complete in 5/7 cases and was caused by a single tablet in all but one case; obstruction was presumably caused by swelling of dry konjac when hydrated by body fluids; none of the patients died. Expansion rates of 5 tablets (500 mg konjac flour each) immersed in water varied, but tablets increased their mean volumes from one to approximately 16 ml in 10 min; final volumes ranged from 12 to 17.5 ml. It is important to note that konjac flour in food is not in this dry form and there are no reported cases of oesophageal obstruction caused by hydrated konjac gels, such as those traditionally eaten in Japan (Henry *et al.*, 1986).

Inhalation of konjac dust ("dancing powder" in factories producing konnyaku, a popular food in Japan made from konjac tubers) in the workplace has been reported to produce allergic bronchial asthma (known as konnyaku asthma) in sensitized individuals (Nakazawa, 1983). In Japan, konnyaku asthma occurs in workers exposed to konjac dust and in people who live close to konjac processing facilities. An epidemiological study of Japanese plant employees and nearby residents conducted in 1980 found that 0.1% of the population (15 675 people) had konnyaku asthma. Konnyaku asthma can be treated by desensitization therapy and disappears when the individual is no longer exposed to konjac dust. It should be noted that inhalation of konjac powder has also been reported to cause allergic asthma in sensitized guinea pigs (Banno, 1979), although application of mechanically ground konjac to the skin of guinea pigs did not produce skin sensitization reactions (Kotkoskie, 1992). In both humans and animals, konjac powder or dust has been shown to produce allergic bronchial asthma by a type I or anaphylactic immune reaction (Nakazawa, 1983).

3.   COMMENTS

The Committee reviewed data from acute and short-term toxicity studies, as well as studies on embryotoxicity, genotoxicity, nutrient absorption, anti-carcinogenicity, gastrointestinal effects, and observations in humans. However, the Committee was concerned about the lack of information on the fate of konjac flour in the gut and the inadequacy of the short-term toxicity studies. The Committee was informed of the existence of a 13-week toxicity study in dogs and a 4-week toxicity study in rats that were not made available for review at the present meeting.

Human studies were conducted for up to 65 days at dose levels of up to 8.6 g konjac flour/person/day. Volunteers consuming approximately 5.2 g or more konjac flour/person/day reported symptoms such as loose stools, flatulence, diarrhoea and abdominal pain or distension. Studies with normal and diabetic volunteers demonstrated that consumption of 7.2-8.6 g konjac flour/person/day for 17 days significantly decreased mean fasting serum glucose levels; in addition, a dose of 3.9-5.0 g konjac flour/person consumed with a single meal (or administered with glucose) was reported to delay the increase in serum glucose and insulin levels for several hours following the meal, thereby also delaying their return to baseline levels. Consumption of test meals containing 3.9 g konjac flour appeared to impair vitamin E absorption (up to 30% decrease in peak serum levels) and influenced the pharmacokinetics of the co-administered drug glibenclamide. On the other hand, intestinal absorption of vitamin B_{12} or the drug paracetamol were not affected by consumption of meals containing konjac flour (3.9 g konjac flour/person for vitamin B_{12} and 5 g konjac flour/person for paracetamol).

4.   EVALUATION

On the basis of the available toxicological data, particularly data from human studies, the long history of use of konjac as a food in China and Japan, and estimates of konjac flour consumption from traditional and anticipated food additive uses, the Committee allocated a temporary ADI "not specified" for konjac flour. The results of additional short-term toxicity studies, which the Committee was informed have been conducted in rats and dogs, together with adequate data on the fate of konjac flour in the gut are required for review in 1996. In view of the observed impairment of absorption of vitamin E, information on the influence of konjac flour on the bioavailability of fat soluble vitamins is also required for review by 1996. The Committee noted that consumption of dry konjac flour has been associated with oesophageal obstruction, and recommended that konjac flour be consumed only in the hydrated form.

5.   REFERENCES

BANNO, H. (1979). Cyclic GMP and cyclic AMP levels in the nasal mucosa, trachea, lung, and plasma of guinea pigs sensitized by the inhalation of konjac powder. *Allergy (Jpn.)* **28**, 595-601.

BIANCARDI, G., PALMIERO, L., & GHIRARDI, P.E. (1989). Glucomannan in the treatment of overweight patients with osteoarthrosis. *Curr. Ther. Res.* **46**, 908-912.

BURGER, I.H., EARLE, K.E., & BAILIE, H. (1992). Evaluation of Konjac flour for use in a commercially prepared cat food. Submitted to WHO by Waltham Center for Pet Nutrition, Waltham-on-the-Wolds, Leicestershire, England.

DOI, K., MATSUURA, M., KAWARA, A., UENOYAMA, R., & BABA, S. (1982). Effect of glucomannan (konjac fiber) on glucose and lipid metabolism in normal and diabetic subjects. *Int. Cong. Ser.-Excerpta Med (Genet. Environ. Interact. Diabetes Mellitus).* **549** , 306-312.

DOI, K., MATSUURA, M., KAWARA, A., TANAKA, T., & BABA, S. (1983). Influence of dietary fiber (konjac mannan) on absorption of vitamin B_{12} and vitamin E. *Tohoku J. Exp. Med.* **141** (Suppl.) 677-681.

EBIHARA, K., MASUHARA, R., & KIRIYAMA, S. (1981). Effect of konjac mannan, a water-soluble dietary fiber, on plasma glucose and insulin responses in young men undergoing glucose tolerance test. *Nutr. Rep. Int.* **23**, 577-583.

FUJIWARA, S., HIROTA, T., NAKAZATO, H., MUZUTANI, T., & MITSUOKA, T. (1991). Effect of konjac mannan on intestinal microbial metabolism in mice bearing human flora and in conventional F344 rats. *Fd. Chem. Toxic.* **29**, 601-606.

HENRY, D.A., MITCHELL, A.S., AYLWARD, J., FUNG, M.T., McEWEN, J., & ROHAN, A. (1986). Glucomannan and risk of œsophageal obstruction. *British Medical Journal* **292**, 591-592.

HUANG, C.-Y., ZHANG, M.-Y., PENG, S.-S., HONG, J.-R., WANG, X., JIANG, H., ZHUANG, F., BAI, Y., LIANG, J., YU, Y., LUO, Z., ZHANG, X., & ZHAU, Z.(1990). Effect of konjac food on blood glucose level in patients with diabetes. *Biomed. Environ. Sci.* **3**, 123-131.

JAPAN FOOD RESEARCH LABORATORIES, Osaka, Japan for Shimizu Chemical Industries (1984). On change in molecular size distribution caused by acid hydrolysis. Unpublished report No. OS27060285-2. Submitted to Food and Drug Administration by Hazelton Laboratories Corp., Herndon, VA, USA. Food Master File 000348 Vol. 2, 237-245.

KIRIYAMA, S., ENISHI, A., & YURA, K. (1974). Inhibitory effect of konjac mannan on bile acid transport in the everted sacs from rat ileum. *The J. of Nutr.*, **104**, 69-78.

KONISHI, F., OKU, T., & HOSOYA, N. (1984). Hypertrophic effect of unavailable carbohydrate on cecum and colon in rats. *J. Nutr. Sci. Vitaminol.*, **30**, 373-379.

KOTKOSKIE, L.A., WEINER, M.L., FREEMAN, C., BATT, K.J., JACKSON, G.C., HARDY, C.J., & FLETCHER, M.J. (1992). Acute toxicity studies with konjac flour. *Toxicolo. Letters Suppl.* 281.

MIZUTANI, T., & MITSUOKA, T. (1982). Effect of konjac mannan on spontaneous liver tumorigenesis and fecal flora in C3H/He male mice. *Cancer Letters* **17**, 27-32.

MIZUTANI, T. & MITSUOKA, T. (1983). Effect of konjac mannan on 1,2-dimethylhydrazine-induced intestinal carcinogenesis in Fisher 344 rats. *Cancer Letters* **19**, 1-6.

MORGAN, L.M., TREDGER, J.A., WRIGHT, J., & MARKS, V. (1990). The effect of soluble- and insoluble-fibre supplementation on post-prandial glucose tolerance, insulin, and gastric inhibitory polypeptide secretion in healthy subjects. *British J. Nutr.* **64**, 103-110.

NAKAZAWA, T. (1983). Studies on agriculture and asthma. *Jpn. J. Traumatol. Occup. Med.* **32**, 10-17.

NISHINARI, K., WILLIAMS, P.A., & PHILLIPS, G.O. (1992). Review of the physico-chemical characteristics and properties of konjac mannan. *Food Hydrocoll.* **6**, 199-222.

OKETANI, Y., ICHIKAWA, K., ONO, C., GOFUKU, M., KIWAKI, S., & KIRIYAMA, S. (1984). Toxicity studies on glucomannan (1) Acute toxicity study in mice and rats. *Appl. Pharmacol.* **27**, 127-131.

OKU, T., KONISHI, F., & HOSOYA, N. (1982). Mechanism of inhibitory effect of unavailable carbohydrate on intestinal calcium absorption. *The J. of Nutr.* **104**, 410-415.

PASSARETTI, S., FRANZONI, M., COMIN, U., DONZELLI, R., ROCCA, F., COLOMBO, E., FERRARA, A., DINELLI, M., PRADA, A., CURZIO, M., TITTOBELLO, A. & participating physicians. (1991). Action of glucomannans on complaints of inpatients affected with chronic constipation: a multicentric clinical evaluation. *Ital. J. Gastroenterol.* **23**, 421-425.

REINHOLD, J.G., ISMAIL-BEIGI, F., & FARADJI, B. (1975). Fibre vs. phytate as determinant of the availability of calcium, zinc, and iron of breadstuffs. *Nutr. Rept. Int.* **12**, 75-85.

REINHOLD, J.G., FARADJI, B., ABADI, P. & ISMAIL-BEIGI, F. (1976). Decreased absorption of calcium, magnesium, zinc, and phosphorus by humans due to increased fiber and phosphorus consumption as wheat bread. *J. Nutr.* **106**, 493-503.

SHIMA, K., TANAKA, A., IKEGAMI, H., TABATA, M., SAWAZAKI, N., & KUMAHARA, Y. (1983). Effect of dietary fiber, glucomannan, on absorption of sulfonylurea in man. *Horm. Metabol. Res.* **15**, 1-3.

VENTER, C.S., VORSTER, H. H., & Van der NEST, D. G. (1990). Comparison between physiological effects of konjac-glucomannan and propionate in baboons fed "Western" diets. *J. Nutr.*, **120(9)** 1046-1053.

WALSH, D.E., YAGHOUBIAN, V., & BEHFOROOZ, A. (1984). Effect of glucomannan on obese patients: a clinical study. *International Journal of Obesity* **8**, 289-293.

ZHANG, M.-Y., HUANG, C.-Y., WANG, X., HONG, J.-R., & PENG, S.-S. (1990). The effect of foods containing refined konjac meal on human lipid metabolism. *Biomedical and Environmental Sciences* **3**, 99-105.

PROCESSED *EUCHEUMA* SEAWEED

First draft prepared by
Ms E. Vavasour
Toxicological Evaluation Division
Bureau of Chemical Safety, Food Directorate
Health and Welfare Canada
Ottawa, Ontario, Canada

1   EXPLANATION

Processed *Eucheuma* seaweed (PES) was previously considered by the Committee at its thirtieth and thirty-ninth meetings (Annex 1, references 73 and 101) but it could not be evaluated for use in foods because no relevant toxicological data were available. At its present meeting the Committee reviewed a 90-day feeding study in rats on a processed *Eucheuma* seaweed from *E. cottonii* and a series of genotoxicity studies on a processed *Eucheuma* seaweed from *E. cottonii* were available. Complete details of the 90-day study were not provided.

2   BIOLOGICAL DATA

2.1   Biochemical Aspects

No information available.

2.2   Toxicological Studies

2.2.1   Acute toxicity studies

No new information available

2.2.2 Short-term toxicity studies

Groups of 10 male and 10 female Sprague-Dawley rats, 6 weeks old, were fed diets which contained 0, 0.5, 1.5 or 5.0% PES, or 5.0% refined carrageenan derived from *Eucheuma cottoni* for 3 months. The rats were observed twice daily and the gross appearance of the stools was checked in the morning. Individual body weights and food consumption were measured weekly throughout the study. Standard haematological and clinical chemistry parameters were measured in blood samples taken from all animals at sacrifice. Urinalysis was also conducted on fresh urine and 24-hour urine samples at week 13 of the study. Faecal samples were analyzed for gross appearance and occult blood. Necropsy was performed on all animals at sacrifice, selected organs weighed (brain, pituitary gland, submandibular glands, thymus, lungs, thyroid, heart, liver, caecum, spleen, kidneys, adrenal glands, testes, epididymides, prostate, ovaries and uterus) and 40 tissues and organs preserved for histopathological examination. No individual data were provided.

No deaths were observed during the study. The average daily intakes for each of the dose levels of PES were 382, 1140 and 3887 mg/kg bw/day for males, and 410, 1292 and 4170 mg/kg bw/day for females. A dose-related trend in the incidence of altered stool quality was noted, in particular soft, big-size and fragmented stool. This effect was most apparent (earlier onset, higher frequency of occurrence and larger number of animals affected) in the groups receiving 5% PES or refined carrageenan, especially the latter. Faecal occult blood was not noted in any of the groups. In addition, a higher urine volume and lower urine specific gravity was observed in the 5% PES groups. Toluidine blue staining of the liver, spleen, mesenteric lymph nodes and gastrointestinal tract did not reveal deposition of metachromatic material at microscopic examination. It was concluded that absorption of carrageenan did not occur. No other effects attributable to treatment were evident from the summary of the histopathological results (Philippine Bureau of Food and Drugs 1992).

2.2.3 Long-term/carcinogenicity studies

No new information available

2.2.4 Reproduction studies

No new information available

2.2.5 Special studies on genotoxicity

The results of genotoxicity assays on PES are summarized in Table 1.

2.3 Observations in humans

No information was available.

Table 1. Results of genotoxicity assays on PES

Test System	Test Object	Concentration of Test Material	Results	Reference
Rec assay	*B. subtilis*	25-100 mg/ml	Negative	Sylianco *et al.* 1992
Ames test[1,2]	*S. typhimurium* TA100	25-100 mg/ml	Negative	Sylianco *et al.* 1992
Host-mediated assay	Swiss Webster mice/*S. typhimurium*	625-2 500 mg/kg bw	Negative	Sylianco *et al.* 1992
Micronucleus test	Swiss Webster mice	625-2 500 mg/kg bw	Negative	Sylianco *et al.* 1992

[1] Without S9 metabolic activation.
[2] Only one strain of *S. typhimurium* was used for the Ames assay, though it is standard practice to use 4 strains.

3   COMMENTS

Analytical data provided on the commercial product and on the material used in the toxicity studies were reported to conform to the specifications that were prepared at the present meeting.   The viscosity specification indicated that the carrageenan component was not degraded. Analytical data showed that the relative molecular mass of processed *E. cottonii* was well above that of degraded carrageenan and similar to that of traditionally refined carrageenan, and that the acid-insoluble component of PES was similar to cellulose.   The crude protein content of the commercial batches ranged from 0.1 to 1.5%, with a mean value of 1%. The product did not contain heavy metals at levels of toxicological concern.

In the 90-day feeding study in rats PES was administered at 0.5%, 1.5%, and 5% in the diet, in addition a comparison group was fed traditionally-refined carrageenan at a level of 5%.   The most notable effect from this study was an alteration of stool characteristics in both the groups fed PES and those fed traditionally-refined carrageenan at the 5% level, which was more pronounced in the group receiving traditionally-refined carrageenan.   This effect is to be expected from this kind of poorly absorbed material and was not considered to be of toxicological significance.   No deposits of metachromatic material were observed in the livers of these rats, and no traces of blood were detected in the faeces as would have been expected if the PES had been degraded.   No effects of toxicological significance were observed.

No genotoxic effects were observed in *in vitro* bacterial assays or in an *in vivo* mammalian assay.

4.   EVALUATION

The Committee allocated a temporary ADI of 0-20 mg/kg bw to processed *Eucheuma* seaweed, based on the application of a 200-fold safety factor to the intake associated with the 5% dose level (equivalent to 3890 mg/kg bw/day) in the 90-day study in rats. The ADI was made temporary, pending submission of the complete details from this study, including histopathological data for individual animals. The Committee was informed that additional characterization data on processed *Eucheuma* seaweed existed, and requested that that these data and the individual data from the 90-day rat study should be submitted for review by 1995.

5.   REFERENCES

PHILIPPINE BUREAU OF FOOD AND DRUGS. 1992. Three months subchronic oral toxicity test of dietary Philippine Natural Grade carrageenan in rats.   Interim report.   BFAD protocol no. 91-5. Unpublished report submitted to WHO by the Government of the Philippines.

SYLIANCO, C.Y.L., BALBOA, J., SERRAME, E. AND GUANTES, E. 1992. Mutagenicity, clastogenicity and antimutagenicity potential of carrageenan. Unpublished report submitted to WHO by the Government of the Philippines.

PROPYLENE GLYCOL ALGINATE

First draft prepared by
Dr G.J.A. Speijers and Mrs M.E. van Apeldoorn
National Institute of Public Health and Environmental Protection
Laboratory for Toxicology
Bilthoven, The Netherlands

1. EXPLANATION

Alginates are polyuronic acids which are major components of the cell walls of brown seaweed. Brown seaweeds have been used in food and feed for centuries but it is only since 1929 that alginates have been manufactured on an industrial scale. Alginates have valuable rheological properties which can be varied to a great extent by varying the degree of polymerisation of the polysaccharide or by changing the ionic environment. Thus alginates can provide solutions having a range of viscosities or gels of varying rigidities which may be used as texture modifiers in a wide range of food and industrial applications (Martin, 1986).

Propylene glycol alginate is a reaction product of propylene oxide and alginic acid (Steiner & McNeely, 1951). This substance was evaluated at the thirteenth, fifteenth, and seventeenth meetings of the Committee (Annex 1, references 19, 26, and 32). At the seventeenth meeting an ADI for propylene glycol alginate of 0-25 mg/kg bw was allocated, based on a NOEL of 2 500 mg/kg bw/day in a long-term toxicity study in rats. At that meeting the Committee concluded that only the propylene glycol moiety is absorbed and metabolized, and that the alginate moiety is excreted unchanged in the faeces of rats and mice. Accordingly, the Committee decided that the contribution of propylene glycol alginate to total dietary propylene glycol intake from all sources should be included in the ADI for propylene glycol, which was allocated an ADI of 0-25 mg/kg bw (Annex 1, reference 32).

Alginic acid and its ammonium, calcium, potassium, and sodium salts were evaluated by the Committee at its thirty-ninth meeting (Annex 1, reference 101) when a group ADI "not specified" was allocated.

At its present meeting, the Committee evaluated new data from a 30-day study in rats, genotoxicity assays, a teratogenicity study in rabbits and a study in human volunteers. The previously published monographs have been expanded and are reproduced in their entirety below.

2. BIOLOGICAL DATA

2.1 Biochemical aspects

2.1.1 Absorption, distribution and excretion.

In vitro hydrolysis studies with propylene glycol alginate in simulated gastric juice and simulated intestinal juice showed no hydrolysis in simulated gastric juice, while intestinal juice hydrolyzed 25% in 4 hours, 65% in 12 hours and 80% in 24 hours (McNeely & Shepherd, 1966).

Five grams of propylene glycol alginate/kg bw (as a 10% aqueous solution), labeled with ^{14}C in the alginate moiety, or 1 g of propylene glycol alginate/kg bw (as a 5% aqueous solution), labeled with ^{14}C in the propylene glycol moiety, was administered as a single dose to mice (8/group) by gavage. Absorption, distribution and excretion of radioactivity were followed from 1 hour to 5 days after administration by whole body autoradiography.
Some, but not all, of the label (labeled in the propylene glycol moiety) in a single dose of 1 g propylene glycol alginate/kg bw was absorbed. The unabsorbed portion was excreted in the faeces within 3 days while the absorbed radioactivity was distributed rapidly over the whole body, was concentrated in the liver and was completely removed from all tissues in 3-4 days. These findings are consistent with the fate of absorbed radioactivity from labeled free propylene glycol and its metabolites. Five days after administration of 5 g propylene glycol alginate (labeled in the alginate moiety)/kg bw traces of radioactivity were still noted in the rectum. It was concluded that released propylene glycol was absorbed and metabolized by the usual pathways (to acetate, lactate or glycogen) and had disappeared completely from the body after five days. The alginate moiety and the unhydrolyzed propylene glycol alginate were not absorbed from the gastrointestinal tract, but excreted in the faeces (Sharratt & Dearn, 1972).

2.1.2 Biotransformation

No information available.

2.1.3 Effects on enzymes and other biochemical parameters

No information available.

2.2 Toxicological studies

2.2.1 Acute toxicity studies

The results of acute toxicity studies with propylene glycol alginate are summarized in Table 1.

Table 1. Acute toxicity studies - propylene glycol alginate

Animal	Route	LD_{50} (mg/kg bw)	Reference
mouse	oral	7 800	FDRL, 1976
rat	oral	7 200	FDRL, 1976
hamster	oral	7 000	FDRL, 1976
rabbit	oral	7 600	FDRL, 1976

2.2.1.1 Rats

Groups of 60 rats were dosed with 5 g/kg bw propylene glycol alginate by gavage or were fed a diet containing 50 to 70% propylene glycol alginate for 24 hours. No adverse effects were observed. Autopsy 14 days after treatment did not reveal compound-related abnormalities (Woodard Res. Corp., 1972).

Rats given 10 g propylene glycol alginate/kg bw orally as a suspension in corn oil showed a transient depression. No other effects were noted (Newell & Maxwell, 1972).

2.2.1.2 Rabbits

Rabbits receiving an application of propylene glycol alginate as an aqueous paste on abraded skin or receiving an ocular application of dry powdered propylene glycol alginate did not reveal signs of irritation (Woodard Res. Corp., 1972).

Rabbits injected intravenously, intraperitoneally, intramuscularly or subcutaneously with 6.2, 12.5 or 25 mg propylene glycol alginate/kg bw showed neither effects at the injection site nor any systemic effects (Steiner & McNeely, 1951).

Rabbits injected subcutaneously or intramuscularly with up to 2 ml of a sterile aqueous 2% solution of propylene glycol alginate did not show gross or histological abnormalities at the injection site. Intraperitoneal and intravenous injections of similar amounts did not produce abnormal systemic effects (Ouer et al., 1935).

2.2.2   Short-term toxicity studies

2.2.2.1 Rats

Two groups of 6 female rats received a diet containing 21.5% propylene glycol alginate and 21.5% glucose or a normal diet containing 21.5% glucose for 4 weeks. After 4 weeks of treatment 2 animals/group were killed and the remaining 4 animals/group received a normal diet for an additional 4 weeks. Thereafter the original control group received a diet containing 21.5% propylene glycol alginate and the original test group received a control diet for 2 weeks. The test group showed slight growth retardation but appearance and behaviour were normal. Faeces of the test group were slimy. Histopathy of liver, kidneys and intestine of the 2 animals/group that were killed after the initial 4 weeks treatment time did not reveal abnormalities (MRCL, 1951).

Fifteen male rats received 5% (w/w) propylene glycol alginate in the diet for 30 days. No diarrhoea was seen and bowel habit was normal. Urinalysis did not reveal abnormalities. All rats showed distension of the caecum, 5 rats showed distension of a portion of the ileum. Twelve rats showed distension of the colon to some degree, with soft contents. Soft ill-formed faecal pellets were seen in 10 rats. No further macroscopic changes were seen. Histopathology was not carried out (Anderson et al., 1991).

2.2.2.2 Guinea-pigs

Four groups of 3 guinea-pigs received 0, 5, 10 or 15% propylene glycol alginate in their diet for 26 weeks. Body weight gain was reduced in test groups but mean food intake was similar to controls. Histopathology of various organs revealed no significant lesions (Nilson & Wagner, 1951).

2.2.2.3 Cats

Eight experimental cats and one control cat were fed 0, 5, 10 or 15% propylene glycol alginate in a diet of dog food and canned salmon daily for 88-111 days. Test animals had difficulties in swallowing and eating because of the physical texture of the diet. The animals could not eat more than 100 g dog food and 30 g canned salmon/day and thus lost weight. At dietary levels of 10 and 15% the cats showed frequent soft stools. Macroscopy and microscopy did not reveal abnormalities (no details) (Nilson and Wagner, 1951).

2.2.2.4 Chickens

4 Groups of 13-day old chickens (number/group unknown) received 0, 5, 10 or 15% propylene glycol alginate in their diet for 3-7 weeks. At all dose levels growth rate was reduced due to difficulties with the diet. Histopathology showed

slight transient tissue changes in controls as well as test animals (no details) (Nilson & Wagner, 1951).

2.2.2.5 Dogs

Three groups of 3 male and 3 female Beagle dogs received a diet containing 0, 5 or 15% propylene glycol alginate for one year. Stool conditions were variable at the 15% dietary level. Weight gain and food consumption were normal. No effects on haematological (no details) parameters or serum urea nitrogen, serum alkaline phosphatase, blood glucose or urinalysis (no details) were seen. Organ weights (10) were comparable to controls. Histopathology (21 tissues) did not reveal compound-related changes (Woodard, 1959).

2.2.3   Long-term toxicity/carcinogenicity studies

2.2.3.1 Mice

Four groups of 10 mice (bw 12-18 g) received 0, 5, 15 or 25% propylene glycol alginate in their diet for 12 months. At week 39 one control mouse and one mouse of the group fed 15% in their diet were killed. In the 25% group, increased mortality, a decreased maximum body weight, decreased food intake and increased water consumption were seen. At the 15% dose level a slightly decreased maximum body weight and a slightly decreased food intake were seen. The effects were probably due to increased water absorption of the diet which caused enough bulk to limit food intake (Nilson & Wagner, 1951).

2.2.3.2 Rats

Four groups of 10 male and 10 female rats (age 4 weeks) received during their life span 0, 5, 15 or 25% propylene glycol alginate in their diet. At dose-levels of 15 and 25% in the diet lifespan was slightly reduced and decreased food consumption was seen. Death of rats in control as well as test groups was usually due to myocardial fibrosis, pneumonia and the multiplicity of cumulative processes associated with aging. There were no lesions attributed to toxaemia or to local irritative intestinal effects. The bulky diets caused loose and smeary faeces and weight gain was reduced, probably due to inanition. Organ weights were not determined. Histopathology of major tissues (liver, kidneys, spleen, heart, brain, lung, stomach, small intestines, large intestines, ovaries/testes) did not reveal abnormalities. A fifth group received 15% propylene glycol alginate in a different basal diet. This group showed an increased food and water consumption. Faeces were normal in this group. The group was killed after 37 weeks (Nilson & Wagner, 1951).

Groups of 20 male and 20 female rats received 0% or 5% propylene glycol alginate in their diet for 2 years as the parent generation of a multigeneration study. Two male and two female rats/group were killed after one year for histopathology.

After 2 years survival of this F_0 generation was 67% for males and 78% for females in the control group and 56% for males and 58% for females in the test group. Survival time was 761 days. No difference from controls in general condition, general behaviour, skin, hair, eyes, mean body weight, or haematology (4 males and 4 females/group) was seen. Gross pathology and histopathology of 6 major organs did not reveal treatment-related effects (Morgan, 1959).

2.2.4 Reproduction studies

2.2.4.1 Rats

Groups of 20 male and 20 female rats received 0 or 5% propylene glycol alginate in their diet. After 5-6 months some animals were mated to produce an F_1 generation. 7 Males and 7 females were F_1 controls and 10 males and 10 females the test group. The F_1 generation was fed on similar diets and mated after 4 months to produce the F_2 generation. The F_2 generation consisted of 9 male and 10 female controls and 9 male and 10 female test animals and were also kept on similar diets. F_0 generation survived 761 days, while F_1 and F_2 generation were killed after 202 and 212 days, respectively.

No differences from controls were noted regarding mortality, general condition, mean body weight, fertility, gestation data, lactation and survival for the F_1 and F_2 generation. Haematology was performed in the F_2 generation only and did not show abnormalities. Organ weights were not determined. Gross pathology and histopathology of 6 major organs did not show abnormalities (Morgan, 1959).

2.2.5 Special studies on genotoxicity

The results of genotoxicity studies are summarized in Table 1.

2.2.6 Special studies on teratogenicity

2.2.6.1 Mice

Groups of 22-32 pregnant albino CD-1 mice received daily from day 6 to 15 of gestation 0, 8, 36, 170 or 780 mg propylene glycol alginate/kg bw/dy by gavage as a suspension in corn oil. Up to 170 mg/kg bw/dy there was no effect on nidation or maternal or fetal survival. The number of abnormalities seen in either soft or skeletal tissues did not differ from the number occurring spontaneously in controls. At 780 mg/kg bw/dy maternal toxicity resulted in 7/32 deaths. Surviving dams and fetuses carried to term appeared normal in all respects (FDRL, 1972).

2.2.6.2 Rats

Groups of 24 pregnant Wistar rats received daily by gavage from day 6 to 15 of gestation 0, 7, 33, 155 or 720 mg propylene glycol alginate/kg bw/dy as a

Table 1. Results of genotoxicity assays on propylene glycol alginate

Test system	Test object	Dose-levels	Results	References
Ames test	Salmonella typhimurium (6 strains)	up to 10 mg/pl ate	neg[1]	Ishidate et al., 1984
Ames test	Salmonella typhimurium (2 strains)	5% w/v	negative[2]	SRI, 1972
Ames test	Salmonella typhimurium (3 strains)	up to 0.60%	negative[1]	LBI, 1975
Mitotic recomb.	Saccharomyces cerevisiae D-3	up to 1% w/v	negative[2]	SRI, 1972
Mitotic recomb.	Saccharomyces cerevisiae D4	2.5, 5.0 and 10%	negative[1]	LBI, 1975
Host-mediated assay	Salmonella typhimurium TA 1530 and G46 i.p. in mice	oral doses to mice for 1-5 days up to 5 g/kg bw	negative	SRI, 1972
Host-mediated assay	Sacharomyces cerevisiae D-3 i.p. in mice	oral doses to mice for 1-5 days up to 5 g/kg bw	negative	SRI, 1972
Chromosomal aberration assay	Chinese hamster fibroblasts (CHL cells)	up to 1.0 mg/ ml	negative[2]	Ishidate et al., 1984; 1988
Chromosomal aberration assay	human WI-38 cells	up to 1.0 mg/ ml	negative[2]	SRI, 1972
Micronucleus assay	rat bone-marrow	once orally 0.03, 2.5, or 5.0 g/kg bw or daily for 5 days 0.03, 2.5 or 5.0 g/kg bw	negative	SRI, 1972
Dominant-lethal assay	rats	once orally 0.03, 2.5, or 5.0 g/kg bw or daily for 5 days 0.03, 2.5 or 5.0 g/kg bw	negative	SRI, 1972

1 Assay without and with metabolic activation.
2 Assay without metabolic activation.

suspension in corn oil. On day 20 Caesarean section was carried out and dams and fetuses were examined for pathological and teratological effects. No compound-related effects were observed (FDRL, 1972).

2.2.6.3 Hamsters

Groups of 20 to 23 pregnant golden hamsters received daily by gavage from day 6 to 10 of gestation 0, 7, 33, 150 or 700 mg propylene glycol alginate/kg bw/dy as a suspension in corn oil. On day 14 Caesarean section was carried out. There was no evidence of maternal toxicity or effect on reproduction. Examinations of fetuses did not reveal compound-related abnormalities (FDRL, 1974a).

2.2.6.4 Rabbits

Groups of 10 to 15 pregnant rabbits received daily by gavage from day 6-18 of gestation 0, 8, 37, 173 or 800 mg propylene glycol alginate/kg bw/dy as a suspension in corn oil. On day 29 Caesarean section was carried out. No differences with respect to number of corpora lutea, implantation sites, resorption sites, number of live and dead fetuses or fetal weights were seen. Gross examination of the fetuses did not reveal external congenital abnormalities. Visceral and skeletal examination of fetuses from dosed does did not show any differences compared to control fetuses (FDRL, 1974b).

2.2.7 Special studies on bacteriology

Two rats were fed control diet during 6 months, thereafter they received 5% polyethylene glycol alginate in their diet for 3 weeks followed by 2 weeks on control diet. Bacteriological examination of the intestinal flora showed lower counts of lactobacilli and aerobes but an increased count of coliforms compared to controls. The anaerobic counts were comparable with those of controls (Woodard, 1959).

2.3 Observations in humans

Fifty individuals known to be allergic to numerous substances were tested intradermally with various dilutions of propylene glycol alginate. Fifty other individuals without an allergic history or family history of allergy were used as controls. 11 Individuals showed slight to moderate skin reactions (8 in test group, 3 in control group). When five of those showing the greatest reactions (all in test group) were fed propylene glycol alginate three showed mild allergic reactions which were duplicated in repeated tests. Three control individuals, who showed very slight skin reactions, did not react to oral administration of propylene glycol alginate (Ouer, 1949).

Five healthy male volunteers received 175 mg propylene glycol alginate/kg bw/day orally for 7 days, followed by 200 mg/kg bw/dy for a further 16 days. The daily doses were consumed in three measured portions at intervals each day. The portions were prepared by adding the weighed aliquots of propylene glycol alginate with rapid stirring to 220 ml cold distilled water. The hydrocolloid was then allowed to hydrate for 24 h to a thick but fluid gel to which each volunteer added a pre-determined amount of orange juice prior to consumption. The treatment period was preceeded by a 7-day initial control period during which daily an amount of orange juice, equal to that to be used later, was consumed. During the treatment period enquiries were made with respect to apparent allergic responses. At day 3 of the initial control period, on the last day the of 23-day treatment period and on the last day of the 7-day recovery period the following parameters were examined; fasting blood glucose, plasma insulin, breath hydrogen concentrations, haematological parameters (Hb, Hct, MCV, MCH, MCHC, Er, Leu, Diff, platelets) and biochemical parameters (Na, Cl, K, CO_2, urea, LDH [lactate dehydrogenase], ASAT, bilirubin, alk. phosphatase, phosphate, Ca, protein, albumin, creatinine, urate, lipids, cholesterol, HDL cholesterol and triglycerides). Routine urinalysis was carried out during the initial control week and during the third week of treatment. Five-day faecal collections were made during days 2-6 of the initial control period and during days 16-20 of the treatment period. Faecal transit time, wet wt., dry wt., water content, pH, occult blood, neutral sterols, fat, volatile fatty acids and bile acids in faeces were determined. No allergic reactions were observed. Propylene glycol alginate exerted no significant effects on faecal parameters (pH, water content, wet and dry wts.) Faecal transit time was constant in 3 volunteers, increased in one and decreased in one. Faecal total and individual volatile fatty acids and total and individual bile acids did not show changes. Faecal total neutral sterols and cholesterol decreased in each volunteer. Haematological, biochemical and urinary parameters did not show significant changes (Anderson *et al.*, 1991).

3.   COMMENTS

An *in vitro* study showed partial hydrolysis of propylene glycol alginate in simulated intestinal juice (25% within 4 hours; 80% within 24 hours). Partial hydrolysis was also observed in an *in vivo* mouse study. Absorption, distribution, and excretion studies in mice showed that unhydrolysed propylene glycol alginate and the alginate moiety were not absorbed. Released propylene glycol was rapidly absorbed and metabolized to lactic and pyruvic acids.

In various short- and long-term toxicity studies, 10% or higher propylene glycol alginate in the diet caused reduced growth accompanied by reduced food consumption and loose stools, the common effects in animals fed high doses of bulking agents.

In a long-term toxicity study in mice (12 months) as well as in long-term toxicity studies in rats ($\geq$ 2 years) the NOEL was 5%. There was no indication of a carcinogenic effect. Propylene glycol alginate did not induce gene mutations in bacteria or in yeast cells or chromosomal aberrations in mammalian cells *in vitro* or *in vivo*.

In addition, in a 2-generation reproduction study in rats, 5% propylene glycol alginate in the diet did not cause any effects. Teratogenicity studies in rats, mice, hamsters and rabbits did not reveal any teratogenic activity of propylene glycol alginate at dose levels of up to 800 mg/kg bw/day.

No adverse effects were observed in a recent 23-day study in five human volunteers in which the substance was given orally at a dose of 200 mg/kg bw/day.

4.   EVALUATION

The Committee noted that similar effects - reduced growth, and loose stool - have been observed in animal studies with other poorly absorbed compounds (including modified cellulose, polyalcohols, gums, modified starches and other alginates). The Committee reiterated that the ADI for propylene glycol alginate is limited only by the amount of propylene glycol that might be released. Propylene glycol alginate containes up to 36% propylene glycol. On the assumption that all of this amount is hydrolyzed, and taking into account the ADI of 0-25 mg/kg by for propylene glycol, the Committee allocated an ADI of 0-70 mg/kg bw (100/36 x 25) to propylene glycol alginate.

The Committee was aware of new toxicological studies on propylene glycol, but as the compound was not on the agenda, the data were not reviewed. The Committee recommended that propylene glycol be reviewed at a future meeting. Because the ADI for propylene glycol alginate is based on the ADI for propylene glycol, the Committee also recommended that the former substance be reconsidered at the same meeting.

5.   REFERENCES

ANDERSON, D.M.W., BRYDON, W.G., EASTWOOD, M.A. & SEDGWICK, D.M. (1991) Dietary effects of propylene glycol alginate in humans. *Fd. Add. Contam.* **8** (3), 225-236

FDRL (1972) Food and Drug Research Laboratories Inc. Report on teratologic evaluation of PGA. PB-221 786. Submitted to WHO by Marinalg International, Paris, France.

FDRL (1974a) Food and Drug Research Laboratories Inc. Report on teratologic evaluation of PGA in hamsters. PB-221 786. Submitted to WHO by Marinalg International, Paris, France

FDRL (1974b) Food and Drug research Laboratories Inc. Report on teratologic evaluation of compound FDA 71-18. Propylene glycol alginate in rabbits. PB-267 196. Submitted to WHO by Marinalg International, Paris, France.

FDRL (1976) Food and Drug Research Laboratories Inc. Paper No. 124, as summarized in RTECS. Submitted to WHO by Marinalg International, Paris, France.

ISHIDATE, Jr., M., SOFUNI, K., YOSHIKAWA, K., HAYASHI, M., NOHMI, T., SAWADA, M. AND MATSUOKA, A. (1984) Primary mutagenicity screening of food additives currently used in Japan. *Fd. Chem. Toxicol.* **22** (8), 623-636

ISHIDATE, Jr., M., HARNOIS, M.C. AND SOFUNI, T. (1988) A comparative analysis of data on the clastogenicity of 951 chemical substances tested in mammalian cell cultures. *Mutat. Res.* **195**, 151-213

LBI (1975) Litton Bionetics Incorporated Report PB-245 497 prepared for Food and Drug Administration. Mutagenic evaluation of Compound FDA 71-18 Propylene glycol alginate. Dated 30 June 1975. Submitted to WHO by Marinalg International, Paris, France

MARTIN, G. (1986) Evaluation toxicologique et nutritionnelle des alginates: I. Définition, structure, fabrication, proprietés et applications. *Sciences et Aliments* **6**, (no.4), 473-486

MCNEELY, W.H. & SHEPHERD, V.M. (1966) Report to Kelco Co. Labs.

MORGAN, F.C.(1959) As cited in Woodard (1959)

MRCL (1951) Medical Research Council Laboratories. Unpublished report.

NEWELL, G.W. & MAXWELL, W.A. (1972) Unpublished Report from Stanford Research Institute, Menlo Park Co., submitted to DHEW/Public Health Service, U.S. FDA.

NILSON, H.W. AND WAGNER, J.A. (1951) Feeding tests with some algin products. *Proc. Soc. Exp. Biol. Med.* **76**, 630-635.

OUER, R.A. *et al.* (1935) *J. Biol. Chem.* **5**, 108

OUER, R.A. (1949) Sensitivity to Kelcoid. Preliminary study. *Ann. Allergy* **7**, 681

SHARRATT, M. & DEARN, P. (1972) An autoradiographic study of propylene glycol alginate in the mouse. *Food Cosm. Toxicol.* **10**, 35-40

SRI (1972) Stanford Research Institute Report PB-221 826 prepared for Food and Drug Administration. Study of mutagenic effects of propylene glycol alginate (71-18). Dated June 1972. Submitted to WHO by Marinalg International, Paris, France

STEINER, A.B. & MCNEELY, W.H. (1951) Organic derivatives of alginic acid. *Ind. Eng. Chem.* **43**, 2073

WOODARD, G. (1959) Unpublished Report.

WOODARD RES. CORP. (1972) Unpublished Report on acute toxicity of PGA.

MISCELLANEOUS SUBSTANCES

ß-CYCLODEXTRIN

First draft prepared by
Professor R. Walker
School of Biological Sciences
University of Surrey, Guildford U.K.

1.   EXPLANATION

ß-Cyclodextrin is a cyclic heptamer composed of seven glucose units joined "head-to-tail" by α-1,4 links. It is produced by the action of the enzyme, cyclodextrin glycosyl transferase (CGT), on hydrolyzed starch syrups. CGT is obtained from *Bacillus macerans*, *B. circulans* or related strains of *Bacillus*.

As a result of its cyclic structure, ß-cyclodextrin has the ability to form inclusion compounds with a range of molecules, generally of molecular mass of less than 250. It may serve as a carrier and stabilizer of food flavours, food colours and some vitamins. Intake of ß-cyclodextrin from use as a food additive has been estimated at 1-1.4 g/day. Other applications in decaffeination of coffee/tea and in reducing the cholesterol content of eggs by complexation followed by separation of the complex would make a much lower contribution to intakes.

ß-Cyclodextrin has not been reviewed previously by the Joint FAO/WHO Expert Committee on Food Additives.

2.   BIOLOGICAL DATA

2.1   Biochemical aspects

2.1.1.   Absorption, distribution, and excretion

ß-cyclodextrin is resistant to hydrolysis by acid (Szeftli & Budai, 1976), α- and ß-amylases and yeast. It is thus not readily digested in the upper gastrointestinal tract by gastric or pancreatic enzymes (Jodal *et al.* 1984).

In a preliminary comparative metabolism study in rats, groups each of 2 animals were given ^{14}C-labelled α-cyclodextrin, ß-cyclodextrin or gelatinised potato starch by gavage as approximately 2.5 ml of a 2.5% aqueous solution. Urine, faeces and expired air were collected for 17-23 hours after which residual radioactivity was assayed in the gastro-intestinal tract (caecum and caecal contents separately), liver, kidneys, heart, lung, spleen, gonads and residual carcass. Animals receiving ß-cyclodextrin metabolized the compound more slowly than starch, as indicated by the time course of elimination of $^{14}CO_2$ in expired air, but by the end of collection the total amount of the dose excreted by this route (48.6% and 66.8% of the dose as $^{14}CO_2$ after 17 and 23 hours respectively) was similar to that of the group given starch; excretion of activity in the urine (3.6-5.1%) and faeces (0-5.4%), and the residual levels in organs and carcass were also similar in the groups given ß-cyclodextrin and starch (Andersen et al. 1963).

ß-Cyclodextrin, purity >77%, and glucose, uniformly labelled with ^{14}C, were administered to rats by gavage as solutions in 20% aqueous dextran at dose levels of 13 mg/kg bw for glucose and 36 and 313 mg/kg bw for ß-cyclodextrin. In the case of glucose, blood levels of radioactivity peaked within 10-30 minutes of dosing whereas with the lower dose of ß-cyclodextrin, peak blood levels were observed between 4 and 11 hours following administration. At the lower dose level of ß-cyclodextrin, the respired radioactivity, as a percentage of the dose, was similar to that after dosing with glucose whereas at the higher dose a smaller percentage was respired. In the eighth hour after the high dose (313 mg/kg bw) no more than 3-50ppm ß-cyclodextrin was detectable in blood. It was concluded that ß-cyclodextrin is not absorbed to a significant extent from the stomach or small intestine of rats but that hydrolysis to open chain dextrins/glucose occurs in the large intestine by a combination of the action of the gut microflora and endogenous amylases. This process may be saturated, and unabsorbed material can be excreted in faeces at high dose levels. The oxygen consumption of slices of rat small intestine was measured in the presence of glucose, maltose, starch and ß-cyclodextrin as substrates; the rate of oxygen consumption was increased by all substrates except ß-cyclodextrin (Szejtli et al. 1980; Gerlóczy et al. 1981; 1985).

The intestinal absorption, digestibility by the colonic microflora, and urinary excretion of ß-cyclodextrin were studied. Using everted sacs of rat small intestine in vitro and ligated gut loops in vivo, absorption was shown to be slow, concentration-dependent, not saturable and not inhibited by phloretin; this indicates that a passive transport process is involved. Rat caecal microflora were able to utilize ß-cyclodextrin under anaerobic conditions in vitro, indicating that the compound may be hydrolyzed to glucose by bacterial enzymes. It was concluded by the authors that ß-cyclodextrin may be utilized by the rat but only indirectly by the activity of the gut flora (Szabo et al. 1981a,b).

Fasted male Sprague-Dawley rats were given a dose of 1 500 mg ß-cyclodextrin (about 3 235 mg/kg bw). Only small amounts (0.6-4% of the dose) were excreted in the faeces in a 60 hour period post-dosing and negligible amounts (0-0.9% of the dose) remained in the gastrointestinal tract. In a separate experiment using a similar dose, a large proportion was shown to be converted to glucose between 3 and 8 hours after dosing (Suzuki & Sato, 1985).

In a 13 week short-term study in beagle dogs (see section 2.2.2.3) animals received ß-cyclodextrin at dietary levels of 1.25, 2.5, 5 or 10%, equal to mean daily doses of 570, 1 234, 2 479 or 4 598 mg ß-cyclodextrin/kg bw. Twenty-four-hour urine samples were analyzed for ß-cyclodextrin at weeks 7 and 13, faeces at week 13 and serum was collected 1, 3, and 6 hours after dosing during week 13.

The urinary concentrations of ß-cyclodextrin at week 7 were 332±76, 510±163, 1 222±491 and 4 218±1 833 mg/l in the respective dose groups; the corresponding values at week 13 were 631±707, 467±335, 817±395 and 2 206±528 mg/l. Although, because of the daily dietary dosing regime, it is not possible simply to express the amount excreted as a percentage of dose, approximately 0.6-1.7% of the mean 24-hour dose was excreted in 24-hour urine and the percentage was not dependent on dose. In week 13, faecal concentrations of ß-cyclodextrin (based on dry matter) in the respective dose groups were 1.3, 1.1, 1.8 and 6.5%. Serum levels of ß-cyclodextrin increased in a dose-dependent manner and with time after dosing up to 6 hours. No ß-cyclodextrin was detected in the lowest dose group and only low levels (1 mg/l increasing to 5 mg/l in the 2.5% dose group; serum levels increased from 4 to 8 mg/l in 1 to 6 hours in the 5% dose group and from 8 mg/l to 46 mg/l in the 10% group. These results indicate that a small proportion of the dose may be absorbed from the gastrointestinal tract in the dog (Smith *et al.* 1992).

2.1.2. Biotransformation

Twenty-four out of thirty strains of *Bacteroides* isolated from the human colon were able to degrade ß-cyclodextrin and utilize it as a sole carbon source. Detailed examinations carried out on the dextrinases from two strains, *Bacteroides ovatus* 3524 and *Bacteroides distasonis* C18-7 indicated that cyclodextrinase activity was predominantly cell bound and inducible in both organisms. The products of hydrolysis of crude cyclodextrinase preparations from these two organisms were markedly different, the former producing only glucose whereas the latter produced a series of maltooligomers (Antenucci & Palmer, 1984).

In vitro, ß-cyclodextrin was resistant to hydrolysis by purified α-amylase from *Aspergillus oryzae*. On incubation for 24 h at an initial ß-cyclodextrin concentration of 15.8 mM, only 17% was degraded; the breakdown products were glucose (12%), maltose (2%) and maltotriose (3%) (Jodal *et al.* 1983).

2.2. Toxicological Studies

2.2.1. Acute toxicity studies

The results of acute toxicity studies with ß-cyclodextrin are summarized in Table 1.

Table 1. Results of acute toxicity studies with ß-cyclodextrin.

Species	Sex	Route	LD50 (mg/kg bw)	Reference
Mouse	M	oral	>3 000	Sebestyén (1980)
Mouse	F	oral	>3 000	Sebestyén (1980)
Mouse	M	i.p.	372	Sebestyén (1980)
Mouse	F	i.p.	331	Sebestyén (1980)
Mouse	M	s.c.	419	Sebestyén (1980)
Mouse	F	s.c.	412	Sebestyén (1980)
Rats	M	oral	>5 000	Sebestyén (1980)
Rats	F	oral	>5 000	Sebestyén (1980)
Rats	M	i.p.	373	Sebestyén (1980)
Rats	F	i.p.	356	Sebestyén (1980)
Rats	M & F	i.v.	788	Frank et al. (1976)
Rats	M	s.c.	>1 000	Sebestyén (1980)
Rats	F	s.c.	>1 000	Sebestyén (1980)
Rats	M & F	dermal	>2 000	Sebestyén (1980)
Rats	M & F	inh	>4.9*	Busch et al. 1985
Dog	M	oral	>5 000	Sebestyén (1980)
Dog	F	oral	>5 000	Sebestyén (1980)

* milligrams/litre of air for 4 hours

2.2.2.   Short-term toxicity studies

2.2.2.1. Mice

In a repeat-dose study of very limited scope which was not reported in detail, mature male mice (number not stated) were given daily oral doses of 6 ml of a 1% solution of ß-cyclodextrin for 15 days. No effects were observed on body weight or relative liver weight. ß-Cyclodextrin was detected in excreta (unclear whether urine and/or faeces) by paper chromatography but could not be detected in liver or gastrointestinal tract (limit of detection not stated)(Miyazaki et al. 1979).

2.2.2.2. Rats

In a 13 week oral toxicity study in Long-Evans rats, body weight 80-100 g at commencement, ß-cyclodextrin (purity not specified) was administered by gavage as a suspension in aqueous 1% methylcellulose to groups of 10 male and 10 female animals at daily dose levels of 200, 400 or 600 mg/kg bw; controls (15 animals of each sex) received an equal volume of 1% methylcellulose solution. Following high mortality (4 males, 3 females) due to misdosing in the 400 mg/kg bw group, a repeat experiment was carried out at this dose level with a separate control group of 5 animals. Body weight and food intake were recorded weekly and urinalysis, haematological and clinical biochemical were performed at termination. At autopsy, heart, lung, liver, kidneys and spleen were weighed, and examined macroscopically and histologically together with gonads, stomach, intestine, pancreas, adrenals and brain.

No abnormal clinical signs were observed and there were no deaths other than 1 male in the low-dose group and 1 female in the high-dose groups, attributed to misdosing. There were no significant treatment-related changes in mean body weight, food consumption, or relative organ weights at termination. No effects due to ß-cyclodextrin were observed in haematological parameters (Hb, haematocrit, MCH, RBC, total and differential leucocytes) or in the clinical biochemical indices ASAT, Alk-P-ase, BUN, bilirubin or creatinine; dose-related but non-statistically significant changes were reported for ALAT in females (decreased) and Alk-P-ase (decreased in males, increased in females) but these were not considered to be of toxicological relevance. Urinalysis for colour, pH, protein, glucose, urobilinogen, bilirubin, ketones and sediment gave similar results between treated animals and controls except for blood detected in the urine of some females of the low-dose group. There were no significant, dose-related changes in the incidence of any lesions in any of the tissues examined histologically but there was a high background incidence of parasitic and bacterial infection.

The power of this study was limited by the small number of animals used and the incidence of lesions due to infection but, within these limits, the NOEL was 600 mg/kg bw/day, the highest dose tested (Sebestyén, 1979; Tury, Aobos-Kovacs & Somogyvari, 1979).

Groups of 17 (19 at the highest dose) male and female Sprague-Dawley rats, 4 weeks old at commencement of the study, were given ß-cyclodextrin by gavage in aqueous suspension at daily dose levels of 0, 100, 400 or 1 600 mg/kg bw After 3 months administration an interim sacrifice was made as follows: Control, 5 males & 4 females; 100 mg/kg bw/d group, 3 males & 5 females; 400 mg/kg bw/d group, 5 males & 4 females; 1600 mg/kg bw/d group, 2 males & 4 females. The remaining animals were maintained on the same dosing regime to 6 months. Food and water intake and body weights were determined weekly. At termination, urinalysis (pH, protein, glucose, ketone bodies, blood, bilirubin, urobilinogen) was carried out on 5 animals of each sex in each group; haematological (RBC, WBC, haemoglobin and haematocrit) and serum biochemical analyses (protein, albumin/globulin, GOT, GPT, Alk-P-ase, BUN, bilirubin, total cholesterol and glucose) were carried out on all survivors. At autopsy, the following organs were weighed: brain, pituitary, thyroid, thymus, heart, lung, liver, kidneys, adrenals, spleen, pancreas, testes or ovaries; these organs and stomach and intestinal tract were examined histologically (haematoxylin & eosin).

A total of 18 animals died during the study as follows: 100 mg/kg bw/d, 3 males; 400 mg/kg bw/d, 2 females; and 1600 mg/kg bw/d, 6 males and 7 females. It was claimed that these deaths were due to misdosing, as no abnormalities were detected other than "pneumonia-like" lung pathology. There was a small decrement of weight gain of both sexes in the top-dose group only, otherwise weight gain, food and water intake were similar to controls and there were no treatment-related effects on organ weights, urinalysis or haematological parameters. Serum biochemical indices generally were within the normal range although some significant differences from controls were observed, notably a dose-related increase in alk-P-ase in males and a decrease in blood glucose in females of the top two dose groups. Gross and histopathological examination did not reveal any treatment-related abnormalities. If the deficit in weight gain at the top-dose level is considered an adverse effect in the absence of other, pathological, changes, the NOAEL for this study is 400 mg/kg bw/day by gavage (Makita *et al.*, 1975).

Following a two-week pilot study, a 26 week oral toxicity study was conducted in Long Evans rats, body weight 80-100 g at commencement, in which ß-cyclodextrin (purity not specified) was administered by gavage as a suspension in aqueous 1% methylcellulose to groups of 15 male and 15 female animals at daily dose levels of 200, 400 or 600 mg/kg bw; controls received an equal volume of 1% methylcellulose solution. Additional groups of 6 animals of each sex were similarly dosed for 6 months followed by a 2-month recovery period prior to autopsy. Body weight and food intake were recorded weekly and urinalysis, haematological and clinical biochemical examinations were performed at termination. At autopsy, heart, lung, liver, kidneys, spleen and testes were weighed; macroscopical and histological examinations (haematoxylin, eosin, Oil red O, and PAS) were carried out on heart, lungs, liver, kidneys, spleen, gonads, stomach, intestine, pancreas, adrenals, lymph nodes and thymus.

In the course of the study there were 5 deaths, not dose-related and attributed to intercurrent disease. No adverse effects of treatment on clinical condition were seen in any dose group. Food consumption was reduced in all treated male groups between weeks 18 and 24, body weight gain was reduced in males of the two highest dose groups between weeks 6 and 21 leading to a 10% deficit in weight gain in the top-dose group; females showed little change in food consumption or weight gain. Statistically significant differences were observed in some haematological and clinical biochemical parameters but in most cases these were not systematically related to treatment and/or were within normal physiological ranges. Dose-related increases in blood glucose were observed in all groups, significantly so in females of all dose groups and in males of the top-dose group. Statistically significant increases, seen only at the top dose level, occurred in total bilirubin and Ca (males only), and in Cl, total protein and albumin/globulin ratio (females only) but were considered not to be of toxicological significance. No significant treatment-related changes in organ weights were observed except for a dose-related reduction in spleen weight, significant in all female treatment groups and in males of the top-dose group. However, these changes did not appear to associated with functional or histological alterations in the spleen and no treatment-related histological abnormalities were observed in heart, lung, liver, kidney, adrenals, gastrointestinal tract, gonads, lymph nodes, pancreas or thymus; no nerve tissue was examined histologically.

In the 2 month withdrawal period following 6 months of treatment, the deficit in body weight in the high-dose males was largely recovered. A significant increase in relative lymphocyte numbers was reported in all treated males but not in females. Changes were noted in some organ weights, notably increased relative weights of lungs and kidneys in males of the top two dose groups, a decreased relative spleen weight in males in the top-dose group and decreased relative liver weights in females of the low and high (but not intermediate) dose groups. These changes were small and unaccompanied by obvious functional changes, and were not considered to be of physiological significance. Blood glucose levels remained higher than controls in all treated male groups and in the top-dose female group but were within the normal range as were the other clinical biochemical parameters. The reductions in spleen weights seen in both sexes (up to 40% reduction in top dose males) were reported not to be accompanied by histopathological changes but individual histological details were not provided and a no-observed-effect-level cannot be established from this study (Gergely, 1982; Mészáros & Vetési, 1982).

A 90-day study was conducted by dietary administration of ß-cyclodextrin to male and female Sprague-Dawley-derived OFA rats. The test material, 99.7% pure on a dry weight basis, was administered to groups of 20 male and 20 female animals, 6-8 weeks old at commencement, by replacing starch in a semi-synthetic diet at levels of O, 1.25, 2.5, 5 or 10%; a "carbohydrate control" group received lactose at a dietary level of 10%. Body weight and food intake were recorded weekly; water intake was monitored 3 times per week. Ophthalmological examinations were conducted on all animals at the start and on 10 animals from the two control groups and the highest dose group at termination. Urine volumes and concentrations of ß-cyclodextrin were recorded at 6 weeks and at the end of the study. Blood and urine biochemistry, haematology and histopathology examinations (controls and high-dose group only) were carried out at termination. The histopathological studies included histochemical examination (Perl's reaction) for ferric iron in liver, kidneys, spleen and lymph nodes. Serum analyses included cholesterol, triglycerides, glucose, urea, creatinine, total bilirubin, total protein, albumin, GOT, GPT, Alk-P-ase, Na, K, Ca and Cl⁻; urinalyses included glucose, urea, uric acid, creatinine, total protein, Na, K and Ca. Haematological examinations included haemoglobin, PCV, MCH, MCHC, MCV, RBC, total and differential leucocyte counts and prothrombin time. At autopsy, relative organ weights were determined for brain, gonads, kidneys, spleen, thymus, caecum, heart and liver.

One male from the lowest ß-cyclodextrin dose group died in the course of the study but there were no indications that the death was related to treatment. There were inconsistent differences in food consumption between groups but no significant difference between the 10% ß-cyclodextrin and the 10% lactose groups. The dose achieved in the top-dose group was approximately 4.4 g/kg bw/day and 5.3 g/kg bw/day for males and females respectively. No significant differences were recorded in water consumption between treatment groups in males but the lactose control group showed a reduced intake in weeks 4, 5 and 6. With females there was a slight increase in water consumption for the 5 and 10% ß-cyclodextrin groups. No significant differences in body weight were observed in any of the groups, except for the male lactose control group, and there were no dose-related adverse effects on haematology, serum biochemistry or urine composition. A small fraction of the dose of ß-cyclodextrin was recovered in urine of animals of the top two dose groups and represented 0.1-0.3% of the highest dose administered. The absolute and relative filled caecal weights of the rats, of both sexes, were increased following administration of diets containing ß-cyclodextrin or lactose (a common feature in rats receiving poorly absorbed and slowly digestible carbohydrates). No treatment-related effects which were considered by the authors as indicative of a toxic response were found from the histopathological examination and it was concluded that ß-cyclodextrin appeared to lack toxicological activity at the doses tested (Olivier *et al.* 1991).

A review of the above study was carried out by an *ad hoc* Scientific Advisory Group which essentially confirmed the authors' conclusions. In noting that in the caeca of female rats of the high ß-cyclodextrin dose group there was a significant increase in sub-mucosal lymphoid follicles the reviewers considered that this was not of toxicological importance as it is commonly associated with caecal enlargement. The increase in the presence of sinus macrophages in the lymph nodes seen in both males and females of the high-dose group was considered to be a physiological rather than a toxic response to the high levels of ß-cyclodextrin in the diet. The review group did not comment on the observation that there was a low incidence of hepatic focal fibrosis in animals from the top-dose group (3/20 and 1/20 in males and females respectively) which was not seen in controls or in the group receiving lactose. The group concluded unanimously that this subchronic study was well designed and properly conducted (Blumenthal *et al.* 1990).

2.2.2.3 **Dogs**

The oral toxicity of ß-cyclodextrin (purity not specified) was examined in a 24-week study in beagles. Groups of 3 males and 3 females were given daily oral doses of 0, 100, 250 or 500 mg/kg bw, corrected for body weight changes every three weeks. The material was administered in boluses made from egg yolk and dried breadcrumbs before the standard diet. Food intake, clinical signs (behaviour, pulse rate, respiratory rate) were recorded initially and at the third, sixth, twelfth, eighteenth and twenty-fourth week of treatment; at the same time blood samples were collected for haematology (Hb, PCV, MCHC, WBC, differential leucocytes) and biochemical analyses (ASAT, ALAT, Alk-P-ase, BUN, glucose, bilirubin, total protein, inorganic P and Ca). At autopsy, the following organs were weighed: liver, spleen, kidneys, gonads, heart, lung and brain; in addition to these organs, histological examinations were performed on adrenals, stomach, small and large intestine, pancreas, spinal cord and tissues showing gross lesions.

All animals survived, but one dog from the top-dose group developed fever, lost appetite and showed catarrhal symptoms during the last week of the study, necessitating treatment with anti-distemper serum and antibiotics for four days; treatment with ß-cyclodextrin was continued during this period. Diarrhoea was observed in some cases but did not appear to be due to administration of ß-cyclodextrin and the condition resolved spontaneously or after treatment with Tannocarbon and bolus astringents for 1-2 days. No treatment-related changes in pulse or respiratory rates were detected. There were no significant dose-dependent changes in blood biochemical parameters, although the values for bilirubin were very scattered, presumably due to haemolysis, at 0 and 3 weeks. Haematological examination also did not reveal any treatment-related changes; an increased eosinophil count in some cases was due to parasitic infestation, confirmed at autopsy. There were no significant changes in organ weights although absolute and relative liver weights tended to be lower in all treated groups, and mean relative and absolute spleen weights were increased in all treated groups. Histopathological changes observed were attributed to the method of sacrifice (magnesium sulfate injection) and were not dose-related. The poor condition of some of the animals due to parasitic infestations and the agonal changes due to the method of sacrifice limited the sensitivity of the study but no obvious compound-related toxicity was detected (Haraszti, 1978; Tury et al. 1978).

In a 13-week study, groups of 2 male and 2 female beagles were given ß-cyclodextrin in the diet at levels of 0, 1.25, 2.5, 5 or 10% (the top-dose group received the test material at 5% of the diet for the first week and 10% thereafter). The purity of the ß-cyclodextrin tested was stated to be ≥ 99.0%. The animals were acclimatised for four weeks prior to administration of the test compound during which time they received inoculations and anthelminthic treatment. The condition of the animals and food intake were recorded daily and body weight was measured weekly. Ophthalmoscopic examinations were performed at the beginning and end of the study; blood was collected for comprehensive haematology and clinical biochemical analysis prior to dosing and on weeks 6 and 13; total 24-hour urine samples were collected for analysis in weeks 7 and 13. Urine samples, and faeces collected during week 13, were analysed for ß-cyclodextrin as were blood samples collected 1, 3 and 6 hours after feeding. At termination organ weights were recorded for adrenals, brain, heart, kidneys, liver, lungs, pancreas, pituitary, spleen, thymus, thyroids and gonads. An extensive range of tissues was fixed at autopsy but histopathological examination was limited to the alimentary tract (8 levels), kidneys, liver, pancreas, urinary bladder and all macroscopically abnormal tissues.

The achieved group mean intakes of ß-cyclodextrin averaged over the 13 weeks of the study were 570, 1234, 2479 and 4598 mg/kg bw/day in the 1.25, 2.5, 5 and 10% dietary dose groups, respectively. In the course of the study, liquid faeces were noted spasmodically in all animals, including controls, but the incidence was higher in the top-dose group (46.7%) than in controls (11.8%) or the 5% dose group (15.7%) and the higher frequency was considered to be treatment-related; there was also a significant decrement of weight gain in the top-dose group only, not associated with reduced food intake. No other clinical symptoms attributable to treatment were observed and the ophthalmoscopic examinations were normal.

Haematological parameters were similar to controls except that red cell counts, haematocrit and haemoglobin levels were statistically significantly reduced in the top-dose group at weeks 6 and 13, and in the 5% dose group at week 6 only; however, the changes were small and similar trends were observed in the acclimatisation period so the toxicological significance was considered equivocal. Reductions were observed in the group mean serum levels of cholesterol, HDL and ß-lipoprotein at weeks 6 and 13 for dogs in the 5% and particularly 10% dose groups; in the top-dose group, total protein, albumin, calcium and phospholipid levels were slightly reduced at weeks 6 and 13, and sodium levels were slightly reduced in week 13 only. Other biochemical parameters were unaffected by treatment. Urinalysis indicated that protein levels were elevated in the 5 and 10% dose groups at weeks 6 and 13 but there were no other notable findings due to treatment. At autopsy, organ weights were generally unaffected by treatment; the group mean absolute thymus weight in the top-dose group was significantly lower than controls ($p < 0.5$) but similar to the lowest-dose group and there was no dose-related trend with the mean group weight being non-significantly higher than controls in the 5% dose group. It was concluded that treatment had no conclusive effect on organ weights. No macroscopic abnormalities were observed and there were no observable treatment-related changes in the tissues examined histologically. The authors concluded that the 2.5% dose level (equal to 1234 mg/kg bw/d) was a NOEL and that, in the absence of any treatment-related macroscopic or microscopic pathological findings, the other effects noted were indicative of only a mild toxic response. However, the small number of animals and the restricted histological examination limited the power of this study. ß-Cyclodextrin in dose-dependent concentrations was detected in urine, faeces and blood of these animals dosed orally (see **Biochemical Aspects** above) (Smith et al. 1992).

2.2.3.   Long-term toxicity/carcinogenicity studies

No information available.

2.2.4.   Reproduction studies

No information available.

2.2.5.   Special studies on teratogenicity

2.2.5.1. Rats

A teratogenicity study was conducted in CFY rats in which groups of 40 mated females (30 in control group) with positive vaginal smears were given ß-cyclodextrin by gavage in 1% methyl cellulose suspension at dose levels of 0, 200, 400 and 600 mg/kg bw/dy on days 7-11 *post coitus*. The animals were killed on day 21 and the number of implants, resorptions, live and dead fetuses, fetal weights and rates of congenital anomalies recorded (no details were given of the methodology of the teratological examinations).

The conception rate was poor (about 30%) giving only 11-12 pregnant animals in each group. Five animals from the top and mid-dose groups and 1 from the low-dose group died during the study, the deaths being attributed to bronchopneumonia due to mis-dosing. Maternal weight gain was reduced in a dose-related manner but there were no changes in mean number of implants (12.7 -14.1), resorptions (1.3-7.3%) fetal viability (93-99%) or fetal weight (3.5-3.9 g). There were 5 congenital anomalies reported out of 628 fetuses, 2 in the low-dose group (hydronephrosis, cardiac anomaly), 1 in the mid-dose group (cardiac anomaly) and 2 in the top-dose group (both absence of right kidney); no anomalies were seen in the control group. No details were given of any examination for skeletal anomalies. The authors state that the incidence of congenital malformations corresponded to the "spontaneous" incidence but no anomalies were seen in controls and no historical data were presented to support this conclusion (Jellinek *et al*, undated).

Following a pilot investigation at dose levels of 500 and 2 500 mg/kg bw/day a teratology study was performed in Wistar rats given ß-cyclodextrin as a suspension in 1.25% aqueous methyl cellulose by gavage at doses of 0, 100, 500 and 2 500 mg/kg bw/day on days 7-16 of pregnancy. The group sizes were 26-28 sperm positive females, of which 22-25/group proved to be pregnant. The dams were sacrificed on day 21 and the following parameters monitored: number of corpora lutea and implantations, preimplantation loss, embryonic and late fetal mortality, and number of viable fetuses. About 50% of the fetuses from each litter were examined for soft tissue defects (Wilson's technique) and the remainder were cleared, stained (Alizarin Red or Alcian Blue/Alizarin red) and examined for skeletal anomalies.

The doses used in this study had no effect on the clinical condition, food consumption or weight gain of the dams and there were no significant effects on intra-uterine mortality, viable fetuses or on the incidence or type of congenital malformation. The anomalies recorded in this study were regarded as sporadic and unrelated to treatment, and had been seen previously among fetuses from over 600 control dams.   Under the conditions of this study, there was no evidence of fetotoxicity or teratogenicity (Druga, 1985).

In a further teratogenicity study in Sprague-Dawley rats, groups of 24-30 mated females were given ß-cyclodextrin as a suspension in 1% aqueous methyl cellulose by gavage at doses of 0, 1 250, 2 500 and 5 000 mg/kg bw/day on days 7-16 of pregnancy. The dams were sacrificed on day 21 and the following parameters monitored: number of corpora lutea and implantations, live and dead fetuses and fetal size. About 50% of the fetuses from each litter were examined for visceral anomalies (Wilson's technique) and the remainder were cleared, stained (Alizarin Red) and examined for skeletal anomalies.

A slight growth retardation was observed in the highest dose group, significant from day 8 to 21, which was associated with a reduced food intake; otherwise there was no effect of treatment on weight gain of the dams. No mortality which could be ascribed to the test compound was observed but 5 animals in the top-dose group died as a result of misdosing and oesophageal perforation, reducing the effective number from 30 to 25. There were no statistically significant differences between groups in any of the following: uterine weight (full and empty), placental weight, weight of fetuses, number of fetuses (all were alive), number of implantation sites, resorptions and corpora lutea or sex ratio. There were no significant effects on the incidence or type of congenital malformation. The anomalies recorded in this study were regarded as unrelated to treatment. Under the conditions of this study, there was no evidence of fetotoxicity or teratogenicity at doses of up to 5 000 mg/kg bw; retardation of weight gain of the dam seen at this dose level was not apparent at a dose of 2 500 mg/kg bw/dy (Leroy *et al.* 1991).

2.2.5.2. Rabbits

Following a pilot investigation at dose levels of 250, 500 and 1 000 mg/kg bw/day a teratology study was performed in groups of 12-14 thalidomide-sensitive New Zealand white rabbits. The dams were artificially inseminated and given ß-cyclodextrin as a suspension in 1.25% aqueous methyl cellulose by gavage at doses of 0, 150, 300 and 600 mg/kg bw/day on days 7-19 of gestation. The dams were sacrificed on day 28 of gestation and the following parameters monitored: number of corpora lutea and implantations, preimplantation loss, embryonic and late fetal mortality, and number of viable fetuses. All of the fetuses from each litter were examined for external and visceral abnormalities on the day of autopsy and the fetuses then fixed, stained (Alizarin Red) and examined for skeletal anomalies.

At the doses used, ß-cyclodextrin had no effect on the clinical condition, food consumption or weight gain of the dams and there were no significant effects on intra-uterine mortality, fetal size or number of viable fetuses. The incidence of minor congenital malformations was slightly but not significantly elevated in all treated animals and was not dose-dependent. The anomalies recorded in this study were regarded as sporadic and unrelated to treatment, and under the conditions of this study, there was no evidence of fetotoxicity or teratogenicity (Dóczy 1985).

2.2.6. Special studies on genotoxicity

The results of genotoxicity studies with ß-cyclodextrin are summarized in Table 2.

2.2.7 Special studies on nephrotoxicity

The experimental use of ß-cyclodextrin in dialysis fluids has been associated with a characteristic nephrosis. Groups of 4 rats of 100-125 g body weight were given single subcutaneous injections of ß-cyclodextrin at dose levels of 225, 450 or 900 mg/kg bw and sacrificed 12, 24, 48 or 96 hours later. In a repeat-dose study, similar animals were given doses of 225, 450, 675 or 900 mg/kg daily for 1, 2, 3, 4 or 7 days and killed 24 hours after the last dose. The kidneys were examined by light and electron microscopy. A characteristic nephrosis was observed, manifested as a series of alterations in the vacuolar organelles of the proximal convoluted tubule. The changes started with an increase in apical vacuoles

Table 2. Results of genotoxicity studies with ß-cyclodextrin.

Test system	Test Object	Concentration	Results	Reference
Host-mediated assay in rat	E.coli WP2uvr A trp⁻, S.typhimurium TA1538	Doses to rat of 0, 100 or 1 000 mg/kg bw	-	Igali 1978
Chromosome aberration	Long Evans rat (?)bone marrow	0, 200, 400 or 600 mg/kg bw/d for 3 m.	-*	Czeizel 1978
Mouse micro-nucleus test	Mouse bone-marrow	100 mg/kg bw	-	Weill, 1988
Sex-linked recessive lethal mutation	Drosophila melanogaster	1.6, 8 & 16 mM	-	Parádi 1987
Ames test (1)	S. typhimurium TA98, TA100, TA1535, TA1537, TA1538	0, 0.1, 0.5, 1, 2 & 4 mg/plate	-	Weill, 1987
HPRT mutation (6-thio-guanine resistance) (1)	V79 Chinese hamster cells	10, 30, 100, 300 & 1 000 µg/ml	-	Marzin et al. 1990
In vitro chromosome aberration test (1)	Human lymphocytes	100, 300 & 1 000 µg/ml	-	Marzin et al. 1991

*The number of cells examined was small relative to normal guidelines
(1) With and without rat liver S9 fraction

and appearance of giant lysosomes followed by extensive vacuolation, cell disintegration and amorphous mineralization. These lesions were evident following a minimal single dose of 675 mg/kg bw and a crude dose-response relationship was established. The earliest manifestations, midcellular cytoplasmic vacuoles, were observable 24 hours after injection. Following repeated dosing, light microscopic lesions were found in one rat given 225 mg/kg bw/dy for 4 days and daily injections of 450 mg/kg bw resulted in severe nephrosis but no deaths; all the animals given repeated doses of 900 mg/kg bw/dy died within 4 days. It was concluded by the authors that intracellular concentration of non-metabolisable ß-cyclodextrin by the lysosomal pathway represents a "perversion" of the physiologic function of the proximal tubule, leading to cell death (Frank et al. 1976).

In studies of the use of ß-cyclodextrin in peritoneal dialysates to accelerate removal of i.v. phenobarbital in adult rats, it was observed that a number of the animals given 1.5% ß-cyclodextrin solution in physiological phosphate i.p. at a level of 15% of body weight died overnight. In a follow-up study, blood urea nitrogen

(BUN) was determined after administration of ß-cyclodextrin orally as 10 ml of a 6% suspension or i.p. as a 0.75% solution in phosphate buffer. Following fasting for 5 hours and gavage with single or three daily doses, BUN was within the normal range 24 hours after the last dose. Intra-peritoneal administration of ß-cyclodextrin was accompanied by a significant increase (3-4 fold) in BUN 24 and 72 hours after administration. The BUN levels fell after 100 hours and returned to normal (Perrin *et al.* 1978).

Subcutaneous administration of ß-cyclodextrin at a daily dose level of 450 mg/kg bw in saline on 7 consecutive days resulted in polyuria and proteinuria, a doubling in relative kidney weight and a decrease in the activities of succinic dehydrogenase, alkaline phosphatase, glucose-6-phosphatase and ß-glucuronidase in proximal convoluted tubules (Hiasa *et al.* 1981).

2.2.8 Special studies on skin irritancy/sensitisation

2.2.8.1 Guinea-pigs

Evaluation of the cutaneous delayed hypersensitivity of ß-cyclodextrin was carried out in albino Dunkin-Hartley guinea-pigs using groups of 20 animals of both sexes. Seven applications (induction phase) and challenge were carried out using 0.4 g ß-cyclodextrin moistened with 0.5 ml water. Macroscopic examinations were carried out 6, 24 and 48 hours after removal of the occlusive patches. Histopathological examinations were carried out on 6 animals showing doubtful reactions at 6 hours. No delayed hypersensitivity reactions were provoked by this protocol (Mercier, 1990).

2.2.8.2 Rabbits

A primary dermal irritation study was conducted in New Zealand white rabbits by application of 0.5 g of test compound moistened with 0.5 ml saline was applied to the shaved dorsal skin of 3 animals under occlusion for 24 hours. The mean primary irritation score was 0.50 (minimally irritating) based on a barely perceptible erythema after 24 hours, there was no eschar or oedema and the treatment sites were normal by 24 hours after removal (Reagan & Becci, 1985).

A primary dermal irritation study in albino rabbits using an abraded skin protocol. The index of primary cutaneous irritation which was obtained (0.01) classified ß-cyclodextrin as non-irritant (Leroy *et al.* 1990).

2.2.9 Special studies on eye irritancy

In an ocular irritancy/corrosion test in albino rabbits, ß-cyclodextrin was classified as slightly irritant (Leroy *et al.* 1990).

2.2.10   Special studies on tumour promotion

Subcutaneous injection of ß-cyclodextrin at a dose of 450 mg/kg bw daily for 7 days during week 3 increased the number and size of renal tubular cell tumours in inbred Wistar rats treated with N-ethyl-N-hydroxyethylnitrosamine (EHEN) in the diet at a concentration of 1 000 mg/kg in the preceding 2 weeks. After 32 weeks, the incidence of tumours was 50% in animals treated with the EHEN alone and 100% in animals subsequently given ß-cyclodextrin. In addition, ß-cyclodextrin promoted the development of renal tumours in rats treated with 500 mg EHEN/kg diet, which was a sub-threshold dose for renal tubular cell tumourigenesis (Hiasa et al. 1982).

2.2.11   Special studies on cell-membranes

The interactions between cyclodextrins and membrane phospholipids, liposomes and human erythrocytes were studied in vitro. ß-Cyclodextrin did not alter the differential scanning calorimetric behaviour of phospholipids, and did not increase the permeability of dipalmitoyl-phosphatidylcholine liposomes. No effects on active or passive transport of ^{42}K or ^{86}Rb into erythrocytes was observed at concentrations of up to 10^{-2}mol/litre but at 1.7×10^{-2}mol/litre, ß-cyclodextrin caused a significant increase in passive transport and 8-10% haemolysis (Szejtli et al. 1986).

ß-Cyclodextrin induced haemolysis of human erythrocytes in vitro in isotonic solution with a threshold concentration of 3 mM (3 400 mg/l). Swelling of erythrocytes, associated with release of cholesterol from the membrane, was observed at lower concentrations, approximately 20% of the membrane cholesterol was released from the membrane at a concentration of 2 mM (2 300 mg/l) ß-cyclodextrin (Irie et al. 1982).

2.3   Observations in humans

2.3.1   Absorption, distribution, metabolism and excretion

The fate of ß-cyclodextrin the human gastrointestinal tract was studied in ileostomy subjects and in normal volunteers after administration of 10 g in a fasting state or after 3 doses of 10 g daily with meals. In the ileostomy subjects, the recovery of ß-cyclodextrin in the ileal effluent was 97±10% and 91±5% respectively. In normal subjects, in which utilization was estimated by the breath hydrogen technique and analysis of stools, breath hydrogen was low, and insignificant levels of ß-cyclodextrin were detectable in faeces. It was concluded that ß-cyclodextrin is hardly hydrolyzed or absorbed in the human small intestine but is fermented by colonic microflora with minimal apparent hydrogen production (Flourié et al. 1992).

2.3.2   Human tolerance studies

In three successive periods of one week, eighteen healthy males, aged 23 ± 2 years, were given doses of 0, 24 or 48 g ß-cyclodextrin/day in addition to the normal diet. The volunteers were randomly assigned to the treatment groups in what was stated to be a placebo-controlled, double blind protocol and the test compound was administered in a chocolate drink equally divided over three meals. At the high dose level "to avoid too drastic influences on bowel function" the subjects were given 24 g ß-cyclodextrin on the first day, 36 g on the second day and 48 g on days 3-7. Tolerance was evaluated by subjective assessment of abdominal complaints using a questionnaire. At the end of each 7-day period, breath hydrogen concentration was measured. One of the volunteers was withdrawn from the study on after three days and replaced with a substitute because of too many adverse events, resembling lactose intolerance (abdominal cramps, nausea, diarrhoea) which were not reported before the start of the study. It is not clear what dose this volunteer received before withdrawal or whether the symptoms preceded treatment.

There was a significant increase in complaints of flatulence ($p < 0.05$) at the higher intake level; other scores of abdominal complaints, reported defaecation patterns and breath hydrogen were stated not to change significantly. The authors concluded that the dose of 24 g ß-cyclodextrin/day was well tolerated on a short term basis (van Dokkum & van der Beek 1990).

2.3.3   Sensitization/irritation

In a repeated insult occlusive patch test in 58 subjects (1 male and 57 females aged 21 to 68 years) ß-cyclodextrin did not induce irritation or allergic contact dermatitis. Three subjects showed scattered, transient, barely perceptible to mild, non-specific patch test responses during the induction or challenge phases of the study, none of which were irritant or allergic in nature (Alworth et al. 1985).

3.   COMMENTS

Metabolic studies in animals and humans consistently indicate that ß-cyclodextrin is poorly hydrolyzed or absorbed in the upper gastrointestinal tract but is largely utilized following hydrolysis by the gut microflora in the lower gut. A small proportion of ingested ß-cyclodextrin may be absorbed intact.

A number of acute and short-term toxicity studies were reviewed which indicated low toxicity by the oral route, although most of these studies used smaller numbers of animals or more limited histological examination than would normally be appropriate for establishing an ADI. In a well-conducted short-term toxicity study in rats, there were no effects of toxicological significance other than caecal enlargement and an increased number of macrophages in intestinal lymph nodes at doses of up to 10% ß-cyclodextrin in the diet; these effects are a common feature of poorly absorbed polysaccharides.

In *in vitro* stidies, ß-cyclodextrin sequestered cholesterol from erythrocyte membranes and caused haemolysis, but only at concentrations much higher than those seen in the blood of dogs given ß-cyclodextrin at a level of 10% in the diet. No effects on mucosal cells of the gastrointestinal tract were seen in the high-oral-dose studies. ß-Cyclodextrin was non-genotoxic in a range of tests, and it does not have a structure likely to be associated with such activity. Given its poor bioavailability and lack of genotoxicity, the Committee concluded that a long-term carcinogenicity study was not required for the evaluation of this substance.

When administered parenterally to rats, ß-cyclodextrin was nephrotoxic, but no renal toxicity was observed in any of the short-term toxicity studies using oral administration. In dogs, the urinary excretion of unchanged ß-cyclodextrin was low, even when the compound was given at a dose level of 10% in the diet, indicating that it is unlikely that systemic levels following oral administration would be high enough to cause renal toxicity.

4.   EVALUATION

The Committee was informed that a 1-year oral toxicity study on ß-cyclodextrin in dogs was under way, and requested the results of this study to complete the evaluation of this compound.

Despite its low toxicity, the Committee was concerned about the possible sequestering effects of ß-cyclodextrin on lipophilic nutrients and drugs. In particular, further data on the effects of ß-cyclodextrin on the bioavailability of lipophilic nutrients are required.

The Committee concluded that there were sufficient data to allocate a temporary ADI of 0-6 mg/kg bw for ß-cyclodextrin, based on a NOEL of 2.5% in the diet, equal to 1230 mg/kg bw/day in the study in dogs and a safety factor of 200.

The results of the 1-year study in dogs and information on the effects of ß-cyclodextrin on the bioavailability of lipophilic nutrients are required by 1995.

As this is a novel product with a wide range of potential applications, the Committee requested further information on the range of possible production methods that could be used in its manufacture.

5.   REFERENCES

ALWORTH, K., SHANAHAN, R.W. & DORMAN, N. (1985) Clinical safety evaluation of beta cyclodextrin: Repeated Insult Patch Test. Unpublished report of Essex Testing Clinic Inc. Submitted to WHO by Société Roquette Fréres, Lestrem, France.

ANDERSEN, G.H., ROBBINS, F.M., DOMINGUES, F.J., MOORES, R.G. & LONG, C.L. (1963) The utilization of Schardinger dextrins by the rat. *Toxicol. Appl. Pharmacol.*, **5**, 257- 266. Submitted to WHO by Société Roquette Fréres, Lestrem, France.

ANTENUCCI, R.N. & PALMER, J.K. (1984) Enzymatic degradation of α- and ß-cyclodextrins by *Bacteroides* of the human colon. *J. Agric. Food Chem.* **32**, 1316-1321. Submitted to WHO by Société Roquette Fréres, Lestrem, France.

BLUMENTHAL, H., FLAMM, W.G., FORBES, A. & MUNRO, I. (1990) Unpublished report of a Science Advisory Group convened to review data on toxicity and food applications of ß-cyclodextrin. Submitted to WHO by Flamm Associates, Reston, VA, USA.

BUSCH, B., BIESEMEIER, J.A. & BECCI, P.J. (1985) Acute inhalation toxicity study of beta cyclodextrin in Sprague Dawley rats. Unpublished report No. 8456 of Food and Drug Research Laboratories Inc. submitted to WHO by Société Roquette Fréres, Lestrem, France

CZEIZEL, E. (1978) Study of the chromosomal mutagenic effect of beta-cyclodextrin in Long Evans rats. Unpublished report of the National Institute of Public Health, Budapest, Hungary. Submitted to WHO by Société Roquette Fréres, Lestrem, France.

DÓCZY, K. (1985) Report on the teratology study of beta-cyclodextrine in New Zealand white rabbits. Unpublished report of the Institute for Drug Research, Budapest, Hungary, submitted to WHO by Société Roquette Frères, Lestrem, France

DRUGA, A. (1985) Report on the teratology study of beta-cyclodextrin in LATI:HAN:Wistar rats. Unpublished report of the Institute for Drug Research, Budapest, Hungary, submitted to WHO by Société Roquette Frères, Lestrem, France

FLOURIÉ, B., MOLIS, C., ACHOUR, L., DUPAS, H., HATAT, C. & RAMBEAUD, J.C. (1992) Digestibility of ß-cyclodextrin in the human intestine. Unpublished report of INSERM U 290 submitted to WHO by Société Roquette Frères, Lestrem, France

FRANK, D.W., GRAY, J.E. & WEAVER, R.N. (1976) Cyclodextrin nephrosis in the rat. *Am. J. Pathol.*, **83**, 367-382. Submitted to WHO by Société Roquette Fréres, Lestrem, France.

GERGELY, V. (1982) Six months chronic toxicity study of beta-cyclodextrin in Long-Evans rats. Unpublished report. Submitted to WHO by Société Roquette Fréres, Lestrem, France.

GERLÓCZY, A., FÓNAGY, A. & SZEJTLI, J. (1981) Absorption and metabolism of ß-cyclodextrin by rats. Proceedings of the 1st International Symposium on Cyclodextrins, Budapest, Hungary, (Ed. J. Szejtli) Akadémiai Kiadó, Budapest; and Reidel Publishing, Dordrecht, The Netherlands. Submitted to WHO by Société Roquette Fréres, Lestrem, France.

GERLÓCZY, A., FÓNAGY, A., KERESZTES, P., PERLAKY, L. & SZEJTLI, J. (1985) Absorption, distribution, excretion and metabolism of orally administered ^{14}C-ß-cyclodextrin in rat. *Arzneimittel-Forsch./Drug Res.* **35**, 1042-1047. Submitted to WHO by Société Roquette Fréres, Lestrem, France.

HARASZTI, J. (1978) Twenty-four week oral toxicity study of beta-cyclodextrin in beagle dogs. Unpublished report of Institute of Obstetrics, Department of Surgery, Budapest, Hungary. Submitted to WHO by Société Roquette Fréres, Lestrem, France.

HIASA, Y., OSHIMA, M., KITAHORI, Y., YUASA, T., FUJITA, T., IWATA, C., MIYASHIRO, A. & KONISHI, N. (1981) Histochemical studies of ß-cyclodextrin nephrosis in rats. *J. Nara. Med. Ass.* **32**, 316-326.

HIASA, Y., OSHIMA, M., KITAHORI, Y., KONISHI, N., FUJITA, T. & YUASA, T. (1982) ß-cyclodextrin: Promoting effect on the development of renal tubular cell tumours in rats treated with *N*-ethyl-*N*-hydroxyethylnitrosamine. *J.Natl.Cancer Inst.*, **69**, 964- 967.

IGALI, S. (1978) Study of the gene-mutation inducing effect of beta-cyclodextrin by host- mediated assay. Unpublished report of the National Institute of Radiobiology, Budapest, Hungary. Submitted to WHO by Société Roquette Fréres, Lestrem, France.

IRIE, T., OTAGIRI, M., SUNADA, M., UEKAMA, K., OHTANI, Y., YAMADA, Y. & SUGIYAMA, Y. (1982) Cyclodextrin-induced hemolysis and shape changes of human erythrocytes *in vitro*. *J.Pharm.Dyn.*, **5**, 741-744.

JODAL, I., KANDRA, L., HARANGI, J., NÁNÁSI, P. & SZEJTLI, J. (1983) Unpublished report submitted to WHO

JODAL, I., KANDRA, L., HARANGI, J., NÁNÁSI, P. & SZEJTLI, J. (1984) *Stärke*, **36**, 140.

JELLINEK, H., KADAR, A. & CZEIZEL, E. (undated) Unpublished report of the 2nd Department of Pathology, Semmelweiss University of Medicine, Budapest, Hungary submitted to WHO by Société Roquette Frères, Lestrem, France

LEROY, P., OLIVIER, PH., WILS, D., COURBOIS, F. & MINET, P. (1990) Local tolerance tests in the rabbit: index of primary skin irritation; index of eye irritation, beta- cyclodextrose (Kleptose) Unpublished report No. 90014 of the Biotoxicology Laboratory, Roquette Frères submitted to WHO by Société Roquette Frères, Lestrem, France.

LEROY, P., OLIVIER, PH., JOURDAIN, R., MINET, P., WILS, D., VERWAERDE, F., POTIER, M.N., BONIFACE, M., DEMARQUILLY, C., SIOU, G. & GUFFROY, M. (1991) Teratogenicity study of orally administered ß-cyclodextrin in rats. Unpublished report No. 90021 of the Biotoxicology Laboratory, Roquette Frères submitted to WHO by Société Roquette Frères, Lestrem, France.

MAKITA, T., OJIMA, N., HASHIMOTO, Y., IDE, H., TSUJI, M. & FUJISAKI, Y. (1975) Chronic oral toxicity study of ß-Cyclodextrine (ß-CD) in rats. *Oyo Yakuri*, **10**, 449-458. Submitted to WHO by Société Roquette Frères, Lestrem, France.

MARZIN, D., VO PHI, H., NESSLANY, F., LAGACHE, D. & DEHOUCK, M.P. (1990) Mutagenicity test by investigating point mutation at the HPRT locus in V79 Chinese hamster cell culture (6-thioguanine resistance) carried out with the compound ß-cyclodextrine. Unpublished report of the Institute Pasteur de Lille submitted to WHO by Société Roquette Frères, Lestrem, France

MARZIN, D., VO PHI, H., NESSLANY, F., LAGACHE, D. & DEHOUCK, M.P. (1991) Test for chromosome aberrations by *in vitro* human lymphocyte metaphase analysis. Unpublished report of the Institute Pasteur de Lille submitted to WHO by Société Roquette Frères, Lestrem, France

MERCIER, O. (1990) Test to evaluate the sensitizing potential by topical applications in the guinea pig: the epicutaneous maximisation test. Unpublished report of Hazleton France No. 010360 submitted to WHO by Société Roquette Frères, Lestrem, France

MÉSZÁROS, J. & VETÉSI, F. (1982) A six month chronic toxicity study in Long-Evans rats; Expert opinion. Unpublished report submitted to WHO by Société Roquette Frères, Lestrem, France.

MIYAZAKI, Y., KAWAHARA, K. & NOZOE, M. (1979) Influence of cyclodextrin on mice. *Ann. Rep. Coll. Agric., Saga Univ.* **47**, 17-22. Submitted to WHO by Société Roquette Fréres, Lestrem, France.

OLIVIER, P., VERWAERDE, F. & HEDGES, A.R. (1991) Subchronic toxicity of orally administered Beta-Cyclodextrin in rats. *J. American Coll. Tox.*, **10**, 407-419. Submitted to WHO by Société Roquette Fréres, Lestrem, France.

PARÁDI, E. (1987) Study of the recessive lethal mutation-inducing effect of beta-cyclodextrin by Drosophila SLRL assay. Unpublished report of 31st August 1987. Submitted to WHO by Société Roquette Fréres, Lestrem, France.

PERRIN, J.H., FIELD, F.P., HANSEN, D.A., MUFSON, R.A. & TOROSIAN, G. (1978). ß-cyclodextrin as an aid to peritoneal dialysis. Renal toxicity of ß-cyclodextrin in the rat. *Chem. Path. Pharmacol.*, 373-376. Submitted to WHO by Société Roquette Fréres, Lestrem, France.

REAGAN, E.L. & BECCI, P.J. (1985) Primary dermal irritation study of beta cyclodextrin in New Zealand White rabbits. Unpublished report No. 8456A of Food and Drug Research Laboratories Inc. submitted to WHO by Société Roquette Frères, Lestrem, France.

SEBESTYÉN, G. (1979) Three-months oral toxicity study of beta-cyclodextrin in Long-Evans rats. Report of Chinoin Pharmaceutical and Chemical Works. Submitted to WHO by Société Roquette Fréres, Lestrem, France.

SEBESTYÉN, G. (1980) The acute LD_{50} values of beta-cyclodextrin in CFY rats, CFLP mice and mongrel dogs. Report of Chinoin Pharmaceutical and Chemical Works. Submitted to WHO by Société Roquette Fréres, Lestrem, France.

SMITH, T.G., COX, R.A., BUIST, D.P., CROOK, D., HADLEY, J.C. & C. GOPINATH (1992) Beta-cyclodextrin toxicity to dogs by repeated dietary administration for 13 weeks. Preliminary study. Unpublished report No. ROQ 2/911089 of Huntingdon Research Centre Ltd. Submitted to WHO by Société Roquette Frères, Lestrem, France

SUZUKI, M. & SATO, A. (1985) Nutritional significance of cyclodextrins: Indigestibility and hypolipemic effect of α-cyclodextrin. *J. Nutr. Sci. Vitaminol.*, **31**, 209-223. Submitted to WHO by Société Roquette Fréres, Lestrem, France.

SZABO, P., FERENCZY, T., SERFÓZÓ, J., SZEJTLI, J. & LIPTÁK, A. (1981a) Absorption and elimination of cyclodextrin derivatives by rabbits and rats. Proceedings of the 1st International Symposium on Cyclodextrins, Budapest, Hungary, (Ed. J. Szejtli) Akadémiai Kiadó: Budapest and Reidel Publishing: Dordrecht, Holland, 115. Submitted to WHO by Société Roquette Fréres, Lestrem, France.

SZABO, P., FERENCZY, T., SERFÓZÓ, J. AND SZEJTLI, J. (1981b) Investigation of the absorption and elimination conditions of ß-cyclodextrin and its derivatives. Drugs, Biochemistry and Metabolism, MATRAFÜRED, 167-171.

SZEJTLI, J., GERLÓCZY, A. & FÓNAGY, A. (1980) Intestinal absorption of ^{14}C-labelled ß-cyclodextrin in rats. *Arzneimittel-Forsch./Drug Res.*, **30**, 808-810. Submitted to WHO by Société Roquette Fréres, Lestrem, France.

SZEJTLI, J. & BUDAI, Z. (1976) *Acta Chimica Acad. Sci. Hung.* **91**, 73-80

SZEJTLI, J., CSERHÁTI, Y. & SZÖGYI, M. (1986) Interactions between Cyclodextrins and cell membrane phospholipids. *Carbohydrate Polymers*, **6**, 35-49.

TURY, E., DOBOS-KOVÁCS, M & SOMOGYVÁRI, K. (1978) The pathological and histo-pathological study of Beagle dogs subjected to beta-cyclodextrin treatment for twenty-four weeks. Unpublished report of the Departments of Surgery and Pathology, University of Veterinary Science, Budapest, Hungary. Submitted to WHO by Société Roquette Fréres, Lestrem, France.

TURY, E., DOBOS-KOVÁCS, M & SOMOGYVÁRI, K. (1979) The pathological and histo-pathological study of Long Evans rats subjected to beta-cyclodextrin treatment for three months. Unpublished report of the Departments of Surgery and Pathology, University of Veterinary Science, Budapest, Hungary. Submitted to WHO by Société Roquette Fréres, Lestrem, France.

Van DOKKUM, W. & Van der BEEK, E.J. (1990) Tolerance of ß-cyclodextrin in man. Unpublished report No. V 90.419 of TNO, to AVEBE, Foxhol, The Netherlands, submitted to WHO by Dr R Scheuplein, USFDA, Washington, DC, USA.

WEILL, N. (1987) Unpublished report No. 709207 of Hazleton-IFT submitted to WHO by Société Roquette Frères, Lestrem, France

WEILL, N. (1988) Unpublished report No. 801201 of Hazleton-IFT submitted to WHO by Société Roquette Frères, Lestrem, France.

SODIUM IRON EDTA

First draft prepared by
Dr I.C. Munro
CanTox Inc., Mississauga, Ontario
Canada

1   EXPLANATION

The Committee was asked to comment on the safety of sodium iron (III) ethylenediaminetetraacetate (sodium iron EDTA, sodium iron edetate, NaFeEDTA, NaFe(III)EDTA) as a dietary supplement for use in supervised food fortification programmes in populations in which iron-deficiency anaemia is endemic. The Committee was informed that use of iron in this form would be restricted to this specific application and would be supervised.

Sodium iron EDTA has not previously been evaluated by the Joint FAO/WHO Expert Committee on Food Additives. However, disodium and calcium disodium EDTA were evaluated at the seventeenth meeting (Annex 1 reference 32). An ADI of 2.5 mg EDTA CaNa$_2$EDTA/kg body weight/day was established. Sodium iron EDTA was placed on the agenda to provide an assessment of its safety for use in supervised food fortification programmes in populations in which iron deficiency anaemia is endemic.

With respect to iron, a provisional maximum tolerable daily intake of 0.8 mg/kg/bw was established by the Committee at the twenty-seventh meeting (Annex 1, reference 62). The view stated at the twenty-sixth meeting (Annex 1, reference 59), that the tolerable daily intake should not be used as a guide for fortifying processed foods, was reiterated. This monograph discusses the safety of NaFeEDTA for food fortification in developing countries.

2.   BIOLOGICAL DATA

2.1   Biochemical aspects

The biochemistry of EDTA metal complexes is inextricably tied to their chemical properties. An understanding of these chemical properties is essential in interpreting the biochemistry and toxicology of EDTA metal complexes. A brief discussion of the chemical properties of EDTA metal complexes is presented here to facilitate understanding of the material that follows.

Ethylenediaminetetraacetic acid (EDTA) is a hexadentate chelator capable of combining stoichiometrically with virtually every metal in the periodic table (Chaberck and Martell, 1959). With divalent or trivalent metal ions a neutral or anionic metal chelate results. The metal is largely prevented from reacting with competing anions and its solubility is greatly increased. The effectiveness of EDTA as a chelate for a particular metal ion is given by its stability constant with the metal ion. Chelation potential is affected by pH, the molar ratio of chelate to metal ion, and the presence of competing metal ions capable of forming complexes with EDTA (Plumb et al., 1950; Martell, 1960; Hart, 1984). The stability constants for different metal-EDTA complexes vary considerably and any metal which is capable of forming a strong complex with EDTA will at least partially displace another metal.

Of the nutritionally important metals, Fe^{3+} has the highest stability constant (log k of 25.1), followed by Cu^{2+} with 18.4, Zn^{2+} with 16.1, Fe^{2+} with 14.6, Ca^{2+} with 10.6, mg^{2+} with 8.7 and Na^+ with 1.7 (West and Sykes, 1960). The situation is somewhat complicated by each metal having an optimum pH for chelate formation ranging from pH 1 for Fe^{3+}, to pH 3 for Cu^{2+}, pH 4 for Zn^{2+}, pH 5 for Fe^{2+}, pH 7.5 for Ca^{2+}, and pH 10 for mg^{2+} (West and Sykes, 1960). When NaFeEDTA is ingested with foods, the Fe^{3+} ion would be expected to remain firmly bound to the EDTA moiety during passage through the gastric juice, but could be exchanged for Cu^{2+}, Zn^{2+}, Fe^{2+} or Ca^{2+} in the duodenum. Similarly when Na_2EDTA and Na_2CaEDTA are consumed with foods, the Na^+ and Ca^{2+} ions would be predominantly exchanged in the gastric juice for Fe^{3+} ions, which could again in turn be exchanged for Cu^{2+}, Zn^{2+}, Fe^{2+} or Ca^{2+} further down the gastrointestinal tract. The extent to which the metal EDTA complexes form is dependent on the pH and the concentration of competing metals as well as competing ligands. The lower stability constant and higher pH optimum of the mg-EDTA chelate make reaction with this metal less likely.

An appreciation of the chelating properties of EDTA with respect to iron provide the basis of our understanding of the observed effects of EDTA on food iron absorption. Ferric food iron is poorly absorbed by human beings because it is precipitated from solution above pH 3.5 unless suitable complexing agents are present. It may therefore be partially insoluble in the upper small intestine where most nonhaem iron is absorbed (Conrad and Schade, 1968; MacPhail et al., 1981).

When EDTA is present in a meal, iron (primarily Fe^{3+}) remains complexed with EDTA under the acidic conditions prevailing in the stomach. The chelate holds the iron in solution as the pH rises in the upper small intestine, but the strength of the complex is progressively reduced allowing at least partial exchange with other metals and the release of some of the iron for absorption. There is convincing evidence that iron chelated by EDTA (NaFeEDTA) is available for absorption via the physiologically regulated pathways responsible for iron uptake (Candela et al., 1984). The results of absorption studies with NaFeEDTA indicate that iron is dissociated from the EDTA moiety prior to absorption. The results of these studies are summarized in Section 2.1.1.

2.1.1   Absorption and excretion

2.1.1.1   Absorption and excretion of Fe from NaFeEDTA - Injection studies

When NaFeEDTA is injected intravenously into rats most of the iron (70-90%) is lost through the urine within 24 hours (Najarajan *et al.*, 1964; Anghileri, 1967). A small proportion enters the physiological iron pool destined primarily for haemoglobin synthesis probably because of the slow release of iron to the iron transport protein, transferrin, in the circulation (Bates *et al.*, 1967). After intramuscular or intraperitoneal injection a greater proportion of the iron is available for physiological exchange with compartments in the bone marrow and liver. The longer contact time between transferrin and EDTA, allows for greater transfer of iron from the chelate to the physiological transport protein (Rubin *et al.*, 1970).

FeEDTA administered intravenously to humans was almost quantitatively excreted in urine (Lapinleimu and Wegelius, 1959).

2.1.1.2   Absorption and excretion of Fe from NaFeEDTA - oral studies

Human iron deficiency anaemia was successfully treated with FeEDTA given orally with 84% of labelled FeEDTA excreted in the faeces and none in the urine. Red cells, however, contained labelled Fe and reticulocytosis occurred (Will and Vilter, 1954).

Studies carried out in swine using a doubly labelled $Na^{55}Fe[2-^{14}C]EDTA$ preparation demonstrated rapid transfer of ^{55}Fe to the plasma with a peak at 1 hour and subsequent incorporation of 4.6% of the administered dose into circulating haemoglobin (Candela *et al.*, 1984). A small fraction (0.3%) of the ^{55}Fe administered was excreted in the urine. In contrast to the ^{55}Fe only a small percentage of the ^{14}C could be detected in the plasma at any time. Absorption occurred over an extended period (5-20 hours). A total of about 5% of the ^{14}C labelled EDTA was eventually absorbed in the duodenum and jejunum and quantitatively excreted in the urine.

In a parallel experiment when 5 mg Fe as $Na^{59}FeEDTA$ was given to six fasting human volunteers, mean radioiron absorption as measured by red blood cell utilization was 12.0%. Only 0.3% of the administered dose of iron was excreted in the urine. The studies demonstrate that Fe and EDTA are absorbed independently when NaFeEDTA is administered by mouth (Candela *et al.*, 1984).

Similar conclusions were reached in an earlier human absorption study carried out by MacPhail *et al.* (1981). $Na^{59}FeEDTA$ was administered to human volunteers. Between 3 and 25% of the ^{59}Fe was absorbed, but less than 1% of the administered ^{59}Fe appeared in the urine over the subsequent 24 hours. All ^{59}Fe absorbed in the form of the intact Na^{59}FeEDTA complex would be expected to be excreted in the urine within 24 hours (based on the results of Nagarajan *et al.*, 1964 and Anghileri, 1967) demonstrating again that most of the iron is released from the EDTA complex before absorption. Similar conclusions have been reached with another iron chelator (nitrilotriacetic acid), the properties of which have been studied extensively in experimental animals (Simpson and Peters, 1984).

2.1.1.3 Absorption and excretion of EDTA from EDTA metal chelates

Rats

^{14}C-labelled CaNa$_2$EDTA, when fed to rats at 50 mg/kg bw, was absorbed only to an extent of 2 to 4%; 80 to 90% of the dose appeared in the faeces within 24 hours, and absorption was still apparent at 48 hours. At the low pH of the stomach the calcium chelate is dissociated with subsequent precipitation of the free acid (EDTA), and this is only slowly redissolved in the intestine (Foreman *et al.*, 1953).

In feeding experiments in rats receiving disodium EDTA at dietary levels of 0.5, 1.0 or 5.0%, the faeces contained 99.4, 98.2 and 97.5% of the excreted material (Yang, 1964).

Similar experiments conducted also in rats gave essentially the same results. Thirty-two hours after a single dose of 95 mg disodium EDTA/rat, 93% was recovered from the colon. After doses of 47.5, 95.0 and 142.5 mg disodium EDTA the amount of EDTA recovered in the urine was directly proportional to the dose given, suggesting that EDTA was absorbed from the gastrointestinal tract by passive diffusion. The motility of the intestine was not affected by the compound (Chan, 1964).

When 200 mg CaNa$_2$EDTA was introduced into the duodenum of rats an absorption rate of 6.5 to 26% was observed (Srbrova and Teisinger, 1957).

The maximum radioactivity in the urine after application of ^{14}C-labelled CaNa$_2$EDTA to the skin was only 10 ppm (0.001%) (Foreman and Trujillo, 1954).

Humans

Experiments in humans also revealed poor absorption; only 2.5% of a 3 g dose given was excreted in the urine (Srbrova and Teisinger, 1957). These authors also confirmed the dissociation of the calcium chelate in the stomach. A dose of 1.5 mg of ^{14}C-labelled CaNa$_2$EDTA given in a gelatine capsule to normal healthy men was absorbed to an extent of 5% (Foreman and Trujillo, 1954).

The absorption of the EDTA moiety from orally administered NaFeEDTA has not been measured directly in humans. However physicochemical considerations indicate that EDTA absorption from NaFeEDTA should be similar to that from other metal complexes, such as $CaNa_2EDTA$ and CrEDTA. As described above, poor absorption of the intact NaFeEDTA can be inferred from the measurements of urinary radioiron excretion after the oral administration of $Na^{59}FeEDTA$ made by MacPhail and coworkers in 1981.

Similar results have been obtained with a tightly bound chelate, $^{51}CrEDTA$ from which any released metal is very poorly absorbed (Bjarnason et al., 1983; Aabakken and Osnes, 1990). Only 1-5% of a dose of $^{51}CrEDTA$ given in a fasting state is absorbed by the healthy intestinal mucosa. In the presence of disorders of the gastrointestinal tract the absorption may be doubled. The $^{51}CrEDTA$ that is absorbed appears to be taken up through intercellular junctions as the intact complex. The amount absorbed has been used as a measure of the integrity of the bowel mucosa.

In summary, most of the iron in NaFeEDTA is released to the physiological mucosal uptake system before absorption. Only a very small fraction of the NaFeEDTA complex (less than 1%) is absorbed intact and this is completely excreted in the urine. An additional small fraction (less than 5%) of the EDTA moiety is absorbed, presumably bound to other metals in the gastrointestinal tract, and is also completely eliminated in the urine.

2.1.1.4 Bioavailability of iron from NaFeEDTA

The results of iron absorption studies comparing the bioavailability of iron from $FeSO_4$ and NaFeEDTA fortified foods are listed in Table 1. For purposes of comparison the individual absorption values have been standardized to a reference absorption of 40% to remove the influence of varying iron requirements in different subjects. A reference absorption value of 40% is assumed to represent borderline iron deficiency (Hallberg et al., 1978). The bioavailability of iron from $FeSO_4$ varies over a wide range and correlates with the relative proportions of enhancers and inhibitors known to be present in the meals.

Table 1. Comparison of iron absorption from meals of different iron bioavailability fortified with ferrous sulfate or NaFeEDTA; Standardized Iron Absorption (%)[a]

Components of Meal		A FeSO$_4$	B NaFeEDTA	Ratio B/A	Reference
1.	Rice Milk	1.7	4.5	2.6	Viteri et al., 1978
2.	Beans, Maize, Coffee	2.0	5.3	2.7	Viteri et al., 1978
3.	Egyptian flat bread[b]	2.1	5.3	2.5	el Guindi et al., 1988
4.	Bran	2.7	7.8	2.9	MacPhail et al., 1981
5.	Beans, Plantain, Rice, Maize, Soy[c]	3.1	7.0	2.3	Layrisse and Martinez-Torres, 1977
6.	Rice	3.9	11.5	2.9	MacPhail and Bothwell, unpublished, 1992
7.	Maize Meal	4.0	8.2	2.1	MaPhail et al., 1981
8.	Beans, Plantain, Rice, Maize, Soy, Orange Juice[c]	4.2	7.4	1.8	Layrisse and Martinez-Torres, 1977
9.	Beans, Plantain, Rice, Maize, Soy, Meat[c]	4.3	9.6	2.2	Layrisse and Martinez-Torres, 1977
10.	Potato	5.9	7.3	1.2	Lamparelli et al., 1987
11.	Wheat	6.2	14.6	2.3	Martinez-Torres et al., 1979
12.	Milk	10.2	16.8	1.6	Layrisse and Martinez-Torres, 1977
13.	Sweet Manioc	14.1	16.6	1.2	Martinez-Torres et al., 1979
14.	Sugar cane Syrup[c]	33.1	10.8	0.3	Martinez-Torres et al., 1979

a. Geometric means standarized to a reference (Ferrous ascorbate) absorption of 40%
b. A mixture of FeSO$_4$ and Na$_2$EDTA was used in this study.
c. Comparison between FeSO$_4$ and NaFeEDTA not in the same individuals.

Enhanced bioavailability was most marked in meals with poor FeSO$_4$ bioavailability (FeSO$_4$ absorptions less than 4%). Between 2.1 to 2.9 times as much iron was absorbed under such circumstances. This point is exemplified by the results of the study by Viteri et al. (1978) (see Table 1) in which iron absorption from a NaFeEDTA-fortified meal of beans, maize, and coffee was 2.7 times greater than that from the same meal containing $FeSO_4$ (Viteri et al., 1978).

In contrast, the absorption of iron from NaFeEDTA eaten with identical meals varies only two to three fold. More iron was absorbed from the meals containing NaFeEDTA in all but one case in which Na_2EDTA and $FeSO_4$ were eaten with sugar cane syrup (see Table 1). The absorption of Fe from NaFeEDTA has been studied in a wide variety of meals. Comparisons with iron absorption from simple iron salts have not always been made. However, some studies provide useful information about the suitability of three staple food items as potential vehicles for fortification with NaFeEDTA. This information is summarized in Table 2. Some studies listed in Table 1 have been included under the appropriate categories (all values are corrected to 40% reference absorption, or a serum ferritin of 27 $\mu g/l$). It is evident that approximately 10% of the fortification iron added would be absorbed by iron deficient individuals if these staple foods were used as the vehicle for delivering the fortificant.

Table 2. Percentage iron absorption from meals containing NaFe(III)EDTA

Vehicle	No. of Studies	Standardized Iron Absorption (Range)	References
Wheat	4	10.1 (5.3 - 14.6)	Martinez-Torres et al., 1979 and el Guindi et al., 1988
Maize	7	9.1 (7.6 - 12.0)	Martinez-Torres et al., 1979 and MacPhail et al., 1981
Cassava	3	13.5 (11.0 - 16.4)	Martinez-Torres et al., 1979

2.1.1.5 Effect of NaFeEDTA on bioavailability of intrinsic food iron

Conclusions drawn from much of the experimental work on food iron absorption and iron fortification are based on the observation that soluble iron added to a meal and the intrinsic nonhaem food iron behave as a common pool, which is equally susceptible to enhancers and inhibitors of iron absorption present in the meal (Cook et al., 1972; Hallberg and Bjorn-Rasmussen, 1972); NaFeEDTA shares this property. When Na[59]FeEDTA was added to meals containing foods labelled intrinsically with [55]Fe, the ratio between the proportions of iron absorbed from the two sources was close to unity (Layrisse and Martinez-Torres, 1977; Matrinez-Torres et al., 1979; MacPhail et al., 1981), with the exception of one study in which Na[59]FeEDTA fortified sugar was sprinkled onto [55]Fe-labelled maize immediately before it was eaten (MacPhail et al., 1981). These results indicate that the Na[59]FeEDTA equilibrates with the common pool, since without such equilibration, the amount of food iron absorbed would be much lower than the amount absorbed from NaFeEDTA (MacPhail et al., 1981). Inadequate mixing of the NaFeEDTA-fortified sugar with the maize meal probably accounted for the lack of equilibration in the one inconsistent study reported by Macphail *et al.* (1981). These results reveal another important property of NaFeEDTA. Equilibration of NaFeEDTA with the common pool iron improves the bioavailability of the intrinsic food iron as well. Therefore NaFeEDTA improves iron balance by supplying iron in a form less affected by dietary inhibitors, but also improves the absorption of nonhaem iron in the meal derived from other sources.

This point is further illustrated by the results of a number of studies which demonstrate that the positive effects of EDTA on iron absorption are shared by other elements of the common pool, such as another iron salt added to the meal. When $FeSO_4$ and NaFeEDTA were fed to humans on separate days in the same type of meal (maize porridge), iron absorption from the NaFeEDTA fortified meal was significantly better. However the iron from $FeSO_4$ was as well absorbed as that from NaFeEDTA when they were fed together in the same meal (Macphail *et al.*, 1981; Martinez-Torres *et al.*, 1979). More direct evidence of reciprocal exchange between food iron and iron added as NaFeEDTA was provided by experiments in which subjects were given maize porridge fortified with equimolar quantities of [59]$FeSO_4$ and Na[55]FeEDTA (McPhail *et al.*, 1981). The ratio between the two isotopes was almost the same in the meal and the urine. This implies that exchange of iron between $FeSO_4$ and NaFeEDTA must occur before absorption of the chelate, since only the small amount of iron (less than 1%) absorbed as the intact chelate would subsequently appear in the urine (for explanation see section 2.1).

2.1.1.6 The effect of Na_2EDTA on iron absorption

Na_2EDTA is widely used as a food additive to prevent oxidative damage by free metals. Since Na_2EDTA readily chelates iron in the gut to form NaFeEDTA, its effect on iron absorption is of interest. In a recent study (el Guindi *et al.*, 1988) Na_2EDTA was added, together with an equimolar quantity of iron as $FeSO_4$, to bread with a high concentration of phytate (an inhibitor of iron absorption). The combination was associated with a 2.6x enhancement in iron absorption when compared with results with $FeSO_4$ used alone. Mean percentage iron absorption was approximately equivalent to that reported in other similar studies using NaFeEDTA. It is evident that the same effect on iron absorption can be achieved in meals containing compounds that inhibit iron absorption by adding Na_2EDTA and a soluble iron salt as is the case for adding NaFeEDTA.

The effects of Na_2EDTA on iron absorption appear to be influenced by the molar ratio of EDTA to iron. Earlier work suggested that increasing the molar ratio of Na_2EDTA to Fe was associated with a progressive reduction in iron absorption (Cook and Monsen, 1976).

These observations have been extended recently: iron absorption from a series of rice meals containing Na_2EDTA and iron in a molar ratio of 1:1 was compared to rice containing Na_2EDTA and iron in molar ratios (EDTA:Fe) ranging from 0:1 to 4:1. Statistically significant enhancement of absorption occurred at ratios of Fe:EDTA between 1:4 and 1:1. The enhancing effect of EDTA on iron absorption appeared to be maximal at a molar ratio (EDTA:Fe) of approximately 1:2, not 1:1 as previously assumed. At this molar ratio over three times as much iron was absorbed from the EDTA containing meal as was the case for the control meal containing no EDTA (MacPhail and Bothwell, unpublished data, 1992).

2.1.2   Distribution

After parenteral administration to rats, 95 to 98% of injected ^{14}C-labelled $CaNa_2EDTA$ appeared in the urine within six hours. All the material passed through the body unchanged. Peak plasma levels were found approximately 50 minutes after administration. Less than 0.1% of the material was oxidized to [14]CO_2, and no organs concentrated the substance. After i.v. injection, $CaNa_2EDTA$ passed rapidly out of the vascular systems to mix with approximately 90% of the body water, but did not pass into the red blood cells and was cleared through the kidney by tubular excretion as well as glomerular filtration (Foreman et al., 1953). The same was also found in man using ^{14}C-labelled $CaNa_2EDTA$. Three thousand milligrams were given i.v. to two subjects and were almost entirely excreted within 12 to 16 hours (Srbrova and Teisinger, 1957). These results indicate that intact $CaNa_2EDTA$, and presumably other EDTA metal complexes are rapidly excreted and do not accumulate.

2.1.3   Biotransformation

Neither the iron nor the EDTA moiety of NaFeEDTA undergoes biotransformation. Evidence for this conclusion comes from studies discussed in the previous section which indicated that both EDTA and iron are excreted unchanged following ingestion of NaFeEDTA.

2.1.4   Influence of EDTA compounds on the biochemistry of metals

EDTA removes about 1.4% of the total iron from ferritin at pH 7.4 to form an iron chelate (Westerfeld, 1961). Transfer of Fe from Fe-transferrin to EDTA *in vitro* occurs at a rate of less than 1% in 24 hours. *In vivo* studies in rabbits demonstrated transfer of iron only from FeEDTA to transferrin and not the reverse. It appeared that tissue iron became available to chelating agents including EDTA only when an excess of iron was present (Cleton et al., 1963). Equal distribution between a mixture of EDTA and siderophilin was obtained only at EDTA:siderophilin ratios of 20-25:1 (Rubin, 1961).

Addition of 1% Na_2EDTA to a diet containing more than optimal amounts of iron and calcium lowered the absorption and storage or iron in rats and increased the amount present in plasma and urine. The metabolism of calcium, however, was apparently unaffected (Larsen et al., 1960). A diet containing 0.15 mg of iron, 4.26 of calcium and 1 mg of EDTA/rat (equivalent to 100 ppm (0.01%) in the diet) for 83 days had no influence on calcium and iron metabolism, e.g. the iron content of liver and plasma (Hawkins et al., 1962).

Copper absorption and retention were improved at 500 mg EDTA/kg but not at 200 mg or 1 000 mg EDTA/kg. Apart from a very small increase in urinary copper excretion, dietary EDTA had no influence on copper metabolism (Hurrell et al., 1993).

$CaNa_2EDTA$ increased the excretion of zinc (Perry and Perry, 1959), and was active in increasing the availability of zinc in soybean containing diets to poults (Kratzer et al., 1959). $CaNa_2EDTA$ enhanced the excretion of Co, Hg, Mn, Ni, Pb, Ti and W (Foreman, 1961). The treatment of heavy metal poisoning with $CaNa_2EDTA$ has become so well established that its use for more commonly seen metal poisonings, e.g. lead, is no longer reported in the literature (Foreman, 1961). EDTA could not prevent the accumulation of ^{90}Sr, [106]Ru, [141]Ba and [226]Ra in the skeleton. [91]Y , [239]Pu and [238]U responded fairly well to EDTA, the excretion being accelerated (Catsch, 1961).

Food fortification with NaFeEDTA may be expected to increase Zn and Cu absorption and retention but not Ca nor Mg. A diet containing RDA quantities of each metal (800 mg Ca and, 350 mg, 10 mg Zn, and 2 mg Cu) which was fortified with 10 mg Fe as NaFeEDTA would contain a 1.5 molar excess of EDTA over Zn, an 8-fold molar excess of EDTA over Cu, but 80 times less EDTA than Ca and 50 times less EDTA than mg on a molar basis. The small quantity of chelate with respect to Ca and mg would be unlikely to have any detrimental effect. Both NaFeEDTA and NaEDTA may increase the absorption and retention of Zn and Cu when added to low bioavailability diets. This conclusion is supported by experiments with turkey poults (Kratzer et al., 1959), chicks (Scott and Ziegler, 1963) and rats (Forbes, 1961) which have demonstrated that Zn bioavailability and animal growth is improved when Na_2EDTA is added at 150-300 mg/kg to animal rations based on soybean protein isolate. The enhancing effect of EDTA on zinc absorption in these studies can be explained by a combination of two factors. Firstly, EDTA forms soluble chelates with Zn from which the metal is potentially absorbable, and secondly, Zn is prevented from forming non-absorbable complexes with phytic acid. EDTA does not enhance Zn absorption when absorption inhibitors are absent from the meal as evidenced by the observation that Na_2EDTA (1 000 mg/kg) improved Zn absorption in rats fed a casein-based diet with added phytic acid, but had no effect in the absence of phytic acid (Oberleas et al., 1966).

Other chelating substances can also enhance Zn absorption from low bioavailability diets. Vohra and Kratzer compared the growth promoting effect of chelates with stability constants (log k) for Zn varying from 5.3 to 18.8 in turkey poults fed zinc deficient diets based on soy protein isolate. They found that ethylenediaminediacetic acid-dipropionic acid, hydroxyethyl-EDTA, and EDTA (stability constants 14.5, 14.5 and 16.1, respectively) were the most effective (Vohra & Kratzer, 1964).

These earlier observations were made with Na_2EDTA. However, NaFeEDTA has been shown to have similar properties in a recent study. Zinc, copper, and calcium balances were performed in rats fed low Zn (6.1 mg/kg) soybean based diets containing 36 mg/kg added Fe as either ferrous sulfate or NaFeEDTA. In some experimental groups additional Na_2EDTA was added to the diet containing NaFeEDTA to give dietary EDTA levels of 200, 500 and 1 000 mg/kg. Changing the iron compound in the diet from ferrous sulfate to NaFeEDTA at a level of 200 mg/kg increased apparent Zn absorption, urinary Zn excretion and Zn retention significantly (p < 0.05), but caused no changes in Cu nor Ca absorption or excretion. Increasing the dietary EDTA level to 500 mg/kg (molar ratio EDTA:Zn, 19:1) and 1 000 mg/kg (molar ratio EDTA:Zn, 38:1) further increased both Zn absorption and urinary Zn excretion. At the highest dietary EDTA level (1 000 mg/kg), Zn retention was significantly higher than with no dietary EDTA, but lower than with 500 mg/kg EDTA. This resulted from an increase in urinary excretion of Zn to 15.6% of intake. Similar results were obtained with a Zn-sufficient (30 mg/kg) soybean diets, but more EDTA was required to achieve optimal ratios for improved absorption.

These studies demonstrate that an 11-fold molar excess of EDTA over Cu increased Cu absorption and retention but that neither a 4.5 nor 23-fold molar excess had a significant effect. A human diet containing the RDA for Zn and Cu which was fortified with 10 mg Fe as NaFeEDTA would be expected to contain a 1.5 molar excess of EDTA over Zn and an 8-fold molar excess of EDTA over Cu. NaFeEDTA fortification would therefore be expected to have very little effect on Zn and Cu balance. A small beneficial effect could occur in meals containing little Zn or Cu or large quantities of phytate (Hurrell et al., 1993).

The applicability of the observations made in experimental animals to human nutrition has been confirmed by recent observations made by Hurrell's group. The metabolism of Zn and Ca was studied using a stable isotope technique in 10 adult women fed a breakfast meal of bread rolls made from 100 g high extraction wheat flour and fortified with 5 mg Fe as $FeSO_4$ or NaFeEDTA. The test meals contained a 3.3 molar excess of EDTA over Zn but some 10-fold less EDTA than Ca. Changing the Fe fortification compound from ferrous sulfate to NaFeEDTA significantly increased ^{70}Zn absorption (p < 0.05) from this meal from 20.9% to 33.5%. Urinary ^{70}Zn excretion also rose from 0.3% to 0.9%. Calcium metabolism was similar with the two different iron compounds (Davidsson et al, 1993).

Earlier studies using less precise methodology have led to similar conclusions. Adding NaFeEDTA to a low bioavailability Guatemalan meal did not influence Zn absorption by human subjects. However, as these workers measured Zn absorption based on plasma Zn concentrations after ingesting 25 mg Zn with a meal, the molar concentration of EDTA was some 10-fold less than that of Zn and an improvement in Zn absorption would not be expected (Solomons et al. (1979).

Finally, no significant changes in plasma Zn concentration were observed in field studies in which NaFeEDTA was used as a food fortificant over a two year period (Viteri et al., 1983, Ballot et al., 1989b).

2.1.5   Effects on enzymes and other biochemical parameters

EDTA had a lowering effect on serum cholesterol level when given orally or i.v. It may have acted by decreasing the capacity of serum to transport cholesterol (Gould, 1961). Disodium EDTA had a pyridoxin-like effect on the tryptophan metabolism of patients with porphyria or scleroderma, due to a partial correction of imbalance of polyvalent cations (Lelievre and Betz, 1961).

In vitro, 0.0033 M EDTA inhibited the respiration of liver homogenates and of isolated mitochondria of liver and kidney (Lelievre and Betz, 1961). The acetylation of sulfanilamide by a liver extract was also inhibited (Lelievre, 1960). EDTA stimulated glucuronide synthesis in rat liver, kidney and intestines but inhibited the process in guinea-pig liver (Pogell and Leloir, 1961; Miettinen and Leskinen, 1962). Of the heavy metal-containing enzymes, EDTA at a concentration of about 10^{-3} M inhibited aldehyde oxidase and homogentisinase. Succinic dehydrogenase, xanthine oxidase, NADH-cytochrome reductase and ceruloplasmin (oxidation of p-phenylenediamine) were not inhibited (Westerfeld, 1961). Disodium EDTA was found to be a strong inhibitor for δ-aminolevulinic acid dehydrogenase, 5.5×10^{-6} M causing 50% inhibition (Gibson *et al.*, 1955). The i.p. injection of 4.2 mmol/kg bw (equivalent to 1722 mg/kg bw) $CaNa_2EDTA$ caused in rats an inhibition of the alkaline phosphatase of liver, prostate and serum up to four days depending on the dose administered; zinc restored the activity (Nigrovic, 1964).

In vitro, EDTA inhibited blood coagulation by chelating Ca. The complete coagulation inhibition of human blood required 0.65-1.0 mg/ml. The i.v. injection of 79-200 mg EDTA/rabbit had no effect on blood coagulation (Dyckerhoff *et al.*, 1942).

I.v. injections of Na_2EDTA and $CaNa_2EDTA$ had some pharmacological effect on the blood pressure of cats; 0-20 mg/kg bw $CaNa_2EDTA$ (as Ca) produce a slight rise; 20-50 mg/kg, a biphasic response; and 50 mg/kg, a clear depression (Marquardt and Schumacher, 1957).

One per cent Na_2EDTA enhances the absorption of ^{14}C-labelled acidic, neutral and basic compounds (mannitol, inulin, decamethenium, sulfanilic acid and EDTA itself) from isolated segments of rat intestine, probably due to an increased permeability of the intestinal wall (Schanker and Johnson, 1961).

2.2   Toxicological studies

2.2.1   Acute toxicity studies

The results of acute toxicity studies with disodium EDTA are summarized in Table 3.

Table 3. Results of acute toxicity studies with disodium EDTA.

Animal	Route	LD_{50} (mg/kg bw)	References
Rat	oral	2 000 - 2 200	Yang, 1964
Rabbit	oral	2 300	Shibata, 1956
	i.v.	47[a]	Shibata, 1956

[a]Dose depending on the rate of infusion

The results of acute toxicity studies with Ca-disodium EDTA are summarized in Table 4.

Table 4. Results of acute toxicity studies with Ca-disodium EDTA.

Animal	Route	LD_{50} (mg/kg bw)	References
Rat	oral	10 000±740	Oser et al., 1963
Rabbit	oral	7 000 approx.	Oser et al., 1963
	i.p.	500 approx.	Bauer et al., 1952
Dog	oral	12 000 approx.	Oser et al., 1963

The oral LD_{50} in rats is not affected by the presence of food in the stomach or by pre-existing deficiency in Ca, Fe, Cu or Mn (Oser et al., 1963).

Oral doses of over 250 mg/animal cause diarrhoea in rats (Foreman et al., 1953).

There are many reports in the literature on kidney damage by parenteral over-dosage of CaEDTA. A review was given by Lechnit (1961). Lesions simulating "versene nephrosis" in man have also been produced in rats. Disodium EDTA in doses of 400-500 mg i.p. for 21 days caused severe hydropic degeneration of the proximal convoluted tubules of the kidneys. $CaNa_2EDTA$ produced only minimal focal hydropic changes in 58% of animals, disappearing almost two weeks after stopping the injections (Reuber and Schmieller, 1962).

2.2.2   Short-term toxicity studies

2.2.2.1   Rats

Groups of five male rats received 250 or 500 mg/kg bw/dy $CaNa_2EDTA$ i.p. daily for three to 21 days and some were observed for an additional two weeks. Weight gain was satisfactory and histology of lung, thymus, kidney, liver, spleen, adrenal, small gut and heart was normal except for mild to moderate renal hydropic change with focal subcapsular swelling and proliferation in glomerular loops at the

500 mg level. There was very slight involvement with complete recovery at the 250 mg level. Lesions were not more severe with simultaneous cortisone administration (Reuber and Schmieller, 1962).

Groups of three male and three female rats were fed for four months on a low mineral diet containing one-half the usual portion of salt mixture (i.e. 1.25% instead of 2.50%) with the addition of 0% and 1.5% $CaNa_2EDTA$. The test group showed a reduced weight gain, but there was no distinct difference in general condition of the animals (Yang, 1964).

Groups of five male rats were given 250, 400 or 500 mg/kg bw/dy disodium EDTA i.p. daily for three to 31 days; some groups were observed for another two weeks. At the 500 mg level all rats became lethargic and died within nine days, the kidneys being pale and swollen, with moderate dilatation of bowel and subserosal haemorrhages. Histological examination of a number of organs showed lesions only in the kidneys. Animals at the 400 mg level died within 14 days, kidney and bowel symptoms being similar to the 50 mg level. One rat at the 250 mg dose level showed haemorrhage of the thymus. All three groups showed varying degrees of hydrophic necrosis of the renal proximal convoluted tubules with epithelial sloughing: recovery occurred in all groups after withdrawal of disodium EDTA (Reuber and Schmieller, 1962).

2.2.2.2 Rabbits

Eight groups of three rabbits were given either 0.1, 1, 10 or 20 mg/kg bw/dy disodium EDTA i.v., or 50, 100, 500 or 1 000 mg/kg bw/dy orally for one month. All animals on the highest oral test level exhibited severe diarrhoea and died. In the other groups body weight, haemograms, urinary nitrogen and urobilinogen were unaffected. Histopathological examination of a number of organs showed degenerative changes in the liver, kidney, parathyroid and endocrine organs and oedema in muscle, brain and heart at all levels of treatment (Shibata, 1956).

2.2.2.3 Dogs

Four groups of one male and three female mongrels were fed diets containing 0, 50, 100 and 200 mg/kg bw/dy $CaNa_2EDTA$ daily for 12 months. All appeared in good health, without significant change in blood cells, haemoglobin and urine (pH, albumin, sugar, sediment). Blood sugar, non-protein nitrogen and prothrombin time remained normal. Radiographs of ribs and of long bones showed no adverse changes at the 250 mg level. All dogs survived for one year. Gross and microscopic findings were normal (Oser et al., 1963).

2.2.3   Long-term toxicity/carcinogenicity studies

2.2.3.1 Mice

Groups of 50 male and 50 female B6C3F$_1$ mice received trisodium EDTA (Na$_3$EDTA) in the diet at concentrations of 3 750 or 7 500 ppm for 103 weeks, followed by one week during which standard diet without EDTA was fed. A control group consisting of 20 mice of each sex received the standard diet. Food was available *ad libitum* and fresh food was provided three times per week.

Animals were examined for signs of toxicity twice per day, and were weighed and palpated for masses regularly (schedule not stated). Gross and microscopic pathological examinations were performed on animals found dead or moribund and on those sacrificed at the end of the study. Microscopic examinations were conducted on the following tissues and organs: skin, lymph nodes, mammary gland, salivary gland, bone marrow, trachea, lungs and bronchi, heart, thyroid, parathyroids, oesophagus, stomach, small intestine, liver, gallbladder, pancreas, spleen, kidneys, adrenals, urinary bladder, prostate or uterus, testis or ovary, brain and pituitary.

Survival rates were comparable among treated and control animals of both sexes. No treatment-related clinical signs of toxicity were noted during the study. Body weight gain was decreased in high-dose males during the second year of the study (no statistical analysis). From the graphical representation of the data, it appears that the body weights in the high-dose group were approximately 10% below that of controls during the last nine months of the study. In females, average body weights in treated groups were consistently lower than the average control body weight for most of the study period, however, the differences among the three groups were very slight. No tumours or non-neoplastic lesions attributable to treatment were observed (NCI, 1977).

2.2.3.2 Rats

Rats were fed for 44 to 52 weeks on a diet containing 0.5% disodium EDTA without any deleterious effect on weight gain, appetite, activity and appearance (Krum, 1948).

In another experiment three groups of 10 to 13 males and females were fed a low-mineral diet (0.5% Ca and 0.013% Fe) with the addition of 0, 0.5 and 1% disodium EDTA for 205 days. At the 1% level some abnormal systems were observed: growth retardation of the males, lowered erythrocyte and leucocyte counts, a prolonged blood coagulation time, slightly but significantly raised blood calcium level, a significantly lower ash content of the bone, considerable erosion of the molars and diarrhoea. Gross and histological examination of the major organs revealed nothing abnormal. Rats fed for 220 days on an adequate mineral diet containing 1% disodium EDTA showed no evidence of dental erosion (Chan, 1964).

In a two-year study, five groups of 33 rats each were fed 0, 0.5, 1 and 5% disodium EDTA. The 5% group showed diarrhoea and consumed less food than the rats in other groups. No significant effects on weight gain were noted nor were blood coagulation time, red blood cell counts or bone ash adversely affected. The mortality of the animals could not be correlated with the level of disodium EDTA. The highest mortality rate occurred in the control group. Gross and microscopic examination of various organs revealed no significant differences between the groups (Yang, 1964).

Four groups of 25 male and 25 female rats were fed diets containing 0, 50, 125 and 250 mg/kg bw/dy $CaNa_2EDTA$ for two years. Feeding was carried on through four successive generations. Rat were mated after 12 weeks' feeding and allowed to lactate for three weeks with one week's rest before producing a second litter. Ten male and 10 female rats of each group (F_1 generation) and similar F_2 and F_3 generation groups were allowed to produce two litters. Of the second litters of F_1, F_2, and F_3 generations only the control and the 250 mg/kg bw/dy groups were kept until the end of two-years' study on the F_0 generation. This scheme permitted terminal observation to be made on rats receiving test diets for 0, 0.5, 1, 1.5 or 2 years in the F_3, F_2, F_1 and F_0 generations, respectively. No significant abnormalities in appearance and behaviour were noted during the 12 weeks of the post weaning period in all generations. The feeding experiment showed no statistically significant differences in weight gain, food efficiency, haematopoiesis, blood sugar, non-protein nitrogen, serum calcium, urine, organ weights and histopathology of liver, kidney, spleen, heart, adrenals, thyroid and gonads. Fertility, lactation and weaning were not adversely affected for each mating. Mortality and tumour incidence were unrelated to dosage level. The prothrombin time was normal. There was no evidence of any chelate effect on calcification of bone and teeth. Liver xanthine oxidase and blood carbonic anhydrase activities were unchanged (Oser *et al.*, 1963).

Groups of 50 male and 50 female Fisher F344 rats received trisodium EDTA (Na_3EDTA) in the diet at concentrations of 3 750 or 7 500 ppm for 103 weeks, followed by one week during which standard diet without EDTA was fed (NCI, 1977). A control group consisting of 20 rats of each sex received the standard diet of Wayne Lab Blox Meal. Food was available *ad libitum* and fresh food was provided three times per week.

Animals were examined for signs of toxicity twice per day, and were weighed and palpated for masses regularly (schedule not stated). Gross and microscopic pathological examinations were performed on animals found dead or moribund and on those sacrificed at the end of the study. Microscopic examinations were conducted on the following tissues and organs: skin, lymph nodes, mammary gland, salivary gland, bone marrow, trachea, lungs and bronchi, heart, thyroid, parathyroids, oesophagus, stomach, small intestine, liver, gallbladder, pancreas, spleen, kidneys, adrenals, urinary bladder, prostate or uterus, testis or ovary, brain and pituitary.

Survival was comparable among control and treated groups of male rats. There was a significant dose-related increase in survival in treated groups of females compared to controls. Body weights were comparable among treated and control groups, and there were no clinical signs of toxicity in treated animals. No tumours or non-neoplastic lesions attributable to treatment were observed (NCI, 1977).

2.2.4 Reproduction studies

2.2.4.1 Rats

Groups of six rats were maintained for 12 weeks on diets containing 0.5, 1 and 5% disodium EDTA. No deaths occurred and there were no toxic symptoms except diarrhoea and lowered food consumption at the 5% level. Mating in each group was carried out when the animals were 100 days old. Mating was repeated 10 days after weaning the first litters. Parent generation rats of 0, 0.5 and 1% levels gave birth to normal first and second litters. The animals given 5% failed to produce litters (Yang, 1964).

To elucidate possible teratogenic effects, daily doses of 20-40 mg EDTA/rat were injected i.m into pregnant rats at days six to nine, 10 to 15 and 16 to the end of pregnancy. A dose of 40 mg was lethal within four days but 20 mg was well tolerated, allowing normal fetal development; 40 mg injected during days six to eight or 10 to 15 produced some dead or malformed fetuses, especially polydactyly, double tail, generalized oedema or circumscribed head oedema (Tuchmann-Duplessis and Mercier-Parot, 1956).

In a four generation study, groups of rats received $CaNa_2EDTA$ at doses of 50, 125 or 250 mg/kg/day via the diet. No reproductive or teratogenic effects were observed in any of the three generations of offspring (Oser et al., 1963). This study is discussed in greater detail in Section 2.2.3 of this monograph.

Groups of pregnant Sprague-Dawley rats were fed Na_2EDTA in standard diet at levels of 2 or 3% from day 1 to 21 of gestation. Another group of pregnant rats received 3% Na_2EDTA in standard diet from day 6 to 14 of gestation. A third group received 3% Na_2EDTA and 1 000 ppm zinc in the diet from day 6 to 21 of gestation. Controls received standard diet, which contained 100 ppm zinc. The number of mated animals per group ranged from 5 to 16. on day 21 of gestation fetuses were removed, fixed in Bouin's solution and stored in 70% ethanol. Fetuses were examined under a dissecting microscope for gross external abnormalities. Razor cut sections were examined for abnormalities of the eye and head. In rats fed 2% EDTA during pregnancy, litter size was normal and fetuses were alive. Gross congenital malformations were apparent in 7% of the treated in fetuses, compared to 0% in controls. In rats fed 3% EDTA during pregnancy, almost half of the implantation sites had dead fetuses or resorptions. Full term young were significantly smaller than controls and 100% of them were malformed. Maternal toxicity as manifested by diarrhoea was observed in rats fed 2 or 3% EDTA in the diet. Malformations included severe brain malformations, cleft palate, malformed digits, clubbed legs and malformed tails. The detrimental effects of EDTA were prevented by supplementation of the diet with 1 000 ppm zinc. These findings suggest that the teratogenic effects observed in rats fed EDTA at very high levels in the diet are due to zinc deficiency (Swenerton and Hurley, 1971).

Groups of pregnant CD rats were treated with Na$_2$EDTA via the diet at a dose of 954 mg/kg/day (3% in the diet; 42 rats), by gastric intubation at doses of 1 250 mg/kg/day (split dose of 625 mg/kg twice/day; 22 rats) or 1 500 mg/kg/day (split dose of 750 mg/kg twice/day; 8 rats), or by subcutaneous injection at a dose of 375 mg/kg/day (25 rats). Animals were dosed on gestation day 7 through 14. The number of control animals for each exposure route were: diet, 38; gavage, 20; subcutaneous injection, 14. Fetuses were removed at day 21 of gestation. One third of the fetuses from each litter (including all stunted fetuses and those with external malformations) were dissected and examined for visceral abnormalities. All fetuses surviving to the time of sacrifice were fixed and examined for skeletal malformations. Maternal toxicity as evidence by decreased food consumption, diarrhoea and diminished weight gain was observed in groups treated by all three dose routes. In the dietary exposure group, there were no maternal deaths, but there was a significant increase in fetal death and 71% of the fetuses were malformed. In the group administered 625 mg/kg/day by gavage, only 64% of the dams survived treatment. In those surviving, the number of fetal resorptions was similar to controls and 20.5% of the fetuses were malformed. Seven out of eight of the dams administered 750 mg/kg/day by gavage failed to survive. In the group administered EDTA by subcutaneous injection, 76% of the dams survived, the number of resorptions was significantly increased above control levels and the proportion of malformed fetuses was similar to controls. The types of malformations were consistent with those observed by Swenerton and Hurley, although these former workers only evaluated external malformations. The results of this study indicate that the route of exposure to EDTA is an important factor in determining its lethality and teratogenicity (Kimmel, 1977).

Groups of 20 pregnant CD rats were administered EDTA, Na$_2$EDTA, Na$_3$EDTA, Na$_4$EDTA or CaNa$_2$EDTA by gavage at a total dose of 1 000 mg EDTA/kg/day in two divided doses per day during gestation day 7 through 14. All fetuses were subjected to gross examination. One third were sliced and examined for visceral abnormalities and the other two thirds were dissected, processed and examined for skeletal abnormalities. The incidence of diarrhoea was increased in all treated groups. Food intake was decreased in treated groups as was weight gain during the treatment period. Litter size and fetal mortality were unaffected by treatment in all groups. No treatment-related teratogenic effects were observed in any group (Schardein et al., 1981).

2.2.5   Special studies on embryotoxicity

2.2.5.1 Chickens

Disodium EDTA injected at levels of 3.4, 1.7 and 0.35 mg/egg gave 40, 50 and 85% hatch, respectively. At the highest level, some embryos which failed to hatch showed anomalies (McLaughlin and Scott, 1964).

2.2.6   Special studies on genotoxicity

Na_3EDTA was tested for mutagenicity in the L5178Y tk^+/tk^- mouse lymphoma cell forward mutation assay. Two experiments were conducted with S9, and three without S9, using EDTA concentrations of up to 5 000 ug/ml. No mutagenicity was observed with or without S9 (McGregor et al., 1988).

Na_3EDTA was tested for mutagenicity in Salmonella typhimurium strains TA98, TA100, TA1535, TA1537 and TA1538 as well as in Escherichia coli WP uvrA, in the presence and absence of S9. Concentrations of up to 1 mg/plate were tested. No evidence of mutagenicity was found in either of these bacterial systems, by four independent laboratories (Dunkel et al., 1985).

2.2.7   Special studies on skin sensitization

Groups of 10 Hartley guinea-pigs received topical application of Na_3EDTA, ethylene diamine (EDA) or epoxy resin (positive control) four times over 10 days to a shaved and depilated area on the back. Following a two week recovery period, animals received a challenge on the clipped flank. Animals originally treated with EDTA were not sensitized to EDTA. Animals originally treated with EDA were sensitized to EDA, but not to EDTA. The results of this study indicate a lack of sensitizing potential of EDTA and a lack of cross-sensitization between EDA and EDTA (Henck et al. 1985).

2.3   Observations in humans

Three comprehensive field trials have been carried out using NaFeEDTA as an iron fortificant in fish sauce (Garby and Areekul, 1974), off-white sugar (Viteri et al., 1983) curry powder (Ballot et al., 1989b). The salient features of these trials are listed in Table 5. All three trials were preceded by some estimate of the iron status of the population and care was taken to establish the acceptability and bioavailability of iron from the chosen vehicle prior to the trials (Garby and Areekul, 1974, Viteri et.al, 1983, Lamparelli et.al, 1987, Ballot et.al, 1989a). The choice of food vehicle in each case reflected the dietary habits of the population.

2.3.1   NaFeEDTA fortified fish sauce

Fortified fish sauce was provided for a period of one year to the population of a Thai village. The packed red cell volume (PCV) values before and after the fortification program showed a significant increase as compared to a control village supplied with unfortified fish sauce. The biggest mean change (+4.7) was seen in a sub-group of women who were anaemic at the start of the trial (initial PCV < 33). Although a similar sub-group of women in the control group also improved during the year (mean change +2.1) the increase in PCV in the fortified group was significantly greater. The same pattern was seen in both men and children with low initial PCV values.

In terms of iron nutrition the increase of 4.7 PCV units over initial values represents an increase of about 187 mg iron, in total body iron or an increase in daily absorption of about 0.5 mg over the duration of the trial (1 year). This is 64% of the expected increase in body iron of 0.8 mg/day calculated on the basis of an anticipated absorption of 8% and an assumed daily intake of 10 ml fortified fish sauce (10 mg Fe). Iron stores were not measured in this trial and the calculation does not take into account any absorbed iron which may have been laid down in stores. The calculated value therefore would be an underestimate of the total amount of iron actually absorbed. Nevertheless it illustrates that fortification with NaFeEDTA is a highly effective method for improving iron status.

Overall this trial demonstrated that fortification of fish sauce at modest levels using NaFeEDTA is feasible, and that it can produce a significant improvement in iron status as assessed by a single simple criterion (PCV) (Garby and Areekul, 1974).

2.3.2   NaFeEDTA fortified sugar

The design of this trial makes interpretation of the results difficult. The analysis is based on the comparative changes in iron status observed in four communities. Three (#13, #14, #16) were test sites, and one was a control site (#15). The initial iron status of individuals drawn from test community #14 was significantly worse than that of individuals from the other test communities and the control community (#15). Unfortunately compliance was poor in this community and also in test community #13. Furthermore seventy percent of the families in test communities number 13 and 14 used fortified sugar for only half of the time. The remaining 30% used it for 80% of the time. Finally, subjects with severe anaemia were given therapeutic iron to improve their iron status prior to the trial.

Despite the presence of these confounding factors, the haemoglobin values rose in both males and females after 20 months of fortification, although the values did not reach statistical significance. Only the children (5-12 years) in communities #13 and #16 showed a significant improvement in haemoglobin levels when compared to children in the control community #15 (+2.2±1.7 and +2.2±1.5 respectively vs +1.6±1.2 g/dl). The greater benefit observed in children may have resulted

Table 5. Outline of field trials using NaFeEDTA to fortify various food vehicles

References	Garby and Areekul, 1974	Viteri, *et al.*, 1983	Ballot, *et al.*, 1989a,b
Geographical region	Thailand	Central America	South Africa
Population studied	Two rural villages	4 rural Guatemalan communities	Urban Indian community in a municipal housing estate
Design of trial	Controlled (one village) not blinded	Controlled (community #15) not blinded	Controlled (random allocation by families) double-blinded
Sample studies	Test village (284) control village (330)	#13 - 186 #14 - 306 #15 - 234 #16 - 296 severe anaemics treated prior to trial	263 Families (672 subjects) 129 control families 134 fortified families Hb < 9 g/dl excluded
Food vehicle	Fish-sauce (salt substitute) 30 g NaCl/l, 10 mg Fe/l distributed by village head-man as required	Off-white sugar distribution: sold to store keepers. Purchased by participants (poor compliance #13 and #14)	Masala (curry powder) distributed directly to families monthly free of charge
Cons. of food vehicle	10 - 15 ml/person/day	33 g/person/day; children highest consumption	5.5 g/person/day
Fe absorption	8%	8%	10%
Level of fortification and intake	1 mg Fe/ml 10 - 15 mg Fe/person/day	13mg Fe/100g 4.29 mg Fe/person/day	1.4 mg Fe/g 7.7 mg Fe/person/day
Acceptability	No changes	Barely perceptible yellowing	Slight darkening of food
Duration of trial	12 months	20 months	24 months
% Abnormal iron status prior to trial	30 - 50 of population anaemic; 34% initial PCV below normal	Low Low Low Comm PCV Sat Ferr #13 31 34 52 #14 43 58 72 #15 35 12 37 #16 21 23 34	Females Males IDA 24 4 ID 53 24
Measurements taken	Packed cell volume (PCV)	Haemoglobin, PCV, %Sat, FEP, Serum Ferritin, Cu, Zn	Haemoglobin, %Sat, Serum Ferritin

IDA = Iron Deficiency anaemia; ID = Iron Deficiency; % Sat = % Saturation of Transferrin; FEP = Free Erythrocyte Protoporphyrin; PCV = Packed Cell Volume; Comm = Community from the fact that sugar consumption was greater in children than in adults when considered relative to body weight. Mean serum ferritin which is a measure of the size of iron stores increased in each of the test communities, but not in the control community. In conclusion it should be noted that the relatively modest improvement in iron status noted in this trial may also have been due, in part, to the fact that the fortification level was considerably less than in the other two trials (4.3 vs 10-15 and 7.7 mg/person/day) (Viteri *et al.*, 1983).

2.3.3 NaFeEDTA fortified masala

The design of the most recent fortification trial differed from those of earlier studies in that it was conducted in a single community with families randomly assigned to control and test groups. The groups were matched for iron status. It was also double-blinded and care was taken to ensure that cross-over between groups did not occur. Fortified or unfortified masala was distributed directly to each family. In addition to evaluating fortification the usual indices of improving iron status (increasing haematocrit or haemoglobin and ferritin) in each individual by using a composite of haemoglobin concentration, percent saturation of transferrin, and serum ferritin concentration, an attempt was made to estimate the total body iron (in mg) in each individual by using a composite of haemoglobin concentration, percent saturation of transferrin and serum ferritin concentration (Cook, *et al*, 1986). This comprehensive index of iron nutrition made it possible to compare subjects with wide variations in iron status and thus to assess both the beneficial and potentially adverse effects of additional iron i.e. development of iron overload (Ballot, *et al.*, 1989a, b).

Significant improvement in body iron as assessed by the index was detectable in the group of women receiving fortified masala after one year of the program (Ballot, *et al.*, 1989a, b). This improvement continued during the second year when the rise in haemoglobin concentration became significantly greater than in the control group. The prevalence of iron deficiency dropped dramatically in the women receiving fortified masala. Iron deficiency anaemia was detected in 22% of individuals at the start of the study, but only to 4.9% after two years. The most significant improvement in iron status was noted in women who entered the trial with iron deficiency (especially in those with anaemia). They showed an increase in calculated body iron of 505 mg which is equivalent to the absorption of an additional 0.7 mg iron/day. The latter figure is close to the predicted improvement in iron balance of 0.8 mg daily based on isotopic absorption studies using NaFeEDTA fortified masala (Lamparelli *et al.*, 1987).

In iron-replete males the rise in calculated body iron was modest and only reached significance in alcohol abusers receiving fortified masala. This suggests that iron-replete males are unlikely to accumulate excessive amounts of iron under these fortification conditions.

3.   COMMENTS

The Committee was concerned about over-fortification or misuse of this product and did not recommend its availability for general use by individuals. The Committee noted that sodium iron EDTA dissociates in the intestine, and iron in this form is approximately twice as bioavailable as iron in the form of iron sulfate. The available studies indicated that only a fraction, if any, of the iron EDTA chelate is absorbed as such, that EDTA from sodium iron EDTA is only poorly absorbed and that the majority is excreted in the faeces. The portion that is absorbed (<5%) is rapidly excreted in urine. The proposed supplementation programme would result in intakes of iron and EDTA of approximately 0.2 and 1.34 mg/kg bw/day, respectively.

4.   EVALUATION

Based on previous evaluations of both iron and EDTA and the available bioavailability and metabolism data, the Committee provisionally concluded that use of sodium iron EDTA meeting the tentative specifications prepared at the present meeting in supervised food fortification programmes in iron-deficient populations does not present a safety problem. The Committee requested that additional studies be conducted to assess the site of deposition of iron administered in this form and further studies to assess the metabolic fate of sodium iron EDTA following long-term administration.

The Committee emphasized that its evaluation pertains only to the use of sodium iron EDTA as a dietary supplement to be used under supervision and expressed its concern about the potential for over-fortification because of the enhanced bioavailability of iron in this form.

The Committee developed new tentative specifications for sodium iron (III) ethylenediaminetetraacetate (NaFeEDTA). In preparing the specifications, the Committee was aware that food-grade NaFeEDTA is not commercially available. However, the Committee was advised, that this substance is being evaluated for its usefulness in fortifying the diet in areas of the world where iron deficiency in the population is endemic, prepared specifications, which it believed would assist in the evaluation. The Committee obtained analytical data and other information on fertilizer-grade NaFeEDTA, which is widely available, and considered this together with the existing specifications for disodium ethylenediaminetetra-acetate and calcium disodium ethylenediaminetetraacetate in formulating the specifications. Because further information on assay and purity data for food-grade material and on analytical methodology is still needed, the specification was designated as tentative.

5.   REFERENCES

AABAKKEN, L. & OSNES, M. (1990). ^{51}Cr-ethylenediaminetetraacetic acid absorption test. Effects of Naproxen, a non-steroidal, antiinflammatory drug. *Scan. J. Gastroenterol.* **25**, 917-24.

ANGHILERI, L.J. (1967). Fate of intravenously injected iron compounds:ferric-fructose complex, iron-EDTA, ferric hydroxide, and iron-albumin labeled with [59]Fe. *Biochemical Pharmacology* **16**, 2033-36, 1967.

BALLOT, D.E., MACPHAIL, A.P., BOTHWELL, T.H., GILLOOLY, M., & MAYET, F.G. (1989a). Fortification of curry powder with NaFe(III)EDTA in an iron deficient population: Initial survey of iron status. *Am. J. Clin. Nutr.* **49**, 156-61.

BALLOT, D.E., MACPHAIL, A. P., BOTHWELL, T.H., GILLOOLY, M. & MAYET, F.G. (1989b). Fortification of curry powder with NaFe(III)EDTA in an iron-deficient population: Report of a controlled iron-fortification trial. *Am. J. Clin. Nutr.* **49**, 162-69.

BATES, G.W., BILLUPS C. & SALTMAN, P. (1967). The kinetics mechanism of iron (III) exchange between chelates and transferrin. *J. Biol. Chem.* **242**, 2816-21.

BAUER, R.O., Rullo, F., Spooner, C., and Woodman, E. (1952) Acute and subacute toxicity of ethylene diamine tetraacetic acid (EDTA) salts *Fed. Proc.* **11**, 321.

BJARNASON, I., PETERS, T.J. & VEALL, N. (1983). A persistent defect in intestinal permeability in coeliac disease demonstrated by a ^{51}Cr-labelled EDTA absorption test. *Lancet* **1**, 323-325.

BOTHWELL, T.H., CHARLTON, R.W., COOK, J.D. & FINCH, C.A. (1979). Iron Metabolism in Man. Blackwell Scientific Publications: Oxford, England.

CANDELA, E., CAMACHO, M.V. MARTINEZ-TORRES, C., PERDOMO, J., MAZZARRI, G., ACURERO, G. & LAYRISSE, M. (1984). Iron absorption by humans and swine from Fe(III)-EDTA. Further studies. *J. Nutr.* **114**, 2204-11.

CATSCH, A. (1961). *Fed. Proc.* **20** (Suppl. 10), 206.

CHABERCK, S.A. & MARTELL, A. E. (1959). Organic sequestering agents. John Wiley and Sons, Inc., New York.

CHAN, M.S. (1964). *Fd. Cosmet. Toxicol.* **2**. 763-765.

CLETON, F., TURNBULL, A. & FINCH, C.A. (1963). Synthetic chelating agents in iron metabolism *J. Clin. Invest.* **42**, 327.

CONRAD, M.E. & SCHADE, S.G. (1968). Ascorbic acid chelates in iron absorption: a role for hydrochloric acid and bile. *Gastroenterology* **55**, 35-45.

COOK, J.D. & MONSEN E.R. (1976). Food iron absorption in man II. The effect of EDTA on the absorption of non-heme iron. *Am. J. Clin. Nutr.* **29**, 614-20.

COOK, J.D. & REUSSER. (1983). Iron fortification: an update. *Am. J. Clin. Nutr.* **38**, 648-59.

COOK, J.D., LAYRISSE, M., MARTINEZ-TORRES, C., WALKER, R.B., MONSEN E. & FINCH, C.A. (1972). Food iron absorption measured by an extrinsic tag. *J. Clin. Invest.* **51**, 805-815.

COOK, J.D., SKIKNE, B.S., LYNCH S.R., & REUSSER, M.E. (1986). Estimates of iron sufficiency in the U.S. population. *Blood* **68**, 726-31.

DAVIDSSON, L., KASTENMEYER, P., AND HURRELL, R. (1993) Sodium iron EDTA (NaFeIIIEDTA) as a food fortificant: the effect n the absorption and retention of calcium and zinc for humans. *Am. J. Clin. Nutr.*, submitted for publication.

DUNKEL, V.C., ZEIGER, E. BRUSICK, D. M^cCOY, E. M^cGREGOR, D., MORTLEMANS, K. ROSENKRANZ H.S., & SIMMON V.F. (1985). Reproducibility of microbial mutagenicity assays:II. Testing of carcinogens and noncarcinogens in *Salmonella typhimurium* and *Escherichia coli. Environ. Mutagen.* **7(Supp.5:1)**, 1-248.

DYCKERHOFF, H., MARX., R. & LUDWIG, B. (1942). *Z. ges. exp. Med.* **110**, 412.

el GUINDI, M., LYNCH, S.R. & COOK, J.D. (1988). Iron absorption from fortified flat breads. *Br. J. Nutr.* **59**, 205-13.

FORBES, R.M. (1961). Excretory patterns and bone deposition of zinc, calcium and magnesium in the rat as influenced by zinc deficiency, EDTA and lactose. *J. Nutr.* **74**, 193-200.

FOREMAN, H. (1961). *Fed. Proc.* **20**, (Suppl. 10), 191.

FOREMAN, H., & TRUJILLO, T.T. (1954). The metabolism of C¹⁴ labeled ethylenediaminetetraacetic acid in human beings. *J. Lab. Clin. Med.* **43**, 566-71.

FOREMAN, H., VIER, M., & MAGEE, M. (1953). The metabolism of C¹⁴ labeled ethylenediaminetetraacetic acid in the rat. *J. Biol. Chem.* **203**, 1045-53.

GARBY, L. & AREEKUL, S. (1974). Iron supplementation in Thai fish-sauce. *Ann. Trop. Med. Parasitol.* **68(4)**, 467-76.

GIBSON, K.D., NEUBERGER, A. & SCOTT, J.C. (1955). The purification and properties of δ-aminolævulic acid dehydrase. *Biochem. J.* **61**, 618-629.

GOULD, R.G. (1961). *Fed. Proc.* **20** (Suppl. 10), 252.

HALLBERG, L. & BJÖRN-RASMUSSEN, E. (1972). Determination of iron absorption from whole diet. A new two-pool model using two radioiron isotopes given as haem and non-haem iron. *Scand. J. Haematol.* **9**, 193-97.

HALLBERG, L., BJÖRN-RASMUSSEN, E., GARBY, L. PLEEHACHINDA, R. & SUWANIK, R. (1978). Iron absorption from South-East Asian diets and the effect of iron fortification. *Am. J. Clin. Nutr.* **31**, 1403-08.

HART, J.R. (1984) EDTA-type chelating agents in everyday consumer products: some medicinal and personal care products. *Journal of chemical education* **61(12)**.

HAWKINS, W.W. *et al.* (1962). *Can. J. Biochem.* **40**, 391.

HENCK, J.W., LOCKWOOD, D.D. & OLSON, K.J. (1985). Skin sensitization potential of trisodium ethylenediaminetetraacetate. *Drug Chem. Toxicol.* **3**, 99-103.

HURRELL, R.F., RIBAS, R. & DAVIDSSON, L. (1993). Sodium iron EDTA as a food fortificant: Influence on zinc, calcium and copper metabolism in the rat. *Brit. J. Nutr.* in press.

KIMMEL, C.A. (1977). Effect of route of administration on the toxicity and teratogenicity of EDTA in the rat. *Tox. Appl. Pharmacol.* **40**, 299-306.

KRATZER, F.H., ALLRED, J.B., DAVIS, P.N., MARSHAL, B.J., & VOHRA, P. (1959) The effect of autoclaving soybean protein and the addition of ethylenediaminetetraacetic acid on biological availability of dietary zinc for turkey poults. *J. Nutr.* **68**, 313-22.

KRUM, J.K. (1948). Thesis, University of Massachusetts.

LAMPARELLI, R.D., MACPHAIL, A.P. BOTHWELL, T.H. BALLOT, D.E. DANILEWITZ, M.D. MACFARLANE, B.J., MAYET F. & BAYNES, R.D. (1987). Curry powder as a vehicle for iron fortification: effects on iron absorption. *Am. J. Clin. Nutr.* **46**, 335-40.

LAPINLEIMU, K. & WEGELIUS, R. (1959). *Antibiotic Med. Clin. Ther. (Br. Edit.)* **6**, 151.

LARSEN, B.A., BIDWELL, R.G.S. & HAWKINS, W.W. (1960). *Can. J. Biochem.* **38**, 51.

LAYRISSE, M. & MARTINEZ-TORRES, C. (1977). Fe(III)EDTA complex as iron fortification. *Am. J. Clin. Nutr.* **30**, 1166-74.

LECHNIT, V. (1961). *Arch. Gewerbepath. Gewerbehyg.* **18**, 495.

LELIÈVRE, P. (1960). *C.R. Soc. Biol. (Paris)* **154**, 1890.

LELIÈVRE, P. & BETZ, E.H. (1961). *C.R. Soc. Biol. (Paris)* **155**, 199.

MACPHAIL, A.P. & T.H. BOTHWELL. (1992). The prevalence and causes of nutritional iron deficiency anemia. In: Nutritional anemias Eds. Fomon, S.J. and Zlotkin. S. Nestle Nutrition Workshop Series 30: 1-12, Nestec Ltd., Vevey, Switzerland / Raven Press, New York.

MACPHAIL, A.P., BOTHWELL, T.H., TORRANCE, J.D., DEOMAN, D.P., BEZWODA, W.R. & CHARLTON, R.W. (1981). Factors affecting the absorption of iron from Fe(III)EDTA. *Br. J. Nutr.* **45**: 215-227.

MARQUARDT, P. & SCHUMACHER, H. (1957). *Arzneimittelforsch*, **7**, 5.

MARTELL, A.E. (1960). Chelation: Stability and selectivity. *Ann. New York Academy of Sciences* **88**, 284-92.

MARTINEZ-TORRES, C., ROMANO, E.L., & LAYRISSE M. (1979). Fe(III)EDTA complex as iron fortification. Further studies. *Am. Clin. Nutr.* **32**, 809-16.

McGREGOR, D.B., BROWN, A., CATTANACH, P., ET. AL. (1988). Responses of the L5178Y tk+/tk mouse lymphoma cell forward mutation assay: III. 72 coded chemicals. *Environ. Mol. Mutagen.* **12**, 85-154.

McLAUGHLIN, J., Jr. & SCOTT, W.F. (1964). Toxicity of some food packaging chemicals measured by the chick embryo technique. *Fed. Proc.* **23**, 406.

MIETTINEN, T.A. & LESKINEN, E. (1962). *Ans. Med. Exp. Fenn.*, **40**, 427.

NAGARAJAN, B., SIVARAMAKRISHNAN, V.M., & BRAHMANANDAM, S. (1964). The distribution of ^{59}Fe in albino rats after intravenous administration in the ionic or chelated form. *Biochemical Journal* **92**, 531-7.

NCI. (1977). Bioassay of trisodium ethylenediaminetetraacetate trihydrate (EDTA) for possible carcinogenicity. National Cancer Institute. Carcinogenesis Tech. Report Series No. 11, 1977.

NIGROVIC, V. (1964). *Arch. Exp. Pathol. Pharmacol.* **249**, 206.

OBERLEAS D., MUHRER, M.E. & O'DELL, B.L. (1966). Dietary metal complexing agents and zinc availability in the rat. *J. Nutr.* **90**, 56-62.

OSER, B.L., OSER, M. & SPENCER, H.C. (1963). Safety evaluation studies of calcium EDTA. *Tox. Appl. Pharmacol.* **5**, 142-62.

PERRY, H.M. & PERRY, E.F. (1959). Normal concentrations of some trace metals in human urine: changes produced by EDTA. *J. Clin. Invest.* **38**, 1452-63.

PLUMB, R.C., MARTELL, A.E. & BERSWORTH, F.C. (1950). Spectrophotometric determination of displacement series of metal complexes of the sodium salts of ethylenediamine-tetraacetic acid. *J. Phys. Colloid. Chem.* **54**, 1208-15.

POGELL, B.M. & LELOIR, L.F. (1961). Nucleotide activation of liver microsomal glucuronidation. *J. Biol. Chem.* **236**, 293-8.

REUBER, M.D. & SCHMIELLER, G.C. (1962). Edetate lesions in rats. *Arch. Environ. Health* **5**, 430-36.

RUBIN, M. (1961). *Fed. Proc.* **20** (Suppl 10.), 149.

RUBIN, M., PACHTMAN, E. ALDRIDGE, M. ZAPOLSKI, E.J. BAGLEY, Jr., D.H., & PRINCIOTTO, J.V. (1970). The metabolism of parenteral iron chelates. *Biochemical Medicine* **3**: 271-88.

SCHANKER, L.S. & JOHNSON, J.M. (1961). *Biochem. Pharmacol.* **8**, 421.

SCHARDEIN, J.L., SAKOWSKI, R., PETRERE, J., & HUMPHREY, R.R. (1981). Teratogenesis studies with EDTA and its salts in rats. *Tox. Appl. Pharmacol.* **61**, 423-28.

SCOTT, M.L. & ZIEGLER, T.R. (1963). Evidence for natural chelates which aid in the utilization of zinc by chicks. *Agr. Fd. Chem.* **11**, 123-25.

SHIBATA, S. (1956). *Folio Pharmacol. Jap.* **52**, 113.

SIMPSON, R.J. & PETERS, T.J. (1984) Studies of Fe^{+++} transport across intestinal brush border membrane of the mouse. *Biochemica et Biophysica Acta* **772**, 220-26.

SIMMONS, W.K. & GURNEY, J.M. (1980). Nutritional anemia in the English-speaking Caribbean and Surinam. Kingston: Caribbean Food and Nutrition Institute J-46-80. Pan American Health Organization.

SOLOMONS, N.W., JACOB, R.A. PINEDA, O. & VITERI, F.E. (1979). Studies on the bioavailability of zinc in man. Effect of the Guatemalan rural diet and the iron-fortifying agent, NaFeEDTA. *J. Nutr.* **109**, 1519-28.

SRBROVA, J. & TEISINGER, J. (1957). *Arch. Gewerbepathol.* **15**, 572.

SWENERTON, H. & HURLEY, L.S. (1971). Teratogenic effects of a chelating agent and their prevention by zinc. *Science* **173**, 62-64.

TUCHMANN-DUPLESSIS, H. & MERCIER-PAROT, L. (1956). *C.R. Acad. Sci.* **243**, 1064.

VITERI, F.E., GARCIA-IBANEZ, R. & TORUN, B. (1978). Sodium iron NaFeEDTA as an iron fortification compound in Central America. Absorption studies. *Am. J. Clin. Nutr.* **32**, 961-71.

VITERI, F.E., ALVARES, E. & TORUN, B. (1983). Prevention of iron deficiency by means of iron fortification of sugar. In: Underwood, B.A., ED. Nutrition intervention strategies in national development. New York, Academic Press, 287-314.

VOHRA, P. & KRATZER, F.H. (1964). Influence of various chelating agents on the bioavailability of zinc. *J. Nutr.* **82**, 249-56.

WEST, T.S. & SYKES, A.S. (1960). Diamino-ethane-tetra-acetic acid. In: Analytical applications of Diamino-ethane-tetra-acetic acid. Poole, England: The British Drug Houses, Ltd. 9-22.

WESTERFELD, W.W. (1961). *Fed. Proc.* **20**, (Suppl 10.), 158.

WILL, J.J. & VILTER, R.W. (1954). A study of the absorption and utilization of an iron chelate in iron-deficient patients. *J. Lab. & Clin. Med.* **44**:499-505.

YANG, S.S. (1964). Toxicology of EDTA. *Fd. Cosmet. Toxicol.* **2**, 763-67.

SUCROSE ACETATE ISOBUTYRATE

First draft prepared by
Ms E. Vavasour
Toxicological Evaluation Division
Bureau of Chemical Safety, Food Directorate
Health and Welfare Canada
Ottawa, Ontario, Canada

1.   EXPLANATION

Sucrose acetate isobutyrate, which is a mixture of esters of sucrose esterified with acetic and isobutyric acids, was evaluated at the nineteenth, twenty-first and twenty-sixth meetings of the Committee (Annex 1, references 38, 44 and 59). At its twenty-first meeting, the Committee concluded that a complete toxicological profile was required for the evaluation of this compound, including carcinogenicity/toxicity studies in two animal species, a 2-year study in dogs with adequate numbers and dose groups to demonstrate a no-effect level and to assess the adverse effects of the substance on liver function, and a multigeneration reproduction/teratogenicity study. This information was not yet available when the compound was again reviewed at the twenty-sixth meeting of the Committee, so no ADI was allocated, although a toxicological monograph summarizing the available toxicological data was prepared (Annex 1, reference 60). With the exception of the 2-year study in dogs, the requested data were available for consideration at the present meeting. The new data that have been made available as well as relevant studies from the previous monograph are summarized in this monograph.

2.   BIOLOGICAL DATA

2.1   Biochemical aspects

2.1.1   Absorption, distribution, and excretion

2.1.1.1   Rats

Male albino Holtzman rats, about 250 g, were intubated with ^{14}C-SAIB of specific activity 0.411 μCi/mg (all ^{14}C-SAIB used this and the following studies was labelled on the sucrose portion of the molecule) in corn oil at dose levels equivalent to 27 or 100 mg/kg bw. The proportion of the administered dose absorbed from the GI tract was greater at the low dose (74-82%) than at the high dose (45-50%).

Elimination of 88 to 90% of the administered dose occurred in 48 hours. The relative proportion of radioactivity eliminated by the various routes varied with the dose. At the high dose level, 54-56% of the absorbed activity was eliminated as CO_2 and 26-28% in the urine. At the lower dose, 63-67% of the absorbed activity was eliminated in CO_2 and 23-25% in the urine. Four days after the administration of the test compound, less than 1% of the administered radioactivity was retained in the gastrointestinal tract (from cardiac valve to rectum), blood, liver and kidney. Chromatography of extracts of the 24-hour faeces of rats showed the presence of SAIB and other metabolites. Most of the radioactivity in urine was in the form of sucrose, although other unidentified substances were also present (Fassett and Reynolds 1962; Reynolds 1972a; Reynolds et al. 1974).

Using the same protocol as in the previous study, male albino Holtzman rats weighing approximately 250 g received 100 mg/kg bw of ^{14}C-SAIB (specific activity, 0.38 μCi/mg) in corn oil by gavage. At termination of the study, 3 or 3.5 hours after dosing, 78-84% of the radioactivity was recovered from the gastrointestinal contents. An additional 7-9% of the radioactivity was recovered from the stomach, intestinal and caecal tissues. Less than 4% of the radioactivity was excreted in the breath, urine and faeces within 3-3.5 hours after dosing, indicating that little absorption had taken place. Extracts of the gastrointestinal contents and organs were found to contain sucrose and partially acylated sucrose esters in addition to unchanged SAIB (Reynolds 1963).

Two rats were given a single oral dose of ^{14}C-SAIB (0.36 μCi/mg) in aqueous emulsion at levels equivalent to 5.8 and 11.2 mg/kg bw. Within 3 days, 59 and 52% of the ^{14}C-labelled SAIB were recovered in breath as respired CO_2, 11 and 13% recovered in the urine, and 23 and 27% recovered in the faeces. The rats retained 6 and 6.6% of the ^{14}C in the carcass; the distribution of radioactivity among the organs was comparable. Total absorption of administered SAIB was 71 and 77% of the administered dose when recovery of label from urine, expired air and whole carcass was combined. The major ^{14}C compounds in the faeces were SAIB or highly acylated sucrose molecules. Chromatographic separation of urine showed 1 or 2 major peaks, which were not identified. In comparison, rats given a single oral dose of ^{14}C-labelled sucrose in aqueous solution at a level of 400 mg/kg bw showed rapid absorption and metabolism of the sucrose to [14]CO_2, the maximum rate of elimination being observed 2 hours post-dosing. Only small amounts of ^{14}C were eliminated in the urine and faeces. At sacrifice (3 days post dosing), the carcass retained 9.6-12.9% of the ^{14}C label. Distribution of radioactivity in the carcass was similar for rats treated with SAIB or with sucrose. No accumulation of radioactivity in a particular organ was observed (Reynolds 1972b; Reynolds et al. 1974).

Female rats received ^{14}C-SAIB (specific activity 1.0 μCi/mg) by oral intubation at a dose level of 50 mg/kg bw. More than 90% of the radioactivity remained in the gastrointestinal tract at 6 hours, of which approximately 60% was situated in the lumen of the small intestine. Less than 30% of this amount was present as SAIB. Only 4.9% of the dose was excreted in the urine, and 2.4% was expired as CO_2 at 6 hours after dosing. Twenty-four hours after administration of the test compound, 90% of the ^{14}C had been excreted and less than 8% remained in the gastrointestinal tract. Metabolism to CO_2 accounted for 45% of the excreted radioactivity. Faecal material contained 33% of ^{14}C, of which 26% was in the form of unchanged SAIB. ^{14}C metabolites present in urine were similar to those obtained from urine of rats given an equivalent dose of ^{14}C sucrose (Phillips et al. 1976).

In a series of experiments with sucrose octaisobutyrate (SOIB), a constituent ester of SAIB, male rats received ≈ 200 mg/kg bw ^{14}C-SOIB (specific activity 0.2 μCi/ml) by corn oil gavage. Radioactivity was not detectable in urine, faeces or breath until 6 hours following dosing, but by 5 days >95% of the dose had been excreted by these routes. The major route of excretion was the faeces (78-93% of the dose); consequently, only a small amount of administered SOIB was absorbed. $^{14}CO_2$ in the breath was the major route of excretion for absorbed SOIB. Radioactivity in bile samples collected from an indwelling catheter for 12 hours after dosing was negligible or only slightly above background and after 48 hours, only 0.2% of the administered dose had been collected from bile. Similarly, radioactivity in terminal blood samples collected at 2, 4, 8, 12, and 24 hours was only detectable in 24-hour samples and included a negligible percentage of the administered radioactivity (Noker 1982; Noker et al. 1986).

2.1.1.2 Dogs

Two dogs received single doses of 3.0 or 4.8 mg/kg bw ^{14}C-SAIB (specific activity 0.36 μCi/mg) in aqueous emulsion by stomach tube. A large proportion of the administered dose (compared with rats at the same dose) was eliminated in the faeces (52.5 and 45.5%, respectively), within 4 days of dosing. Although collection of $^{14}CO_2$ excreted in breath was incomplete, it still represented the major portion of excreted radioactivity (26-28%). Smaller amounts were eliminated in the urine (6 and 7% after 7 and 8 days respectively). Chromatography of faecal extracts indicated the presence of SAIB and highly acylated sucrose esters. Radioactivity in urine samples corresponded almost entirely to sucrose esters while no significant amount of sucrose was detected (Reynolds and Travis 1972; Reynolds et al. 1974).

^{14}C-SOIB (specific activity 0.02 μCi/mg) was administered to male Beagle dogs by corn oil gavage at a dose of ≈ 200 mg/kg bw. Almost no radioactivity was detected as $^{14}CO_2$ during the first 24 hours after dosing. Throughout the 5-day study, the amount of radioactivity excreted as $^{14}CO_2$ accounted for 1% or less of the dose. The major route of elimination was the faeces, accounting for 77 to 94% of the dose. In one of the dogs, essentially the entire dose was recovered within 5 days, indicating that SOIB was not incorporated to any great extent in the tissues. In another study using dogs with indwelling catheters, between 2 and 10% of the dose was retrieved in bile collections made over 48 hours or more after a delay of 4-6 hours following dosing. Chromatographic analysis of the bile samples revealed at least 9 radiolabelled components. Although the identity of none of them could be established, SOIB was not present in the samples and all the components were more polar than the parent compound. The variability in total biliary excretion between individual animals and in the same animals in repeat-dose studies was attributed to differences in degree of absorption of the compound. The results of a separate 12-hour bile collection study were considered to be possibly inaccurate since the anaesthesia (halothane-nitrous oxide) used during the collection period may have resulted in reduced gastric motility (Noker 1984a; Noker et al. 1986).

2.1.1.3 Monkeys

Male Cynomolgus monkeys weighing approximately 2.5 kg received a single dose of ≈ 200 mg/kg bw ^{14}C-SOIB (specific activity 0.08 μCi/mg) by oral gavage in corn oil. The major route of elimination was the faeces, where the amount recovered from individual monkeys ranged from 61 to 85% of that administered. Radioactivity was detected in the breath of one monkey at 12 hours and in the other two monkeys only after 24 hours. During the 5-day observation period, the total amount of SOIB excreted as ^{14}CO$_2$ accounted for less than 2% of the administered dose. For each monkey, 1% or less of the dose was found in the urine. Excretion of radioactivity in the bile was monitored in three monkeys for at least 52 hours. For all 3 monkeys, very low levels of radioactivity were excreted into the bile, corresponding to only 0.1-0.2% of the administered dose. No significant level of radioactivity was detected in the blood or plasma in the 48 hours following dosing (Noker 1984b; Noker et al. 1986).

2.1.1.4 Humans

^{14}C-SAIB (specific activity 0.39 μCi/mg) was incorporated into a simulated non-carbonated soft drink and administered to 3 male subjects. The 3 subjects were each given 2 or 3 single doses at widely spaced intervals. The first dose was administered at a level of ≈ 1 mg/kg bw to each subject, none of whom had been previously exposed to SAIB. Two of these subjects were given a second dose at the same level 7-27 weeks after the first dose and following ingestion of unlabelled SAIB at a level of 1 mg/kg bw/dy for 7 days. The third subject received a single dose at a level of 0.18 mg/kg 25 weeks after the first dose. One subject was given a third dose at a level of 1 mg/kg bw 10 weeks after the second dose and immediately after ingestion of a high-fat meal. All subjects were monitored for elimination of radioactivity in expired air and urine for 30 days or more post-dosing. Elimination of radioactivity from the lungs occurred rapidly. [Only a small amount of the total was eliminated in the 6-8-hour period post-dosing, but excreted radioactivity reached maximum levels 9-15 hours post-dosing.] The subjects excreted 14 to 21% of the dose in the urine, the maximum rate of urinary excretion occurring within 3 hours and decreasing by 48 hours. About 10% or less of the dose was unabsorbed and appeared in the faeces of all subjects. Prior dosing with SAIB or ^{14}C-SAIB had no effect on the pattern of elimination. Chromatographic studies of urine showed several radioactive peaks, which have not been clearly identified; however, the amount present as free sucrose was estimated to be 20%

of the radioactivity and SAIB or highly acylated esters of sucrose were not detected. Chromatographic studies of extracts of faeces showed the presence of radioactive materials which did not correspond with those in the urine and which were probably highly acylated esters of sucrose and SAIB. No effect on blood haematology or selected blood chemical values was detected. In another study, two subjects ingested ^{14}C-sucrose at a level of 400 mg/kg bw, corresponding to the concentration of sucrose in the simulated soft drink administered in the previous study. Forty-two to 59% of the ^{14}C-sucrose was metabolized to ^{14}CO$_2$ within 48 hours, the maximum rate of elimination occurring 3 hours post-dosing. Both subjects eliminated small amounts of ^{14}C in the urine (1.9 and 1.7% of the dose in 48 hours). Most of the radioactivity appeared to have been incorporated into urea and free sucrose was not detected in urine samples (Reynolds et al. 1972; Reynolds et al. 1974).

Two male subjects were given SAIB (100 mg or 1 g) as a single dose. The urinary excretion of sucrose and sucrose esters was less than the limit of detection of the assay procedure used (1 ppm sucrose) in any 24-hour period up to 5 days post-dosing. In another study, 2 male subjects were given 1 g of SAIB/day for 7 days. No urinary excretion of sucrose was detected. No unchanged SAIB or metabolites were detected in faecal samples of one subject given 100 mg of SAIB daily for 7 days. Two subjects were each given sucrose intravenously (100, 250 and 800 mg in a 10% solution w/v on different days) and the urine collected 3, 12 and 24 hours. Approximately 50% of the administered sucrose was recovered in the urine by 3 hours at all 3 dose levels, and there was almost quantitative recovery of the lower dose by 12 hours (Phillips et al. 1976).

2.1.1.5 **Combined species**

The disposition of SAIB following a single oral dose was compared in the rat (5.8, 11.2, 27 and 100 mg/kg bw), dog (3.0 and 4.8 mg/kg bw) and human (0.18 and 1.0 mg/kg bw). The authors concluded that the excretion patterns for humans and rats showed more similarities than did the excretion patterns for humans and dogs. Humans and rats (at the three lower doses) absorbed a larger proportion of the administered SAIB from the intestine and converted a higher proportion to CO$_2$. The results of chromatography of urine extracts indicated that the types of partial sucrose esters differed in dogs compared with rats and humans. More highly acylated sucrose molecules were present in the urine of dogs and more polar esters in the urine of humans and rats (Reynolds et al. 1971; Reynolds et al. 1974).

Comparison of the disposition of SOIB in rats, dogs and monkeys receiving the same single, oral dose (200 mg/kg bw), showed that the three species excreted similar amounts of the administered compound in the faeces and that this was the major route for excretion of SOIB. However, the three species differed in the disposition of absorbed SOIB. Measurement of biliary excretion indicated that the dog excreted substantial amounts of SOIB by this route (3-10% of the administered dose) compared with rats and monkeys (≤ 0.2% of the administered dose). In the rat, the preferred route of elimination of absorbed SOIB was through expired CO$_2$, representing 3-15% of the dose; CO_2 represented 0.1-1.7% of the dose in dogs and monkeys. The authors conclude that the virtual absence of radioactivity in the blood, urine, expired CO_2 and bile of the monkey suggests that this species did not readily absorb SOIB. Chromatographic analysis of the faecal metabolites of SOIB indicated that this compound was hydrolyzed to a different extent in the gut of the rat, dog and monkey with the most extensive hydrolysis occurring in the rat, less extensive in the dog and little intestinal metabolism in the monkey (Noker et al. 1986).

2.1.2   Biotransformation

The bile ducts of 3 rats and 1 dog were cannulated and the bile was collected following single per os doses of ^{14}C-SAIB. The rats eliminated 4.5% of the administered dose in the bile within 15 hours of dosing. Chromatographic separation of the metabolites present in the bile showed that they had properties similar to sucrose or sucrose with few acyl groups attached. In the case of the dog, which was subjected to 3 separate trials, about 6% of the dose was eliminated in the bile within 15 hours of dosing. Separation of the metabolites showed the presence of SAIB or highly acylated sucrose (Reynolds et al. 1975).

Homogenates of the liver and small intestinal mucosa of rats prepared in Krebs-Ringer phosphate buffer (pH 7.4) were incubated with ^{14}C-SAIB. At 0, 1, 2, and 4 hours, samples were removed and assayed for metabolites. The rate and extent of hydrolysis of SAIB by liver homogenates was less than that of the intestinal mucosa, and the rate and extent of hydrolysis decreased with increasing concentrations of SAIB. In another experiment, ^{14}C-labelled SAIB was incubated under anaerobic conditions with preparations derived from the contents of 3 regions of the rat gut, namely, stomach, small intestine and caecum. Preparations from the proximal region of the small intestine showed the greatest hydrolytic activity. The hydrolytic activity of the caecal contents was less than that of the small intestine, and the stomach contents showed no hydrolytic activity. An ex vivo study of the disappearance of radioactivity from loops of the small intestine of rats after introduction of ^{14}C-sucrose and ^{14}C-SAIB showed that sucrose was rapidly cleared from the intestine, whereas the rate of removal of SAIB activity was very slow, less than 13% in 1 hour. When ^{14}C-SAIB was incubated with human faecal homogenates, 40% was hydrolyzed in a 16-hour period, with less than 2% completely hydrolyzed to sucrose. Hydrolysis of SAIB by suspensions of bacteria isolated from human faeces was even less than that of the faecal suspensions (Phillips et al. 1976).

Dogs and rats received a single dose of ^{14}C-SAIB [not specified in previous monograph]. The rats eliminated 7-10% of the dose in the urine in 30-46 hours and the dogs, 2.8-5.2% of the dose in the urine in 29-30 hours. Size exclusion chromatography of the dog and rat urine showed that ^{14}C-labelled molecules larger than sucrose were not present to any significant extent. The nature of the metabolites was not determined, although sucrose, glucose and fructose appeared to be absent. A male subject was given a single dose of ^{14}C-SAIB at a dose level of 1.18 mg/kg bw. Samples of urine were collected before dosing and at 0 and 6.2 hours after dosing, and subjected to various chromatographic procedures. Glucose, fructose and the esters of fructose and sucrose were not present in the urine. Two unidentified peaks were considered to be the principal metabolites of SAIB (Reynolds and Zeigler 1977).

2.2 Toxicological studies

2.2.1 Acute toxicity studies

The results of acute toxicity studies with sucrose acetate isobutyrate are summarized in Table 1.

Table 1. Results of acute toxicity studies with sucrose acetate isobutyrate.

Animal	Route	LD_{50} (g/kg bw)	Reference
Rat	Oral	>5.0	Fassett and Reynolds 1962; Reynolds 1972a

2.2.2 Short-term toxicity studies

2.2.2.1 Mice

Five groups of B6C3F$_1$/CrlBR mice (10/sex/goup) received approximately 0, 0.625, 1.25, 2.5 or 5.0 g SAIB/kg bw/day in the diet for 4 weeks. Body weights, food consumption and physical examinations were recorded at initiation of treatment and weekly during the study. Feeding of SAIB at these doses for 4 weeks had no effect on the biological performance of the treated animals. No treatment-related observations were noted at the terminal necropsy (MacKenzie 1987).

2.2.2.2 Rats

A three-week feeding study was conducted in which groups of 30 Sprague-Dawley rats (15/sex/group) were fed 0, 5 000 or 50 000 ppm SAIB in the diet. Five rats/sex/group were sacrificed after 1, 2 and 3 weeks of treatment. Twice weekly determinations of body weight and food consumption indicated no adverse effect of treatment on these parameters. Daily examination of the rats during the first week revealed a high incidence of respiratory disease which was not related to treatment; no animals died. Gross necropsy at sacrifice did not reveal any treatment-related changes. Absolute and relative liver weights were comparable between control and treated groups (Procter and Chappel 1970a).

In a series of studies, Sprague-Dawley rats were divided into 14 treatment groups of 10 animals/sex/group and fed diets containing SAIB at dietary levels of 1.0, 2.0 and 4.0% (w/w) supplemented with 5% corn oil (w/w). The groups were fed the test diets for 28 or 56 days continuously or for 28 days followed or preceded by 28 days on control diet. Two groups were fed the control diet containing corn oil only for 28 or 56 days continuously. At the termination of the study, animals were sacrificed and blood collected for determination of serum alkaline phosphatase (SAP), ornithine carbamyl transferase (OCT), blood urea nitrogen (BUN), triglyceride, cholesterol and glucose. The animals were autopsied, examined grossly, and absolute and relative liver weights were determined. Liver microsomal enzyme activity (p-nitroanisole demethylase), glucose-6-phosphatase and bilirubin-β-D-glucuronyl transferase were determined and the liver was histologically examined. Weight gain and feed consumption of test and control groups were similar. There were no significant changes in the serum chemistry of the test animals. Gross pathology at autopsy was negative and liver weights (absolute and relative) were similar for test and control groups. Microsomal enzyme activity was similar for test and control animals, with the exception that glucose-6-phosphatase activity was reduced in male rats on the 4% SAIB diet (Krasavage and Terhaar 1971b; Krasavage et al., 1973).

Groups of 50 Holtzman albino rats, 25/sex/group, were maintained on diets containing 0, 1.0 or 5.0% SAIB (w/w) for a period of 95 days. Haematological studies consisting of Hb, Hct and total and differential WBC counts were carried out at days 24, 52 and 87 of the study. Body weight and food intake were determined weekly. The animals were necropsied on day 95 and liver and kidney weights recorded and a complete histological study made of 15 tissues and organs, including the liver, stomach and small intestine. There was a slight reduction in weight gain in the males fed 5% SAIB and a slight increase in the absolute and relative liver weight of females fed 5% SAIB. No compound-related histopathological changes were observed (Fassett et al., 1962).

Four groups of 20 Sprague-Dawley rats (10 males, 10 females; body weight 85-100 g), were maintained on diets for 13 weeks which contained 0, 0.30, 1.80 or 9.12% SAIB dissolved in vegetable oil, to a final concentration of 9.3% oil in the diet. Body weights were determined weekly. Prior to sacrifice at 13 weeks, blood samples were taken and Hb content and total and differential WBC count were determined. At autopsy, absolute and relative organ weights were recorded for liver, kidneys, lungs, testes, spleen and heart and a microscopic examination was made of 10 tissues and organs including the liver. At the highest dose level there was occasional diarrhoea. However, there were no significant differences in weight gain between control and test animals. Organ weight, blood chemistry and histopathology were similar in all groups and showed no compound-related effects (Hint, 1964).

Groups of 80 rats (Sprague-Dawley), 40/sex/group, were maintained on diets containing 0, 2.5, 5.0 or 10% SAIB. A positive control group for the study of liver enlargement and microsomal enzyme induction received phenobarbital daily by gavage at a dose equivalent to 100 mg/kg bw. Half of each group received treatment for 6 weeks, and the other half for 12 weeks. Following 6 and 12 weeks on the test diet, one subgroup (10 rats/sex/group) was subjected to the Zoxazolamine muscle relaxant test and retested 4 weeks after removal from treatment. The other subgroup (10 rats/sex/group) was subjected to extensive histological and biochemical tests at the end of 6 or 12 weeks, which included serum OCT and protein, glycogen, carboxylesterase, lipid and water of the liver. In addition, urinary excretion of ascorbic acid was measured at weekly intervals during treatment. At autopsy, absolute and relative organ weights of the adrenals, heart, kidney and liver were recorded for test and control animals for both subgroups.

Dietary SAIB had no significant effect on the weight gain of test animals except at the low dose (2.5%) level, where there was slight decrease in weight gain of males after 6 weeks and in both sexes after 12 weeks. In general, food consumption in the SAIB groups was not affected. The SAIB-treated rats did not differ from negative controls in their response to the Zoxazolamine muscle relaxant challenge or in urinary excretion of ascorbic acid. In contrast, in the phenobarbital-treated rats, the response to Zoxazolamine was markedly reduced and urinary excretion of ascorbic acid showed a prolonged and marked elevation. On this basis, the authors concluded that induction of microsomal enzymes did not occur in SAIB-treated rats. There were no significant compound-related effects in the organ weights, gross pathology or histopathology in the SAIB-treated animals. The biochemical studies of SAIB-fed animals showed significantly increased glycogen and water content in the livers of the 10% males and females but no increase in hepatic carboxylesterase levels. In contrast, the animals which had been administered phenobarbital had enlarged livers and demonstrated a significant reduction in glycogen and water content, an increase in lipid content, and a marked increase in carboxylesterase activity of the liver (Procter *et al.*, 1971a).

Groups of 20 male and 20 female F-344 rats were fed diets which provided doses of 0, 0.5, 1 or 2 g SAIB/kg bw/day for 52 weeks. Individual body weights and food consumption were recorded weekly. Ophthalmoscopic examinations were performed on all animals at initiation, 6 months and 12 months; a battery of standard haematology, clinical chemistry and urinalysis parameters were measured at 6 and 12 months. A bromosulfophthalein (BSP) clearance test was performed on all animals in the control and high-dose groups during weeks 23 and 48. No information on the conduct of the BSP clearance test was supplied (*i.e.* dose of BSP, clearance times used). All surviving animals were sacrificed after 52 weeks of treatment and the organ weights for heart, kidneys, liver, gonads and brain recorded. Histopathological examination was conducted on kidney, liver, lung and gross lesions from all animals in all dose groups and on 32 additional tissues, including the common bile duct and organs of the GI tract, from all control and high-dose animals. Samples of the liver from 3 control and 3 high-dose animals were also examined by electron microscopy.

Treatment with SAIB did not affect body weight gain, food consumption or the general health of the animals. In addition, results from measurement of haematology, clinical chemistry and urinalysis parameters did not suggest adverse treatment-related effects. Absolute, relative-to-brain or relative-to-body organ weihts were not affected and no unusual histopathological observations were noted. Ultrastructural examination of livers failed to reveal any change in liver cells or in bile canaliculi and sinusoidal linings as a result of treatment with SAIB. A NOEL of 2 g/kg bw/day was assigned for this study (MacKenzie 1990a).

2.2.2.3 Dogs

Three test groups of 8 pure-bred beagle dogs (4 males, 4 females), were maintained on diets containing 0.2, 0.6 and 2.0% SAIB dissolved in cottonseed oil for a period of 90 days. The control group consisted of 12 pure-bred beagles (6 males, 6 females). The total fat content of the diets was adjusted to 12% by addition of cottonseed oil. Physical examinations and clinical studies were made twice prior to commencement of the study and at week 12. The clinical studies included measurement of haemoglobin concentration, haematocrit, total and differential WBC count, blood glucose, BUN, SAP and LDH, and standard urinary parameters. Neurological reflexes were tested and body weight and food intake recorded weekly. At the termination of the study (end of twelfth week), all dogs were sacrificed and autopsied. Absolute and relative organ weights were determined for liver, kidneys, spleen, gonads, adrenals, pituitary and brain. Twenty-three tissues, including the liver, gall bladder and small and large intestines from dogs in the control and 2% groups were examined microscopically. The liver and kidneys of dogs in the 0.2 and 0.6% SAIB groups were also examined microscopically.

There was no significant compound-related effect on food intake or weight gain. Haematological and urine parameters of test animals and controls were comparable and within normal values. Serum chemistry indicated a significant increase in SAP activity of both male and female dogs in the 2% group (approximately two times increase over pretreatment values). At autopsy there was a marked, dose-related increase in relative liver weights in the 0.6% and 2% groups of both sexes when compared with controls; all other organ weights were normal. No compound-related histopathology was observed (Morgareidge, 1965).

In another study, groups of 12 beagle dogs (6/sex/group) were fed diets containing SAIB at 0, 0.5, 1.0, 2.0 and 4.0% for a period of 12 weeks. Test animals in the 4.0% group were maintained for a further 3 weeks on an SAIB-free diet. Body weight and food intake were determined during the course of the study. Fasting blood samples and urine samples were obtained at weeks 4, 8 and 12 and standard haematological, biochemical and urinalysis tests were performed. At these intervals, 30-minute bromosulfophthalein (BSP) and phenosulfophthalein (PSP) retentions were measured. BSP and indocyanine green (ICG) plasma disappearance curves were determined at week 12 for male dogs in the 0 and 4.0% groups. BSP clearance was measured in the 4.0% group during the 3-week withdrawal period. At the end of the test period, the animals were sacrificed, and following completion of gross pathological examination, absolute and relative organ weights were determined for the brain, heart, liver, lung, kidneys, adrenals, gonads, prostate, uterus, pituitary, spleen and thyroid. A microscopic examination was made of samples of 6 tissues including the liver and small and large intestines. Histochemical studies were carried out on liver sections of dogs from the 0.5, 1 and 2% groups, and included evaluation of succinate dehydrogenase, phosphorylase, glucose-6-phosphate dehydrogenase, glycogen, acid phosphatase, alkaline phosphatase, adenosine triphosphatase, and use of Masson's trichrome stain. Additional samples of liver from test animals (not including the 4% groups) were analyzed for protein, glycogen, lipid and water, and carboxylesterase activity. Serum OCT was measured in serum samples obtained terminally. Electron microscopic studies were carried out on liver samples from animals in all groups except the 4.0% group.

Daily clinical observation revealed no change in the treated dogs. Growth and food intake appeared normal in all groups. Urine and haematological analyses were similar in test and control groups and of the biochemical parameters, only SAP values demonstrated an increase in the treated animals which was directly related to dose level and duration of exposure. Marked bromosulfophthalein (BSP) retention occurred among all test animals during the experimental period, but the magnitude of the response was not dose-related. The marked increase in BSP retention in the 4% group was reversible following withdrawal of SAIB from the diet for 3 weeks. Indocyanine green clearance rates were reduced in a manner paralleling the changes observed in the BSP tests. Male dogs treated with SAIB showed a dose-related increase in absolute and relative liver weight which was reversible following 3 weeks on a SAIB-free diet. No liver enlargement was observed in the female dogs. Histochemical studies of liver sections did not reveal any changes in the hepatocytes; however, there was a marked increase in enzyme activity (alkaline phosphatase, adenosine triphosphatase and glucose-6-phosphate dehydrogenase) of the bile canaliculi of treated animals when compared with controls. There was a slight but statistically significant reduction of protein content and a slight increase in glycogen in the liver. Liver lipid was slightly increased at the 2% level. An increase in liver carboxylesterase was observed in the test groups, particularly in the males, but the effect was not dose-related. Serum OCT values assayed in terminal blood samples were similar for test and control animals and within normal range. Light microscopic examination of the liver from treated males showed hepatocellular hypertrophy, dilatation of the bile canaliculi, and an increase in the number of bile pigment granules. Electron microscopic evaluation of the hepatocytes of treated dogs showed various changes, the most consistent being an increase in smooth endoplasmic reticulum (SER). The effect was observed in both treated males and females, but the effect was most pronounced in the males. The structural changes found in the bile canaliculi and the pericanalicular cytoplasmic areas included moderate dilatation of the canaliculi, pronounced microvillous pattern, prominent Golgi bodies and an increased number of microbodies in the intracellular pigment granules. Since effects of the test material on the liver were observed at all dose levels, a NOEL was not observed for this study (Procter *et al.*, 1970).

In a parallel study, a group of 8 beagle dogs (4/sex/group) was fed SAIB at a dietary level of 2.0% for 12 weeks and then maintained for 6 weeks on an SAIB-free diet prior to sacrifice. SAIB caused a slight weight depression that was reversible upon removal of SAIB from the diet. The effect of SAIB on two indicators of liver function, SAP activity and plasma BSP clearance was completely reversed following the 6-week withdrawal period. At autopsy, the liver enlargement reported in organ weight studies, the high activity of alkaline phosphatase, adenosine triphosphatase and glucose-6-phosphate dehydrogenase in bile canaliculi reported in the histochemical studies, and the effect of SAIB administration on liver carboxylesterase activity were fully reversible following this withdrawal period. Electron microscopic examination of the liver indicated that the cellular morphology was completely normal following removal of the SAIB from the diet (Procter et al., 1971b; Procter et al., 1973).

Six male beagle dogs, approximately 6 years old, were fed a control diet containing 5% (w/w) corn oil for 3 weeks and then an experimental diet containing 5% SAIB for 28 days. The dogs were returned to control diet for the next 57 days. Haematocrit, haemoglobin, total and differential WBC counts, ASAT, blood glucose, BUN, serum protein, SAP, OCT, and triglyceride and cholesterol determinations were made twice prior to and at weekly intervals during the feeding study. Four of the dogs then received one day's allotment of the SAIB diet, and ICG plasma clearance rates and SAP were determined after 24 and 48 hours. The study was terminated 3 days later. At the termination of the study, all dogs were sacrificed, absolute and relative liver and kidney weights determined, and 23 tissues and organs, including liver, gall bladder and organs of the GI tract, examined microscopically. Dogs on diets containing 5% SAIB showed a moderate increase in SAP and a prolongation of ICG plasma clearance by the liver. Within 5 weeks of withdrawal of SAIB from the diet, SAP activity was near normal. The ICG clearance rate appeared within normal range 2 weeks after withdrawal of SAIB from the diet. After receiving control diet for 8 weeks, the 4 dogs returned to SAIB-containing diets for 24 hours showed a significant slowing of ICG clearance rate, but SAP did not appear to be increased. All other parameters measured in test and control animals were similar (Krasavage and Terhaar, 1971a; Krasavage et al. 1973).

In another study, groups of 5 male beagle dogs (11-13 months of age) were fed diets containing 5.0% SAIB plus 5% corn oil, or corn oil alone for 91 days. Physical appearance, behaviour, food consumption and body weight were determined daily throughout the study. Indocyanine green plasma clearance rates were determined at 3-week intervals. Serum bilirubin was measured at week 7 of the study and haematological and blood chemistry (haematocrit, haemoglobin, BUN, serum protein, SAP and OCT, triglyceride and cholesterol) studies were carried out at the termination of the study. All dogs were autopsied at the termination of the study, liver and kidney weights recorded, and all tissues (not specified) examined microscopically. Livers were analyzed for glycogen, protein and phospholipid content, and samples were assayed for microsomal enzyme activity (p-nitroanisole demethylase), and for glucose-6-phosphatase and bilirubin-β-D-glycuranyl transferase activities. Liver, kidney, bone, bile and scrapings of the intestinal mucosa were analyzed for alkaline phosphatase activity. Dogs fed SAIB showed a slight increase in SAP, as well as a prolonged indocyanine green clearance time, increased relative and absolute liver weight. Liver glycogen and phospholipid content were increased while liver protein was decreased. Disk electrophoresis and isoenzyme inactivation studies of tissue alkaline phosphatase indicated that the elevation of SAP was related to the liver isoenzyme. The liver content of alkaline phosphatase in SAIB-fed animals was twice that of controls. All other parameters studied were similar in test and control animals (Krasavage and Terhaar, 1971c; Krasavage *et al.*, 1973).

2.2.2.4 Monkeys

Two male and two female *Cynomolgus* monkeys received SAIB by intubation in an orange juice vehicle over a period of 14 days. Dosing started at 1.25 g/kg bw/dy and increased by a factor of 2 with a 72-h rest period between doses, up to a dose of 20 g/kg bw/d. The animals were observed daily for signs of adverse effects. Body weight and food consumption were recorded daily. Seventy-two hours after the last dose, the animals were sacrificed and complete gross postmortem examinations were conducted. No deaths occurred during the study. Moderate amounts of yellow, watery emesis and/or yellow/tan watery stools were observed in some males and some females 1 to 5 hours after dosing. Twenty-four hours after dosing, all the animals passed moderate amounts of loose, tan stools. Gross postmortem examinations did not reveal any changes which could be attributed to an effect of treatment (Tierney and Rinehart, 1979).

Twelve *Cynomolgus* monkeys were assigned to six goups (1/sex/group) in a range-finding study in which doses of 0, 0.5, 1.0, 2.0, 5.0 and 10.0 g SAIB/kg bw/day were administered by gavage in orange juice concentrate for 15 consecutive days. Physical observations, body weight and food consumption were recorded daily. Thirty-minute BSP retention was determined pretest and prior to termination. Following gross necropsy, adrenals, heart, kidneys, liver and all gross lesions were preserved for histopathological examination. In addition, two sections of liver from control and high-dose monkeys were examined by electron microscopy. Treatment with SAIB for 15 days had no effect on body weight or food consumption. Gross postmortem examinations and light microscopic evaluations did not reveal evidence of changes attributable to treatment. Electron microscopy of liver samples from the high-dose male and female revealed glycogen aggregation surrounded by smooth endoplasmic reticulum in hepatocytes which did not represent a significant alteration in ultrastructural organization (Tierney and Rinehart, 1980a).

In another study, the evaluation of selected clinical chemical parameters was conducted in eight *Cynomolgus* monkeys (1/sex/group) fed doses of 0, 2.0, 5.0 and 10.0 g SAIB/kg bw/day under the same conditions as in the previous study. Blood samples were collected pretest and at termination of the study for measurement of ASAT, ALAT, SAP, BUN, total protein, albumin, globulin, creatinine, total bilirubin and bromosulfophthalein retention. Although plasma levels of BSP were presented and the time for clearance indicated, no other details of the clearance test (*e.g.* dose of BSP) were provided. Gross necropsy was conducted at sacrifice. Treatment with SAIB had no effect on body weight or food consumption. There were no differences in the clinical chemistry parameters, including bromosulfophthalein retention, which could be attributed to treatment (Tierney and Rinehart, 1980b).

In a 4-week oral toxicity study with *Cynomolgus* monkeys, doses of 0, 500, 1 450 and 2 400 mg SAIB/kg bw/day were administered by corn oil gavage to 4 groups of 1 monkey/sex/group. Clinical observations were made twice daily and included monitoring of inappetence. Body weights were determined weekly and a complete physical examination was conducted prior to treatment and at the end of 4 weeks. A standard set of haematology and clinical chemistry parameters (including gamma-glutamyl transpeptidase, SAP, OCT and 30-minute BSP clearance) were measured from blood samples collected pretest and at four weeks. Gross necropsy was conducted at sacrifice. Inappetence was noted occasionally throughout the study for most monkeys, although it was observed on 13 separate days in the high-dose female. Consequently, this animal experienced a 12% weight loss over the course of the study. Body weight gains of the other animals were comparable. No abnormalities related to treatment were detected from the physical examinations. The results of haematological and clinical chemistry tests did not indicate an effect of treatment although lowered serum phosphorous levels were detected in the high-dose female. For BSP clearance, only semi-quantitative results were presented, *i.e.* >95% clearance for all groups. This could indicate that the dose used was too low to detect any changes within a standard 30 min. period. The concentration of BSP in blood was not presented. Gross necropsy did not reveal any unusual findings (Blair, 1986).

Groups of 4 male and 4 female *Cynomolgus* monkeys received doses of 0, 500, 1 450 or 2 400 mg SAIB/kg bw/day by corn oil gavage for 52 weeks. Clinical observations, including inappetance, were made twice daily and body weights determined weekly. Complete physical examinations and separate ophthalmoscopic examinations were conducted on all monkeys pretest and during months 3, 6, 9, and 12. Blood samples for determination of a standard set of haematological and clinical chemistry parameters (including SAP, gamma-glutamyl transpeptidase, OCT, BSP clearance and bile acid analysis) were also collected at the same intervals. At termination, gross necropsy was performed, selected organs were weighed, and 40 tissues and organs including liver, GI tract and gross lesions were subjected to histopathological examination.

During the study a few animals had signs of slight anal staining and slightly soft stool. However, there were no signs of inappetance or changes relating to administration of the test material, and none of the animals demonstrated body weight loss over the course of the study. The physical and ophthalmoscopic examinations did not reveal any treatment-related abnormalities. In addition, analysis of the haematological and clinical chemistry parameters obtained during the study indicated that no effect of treatment on these parameters was evident. Semi-quantitative measurements only of BSP clearance were given and blood levels of BSP were not presented. There were no unusual histopathological observations indicating an effect of treatment, including the liver. Since no effects of treatment were observed, the NOEL was the highest dose tested, 2400 mg/kg bw/day (Blair, 1990).

2.2.3   Long-term toxicity/carcinogenicity studies

2.2.3.1 Mice

A carcinogenicity study was conducted with B6C3F$_1$ mice in which 5 groups of 50 mice/sex/group received 0.0, 0.0, 1.25, 2.5 or 5.0 g SAIB/kg bw/day in the diet for 104 weeks. Physical examination, body weight and food consumption data were collected weekly. A standard set of haematology parameters was determined for 15 mice/sex from one control group and from the high dose group at 26, 52, 78 and 104 weeks of the study. Necropsy was performed on all animals dying on test or sacrificed. The weights of liver with gall bladder, lungs and kidneys were recorded for all animals sacrificed at 104 weeks. Histopathology was carried out on lungs, liver, kidneys and gross lesions from all animals and on 44 additional organs and tissues, including the GI tract, from animals that died on test and the control and high-dose animals from the terminal sacrifice.

Survival of the mice from all groups in this study ranged from 66 to 80%. No treatment-related effects on body weight gain were noted. Food consumption was elevated in both male and female mice receiving SAIB in the diet. The difference was frequently statistically significant in the high-dose males. There were no treatment-related differences in the haematology parameters. A dose-related decrease was apparent in the absolute weights of the kidneys of male mice which was statistically significant at the mid and high doses. The relative kidney weights were also lower than controls but the magnitude of the decrease was not related to dose. No unusual histopathological results for the kidney were observed. The authors concluded that this represented a NOEL of 2.5 g SAIB/kg bw/day (mid dose) for the male mouse. There was an increased incidence of hyperplasia of the perivascular and peribronchial lymphoid tissue of the lung in treated female mice which lacked dose-relationship; the result was not considered by the authors to be toxicologically significant. There were no treatment-related increases in the incidence of any tumour type. Based on the reduced kidney weights in the two top doses, a NOEL of 1.25 g/kg bw/day was considered appropriate for this study. The NOAEL was the highest dose tested, 5.0 g/kg bw/day (MacKenzie 1990c).

2.2.3.2 Rats

Groups of 20 (10 male, 10 female) Sprague-Dawley rats were maintained on diets containing 0, 0.38 or 9.38% (w/w) SAIB for 104 weeks. During this period the rats were bred on 3 successive occasions. Body weight and food intake were measured weekly.   All animals dying during the test period and those sacrificed at 104 weeks were autopsied. Relative and absolute organ weights were determined for heart, kidneys, liver, lungs, ovaries, spleen and testes. Histological examinations were made of 18 tissues, including the liver, stomach and ileum, from rats of the control and 9.38% SAIB groups.

Feeding SAIB did not increase the overall number of mortalities (15/20 in control, 13/20 in 0.38% and 14/22 in 9.38% groups) even though 4 males in the 9.38% SAIB group died during the first 10 weeks.   Autopsy revealed massive haemorrhages at multiple sites in each case.   Subsequent measurement of systolic blood pressure in surviving males failed to demonstrate any inter-group difference. There were some differences in food intake and body weight between the various groups at various stages of the study.   At the end of the first year there were no significant differences in body weights of rats from the various groups.   During the second year, however, male survivors receiving treatment at either dose weighed less than the respective controls.   There appeared to be a dose-related increase in the absolute and relative kidneys weights of both the male and female rats.   Due to the disparities in body weight of treated and control males, and the small number surviving (2 or 3 animals/group), no meaningful conclusions could be drawn from the organ weight data for male groups at the termination of the study.   Histological studies did not reveal any compound-related lesions (Harper *et al.*, 1966).

A carcinogenicity study was conducted with F-344 rats in which 5 groups of 50 rats/sex/group received 0.0, 0.0, 0.5, 1.0 or 2.0 g SAIB/kg bw/day in the diet for 104 weeks.   Physical examination, body weight and food consumption data were recorded weekly.   RBC and total and differential WBC counts were performed on all rats prior to study initiation and on all surviving rats at termination.   Clinical chemistry parameters were not measured.   Necropsy was performed on all animals dying on test or sacrificed.   Organ weights were determined for brain, heart, liver, kidneys and gonads for all animals sacrificed at 104 weeks.   Histopathology was carried out on lungs, liver, kidneys and gross lesions from all animals and on 44 additional organs and tissues, including the organs of the GI tract, from animals that died on test and from the control and high-dose animals at termination.

The health of the treated and control animals was comparable throughout the study and survival rates at 104 weeks were similar.   No effect on body weight was seen in the treated male groups;   in females, a small but significant decrement was noted in the body weights of the high-dose group compared with control groups for the first 1½ years.   Food consumption was not affected by treatment. Treatment with SAIB had no effect on haematology, organ weights or macroscopic and microscopic examinations at termination of the study.   There were no treatment-related increases in the incidence of any tumour type.   The NOEL was 2 g/kg bw/day in this study (MacKenzie 1990b).

2.2.4   **Reproduction studies**

2.2.4.1 **Rats**

Groups of 15 female and 5 male Holtzman rats, 60 days of age, were maintained on diets containing 0 or 5% SAIB. These diets were fed to parents and their offspring throughout the study. After 1 month on the diet, the rats were regrouped, 1 male and 3 females/cage. Pregnant females were then housed separately. The parameters recorded for assessing reproductive performance were length of gestation, number of young and live young, number of young weaned and average weight at weaning and post-weaning. Fifty-one days after the last parturition, another mating was attempted. Progeny of the first breeding (F_1) were also bred. At necropsy, liver and kidney weights were measured in both F_0 and F_1 parental animals, and 12 tissues, including liver and stomach, were examined microscopically. Treatment with 5% SAIB did not affect the biological performance of the F_0 generation. The reproductive performance of the test parent generation resulting from the first breeding was equal to or superior to that of controls, based on the parameters measured. At the second breeding, a somewhat lower percentage of pups from the treated groups was reared from birth to weaning compared to controls, and those surviving 2 weeks post-weaning weighed less than the controls. The breeding of the F_1 generation appeared satisfactory. Due to an outbreak of respiratory disease, many F_1 parents and pups died during the test and none of the pups from the SAIB group survived post-weaning. No differences in organ weights or histopathology were detected between treated and control groups (Fassett *et al.*, 1965).

Groups of 20 Sprague-Dawley rats, 10/sex/group, age not indicated, were maintained on diets containing 0, 0.38 and 9.38% w/w SAIB for 5 weeks. Pairs of rats from each dose group (10 pairs) were selected and caged together for 19 days, after which the male was removed. Females were allowed to rear young to weaning at 21 days. Litters were weighed at days 1, 11 and 21 post-partum. All pups were sacrificed at 21 days, sexed and examined for gross abnormalities. The parent rats were bred 3 times during weeks 9-36 of the study, each female receiving a different male at each mating. Reproductive performance was based on number of pups born, conception rate, pups per litter, pups weaned, as well as the weight of pups on days 1, 11 and 21. Reproductive performance as judged from the data presented was slightly better in the 0.38% group than in the control. At the 9.38% level, fewer females became pregnant, fewer pups were born and fewer pups survived to weaning on the basis of the three breedings. The observed effects could have been due to compromised nutritive value of the feed at this high level of inclusion. Performance of the 0.38% group was comparable to controls (Harper *et al.*, 1966).

A three-generation reproduction study was conducted with groups of 30 male and 30 female weanling rats which received 0, 0.5, 1.0 or 2.0 g SAIB/kg bw/day in the diet for 10 weeks (males) or 2 weeks (females) prior to mating.

These F_0 animals were mated for 21 days on a one-to-one basis to produce the F_1 litters. From these litters, groups of 30 rats/sex were selected randomly to continue with the same dosage of SAIB in the diet, and to be mated 10 weeks after weaning to produce the F_{2a} and subsequently, the F_{2b} litters. The F_{2a} litters were mated in a similar fashion to produce the F_3 litters and the F_{2b} litters were used for teratologic evaluation (see Section 2.2.5.1). The study was completed with the necropsy of the F_{2a} females on Day 14 of the F_3 gestation. Rats received the test diet continuously throughout the premating, mating, gestation, lactation and weaning stages of the study. Body weight and food consumption were measured weekly throughout the study with the exception of the mating periods and the 2-week rest period between the F_{2a} and F_{2b} litters. The following reproductive parameters were assessed for the F_1 and F_{2a} litters: mating index, male and female fertility indices, gestation index, numbers of live- and stillborn pups, and pup weights, survival and sex ratio on days 0, 4 and 28 of lactation. Male and female fertility indices and numbers of corpora lutea and implantations were recorded for the F_3 litters. All F_0 and F_1 adult male and female rats were necropsied with particular attention to reproductive organs and macroscopic lesions, the males after completion of parturition and the females after completion of weaning. There were no consistent statistically significant differences in body weight gains, although body weights of the mid- and high-dose F_0 females were lower than controls during the first part of the lactation period, and slightly lower food consumption was noted for the F_{2a} males and females during the premating period. No treatment-related effects were noted on fertility, gestation or survival indices for any of the generations (MacKenzie 1990d). The NOEL was the highest dose tested, 2.0 g/kg bw/day.

2.2.5   Special studies on teratogenicity

2.2.5.1 Rats

The F_{2b} litters from the reproduction study described above were subjected to teratologic evaluation. Groups of 30 male and 30 female F-344 rats from the F_1 generation were subjected to in utero and lifetime exposure to 0, 0.5, 1.0, and 2.0 g SAIB/kg bw/day in the diet. The animals were bred on a one-to-one basis 2 weeks after completion of weaning of the F_{2a} litters. Vaginal smears were taken daily and the presence of a copulatory plug or sperm in the vaginal smear was taken as positive evidence of mating and counted as Day 0 of gestation. The F_1 dams were sacrificed on Day 20 of gestation and examined for the number and distribution of fetuses, the number of fetuses undergoing resorption and the number of corpora lutea. Live fetuses were removed from the uterus, weighed, sexed and examined for gross abnormalities. Approximately one-half of the pups from each litter were examined for soft tissue abnormalities and the remainder were examined for skeletal abnormalities. Weekly measurement of body weight and food consumption in the maternal animals did not reveal any effect of treatment on these parameters. Treatment with SAIB also did not affect mating indices, male fertility indices, female fertility indices, the number of corpora lutea or implantations, implantation efficiency, uterine weights, the number of live fetuses, early resorptions, late resorptions, sex ratios or fetal weights. External, skeletal and soft-tissue fetal examinations also did not reveal any treatment-related effects (MacKenzie 1990d).

2.2.5.2 Rabbits

Groups of 16 inseminated New Zealand white rabbits each received 0, 500, 850 or 1200 mg SAIB/kg bw/day orally by corn oil gavage in two doses on day 7 to 19 of gestation (the day of insemination was counted as day 0). On day 29 of gestation, the dams were sacrificed and the pups delivered by Caesarean section. The number and location of viable and nonviable fetuses, early and late resorptions and the number of total implantations and corpora lutea were recorded. Each fetus was weighed and examined for external malformations, then dissected and examined for visceral malformations, and the carcass prepared for subsequent skeletal examination. Laboured respiration was noted in several of the does from each of the treatment groups during the last few days of the treatment period but in none of the control animals. The authors attributed this to tracheal irritation from the test material. There were no treatment-related effects on body weight gain or food consumption measured on gestation days 0, 7, 13, 20 and 29, nor did macroscopic examination of the does following sacrifice reveal signs of maternotoxicity resulting from administration of the test material. The reproductive parameters and the fetal examinations did not reveal any embryotoxic or teratogenic effects attributable to treatment (Schardein, 1988).

2.2.6   Special studies on genotoxicity

The results of genotoxicity studies with sucrose acetate isobutyrate are summarized in Table 2.

2.2.7   Special studies on liver function

2.2.7.1 Rats

Groups of 5 male Wistar rats were maintained on diets containing 4% SAIB for 7 days. Bromosulfophthalein clearance was measured at 0 (pretreatment) and 24 and 48 hours following withdrawal from the treated feed. SAIB had no effect on bromosulfophthalein clearance (Procter and Chappel, 1971).

Groups of male rats (Sprague-Dawley) (group size not specified) were fed diets containing 4% SAIB and corn oil, or 5% corn oil. Indocyanine green (ICG) clearance was determined on at least 2 rats randomly selected from each group on days 1, 3, 5, 8, 10, 22, 26 and 36 of the study. The ICG plasma clearance rates in rats from the SAIB group was not significantly different from controls (Krasavage and Terhaar, 1972; Krasavage et al., 1973).

Table 2. Results of genotoxicity studies with sucrose acetate isobutyrate.

Test System	Test Object	Concentration of SAIB	Results	Reference
Ames test[1]	S. typhimurium TA1535, TA1537, TA1538, TA98, TA100, S. cerevisiae D4	10-2 000 µg/plate	Negative	Jagannath & Brusick 1978
Ames test[1]	S. typhimurium TA98, TA100	100-10 000 µg/plate	Negative	Bonin & Baker 1980
Ames test[1]	S. typhimurium TA98, TA100, TA1535, TA1537, TA1538	333-10 000 µg/plate	Negative	Lawlor & Valentine 1989
CHO/HGPRT forward mutation assay[1]	Chinese hamster ovary cells	10-1 000 µg/ml	Negative	Young 1985
Unscheduled DNA synthesis assay	Rat hepatocytes	0.25-1 000 µg/ml	Negative	Cifone 1985
In vitro chromosomal aberration assay[1]	Chinese hamster ovary cells	200-2 000 µg/ml	Negative	Ivett 1985
Dominant lethal assay	Rats	20, 200, 2 000 mg/kg bw	Negative[2]	Krasavage 1973

1 Both with and without metabolic activation.
2 Matings were conducted only every 2 weeks instead of every week.

2.2.7.2 Dogs

Two male and 2 female beagle dogs were fed a one day's dietary ration containing 0.1, 0.3 or 0.5% SAIB. All 4 animals were tested for bromosulfophthalein clearance 24 hours after feeding of SAIB and again after 48 hours. A rest period of 1 week was allowed between each dietary level. No bromosulfophthalein retention occurred at the 0.1% dietary SAIB level; 0.3% and 0.5% SAIB resulted in distinct but reversible bromosulfophthalein retention (Procter and Chappel, 1971).

Two series of experiments were carried out with 14 young, adult, male beagle dogs. In the first series, groups of 2 (control) or 3 (treated) dogs received a single dose of 2 g SAIB/kg bw or orange juice vehicle by gavage and 30-minute BSP clearance was measured 2, 4, 6, 10, 12, 18 or 24 hours later. Compared with pre-treatment measurements, plasma BSP concentrations were increased at all post-treatment intervals, and were highest between 4 and 6 hours. Approximately 5 hours post-dosing was considered the maximal BSP retention time in the dog. The second series of experiments was conducted to establish the range of doses of SAIB which produced increased BSP retention in the dog five hours after a single administration. Fifteen-minute BSP retention values were increased 7-10 fold with doses of 25 mg/kg bw to 2 g/kg bw. No dose-response correlation was apparent. At 5.0 mg/kg bw, only 1 of 3 dogs showed increased BSP retention and the authors considered this to be close to a no-effect dose. Throughout the study, none of the dogs showed a marked change in body weight. There were no significant changes in SAP values measured in blood samples at the same intervals as measurement of BSP clearance. Changing the vehicle to corn oil in the last two studies of the second series of experiments eliminated the observations of vomiting and orange-coloured, loose stools which were common in the foregoing experiments (Dickie *et al.* 1980a).

Young, adult, male beagle dogs were tested for 15-minute BSP clearance and SAP levels 5 hours after a single oral administration of either sucrose hexaacetate diisobutyrate (SHADIB) or sucrose octaisobutyrate (SOIB) (constituent esters of SAIB) in a series of experiments. The range of doses used was 100-1 000 mg/kg bw of SHADIB and 5-1 000 mg/kg bw SOIB. In the first 3 experiments, 4 treatment groups of 3 dogs and a vehcile control group of 2 dogs were used; in the fourth experiment, 2 dose groups of 3 dogs and a vehicle control group of 1 dog were used. Compared with pretreatment measurements, a single dose of SHADIB caused a significant increase (5-7 fold) in BSP retention at all doses tested. SOIB administration also resulted in an increase of BSP retention of about 4-5 fold compared with pretreatment values at doses of 25 mg/kg bw and higher. As in the previous experiment, no dose-response correlation was observed and mean BSP retention at 5.0 mg/kg bw SOIB showed only a slight increase over control and pretreatment values. Neither ester appeared to cause any gross clinical effects and neither affected SAP activity. None of the dogs showed a marked change in body weight over the course of the study. The observation of yellow-orange stools and vomiting was eliminated by changing the vehicle from orange juice to corn oil as in the previous experiment (Dickie *et al.* 1980b).

2.2.7.3 Monkeys

Two groups of 3 male squirrel monkeys (*Saimiri sciureus*) weighing approximately 1 kg, were fasted overnight and then received either SAIB (1 g in 2 ml cottonseed oil) or no treatment. Twenty-four hours after treatment the monkeys were tested for bromosulfophthalein clearance. Following a 7-day rest period, the treatment of the groups was reversed. Clearance appeared normal in 2/3 of the animals in each group (Procter and Chappel 1970b).

The same experiment was repeated using doses of 2 g SAIB in 4 ml cottonseed oil to deliver a dose of approximately 2 g/kg bw. Unusually high plasma BSP levels were measured in 3 of the control animals, but these were considered by the authors to be technical errors since BSP clearance following treatment with SAIB was normal in all of the animals (Procter and Chappel, 1971).

Thirty-minute BSP retention and SAP were measured in 10 male *Cynomolgus* monkeys 5 hours after a single oral dose of 5 g SAIB/kg bw, 5 g SOIB/kg bw or corn oil and compared with pretreatment values for these parameters. Treatment had no effect on BSP retention time or SAP. There were no unusual clinical observations or changes in body weight during the study. It should be noted that the authors did not run a time series as in the corresponding dog experiment to determine the optimum interval for measurement of hepatic function following adminstration of the test material (Dickie *et al*. 1980c).

2.3   Observations in humans

Twenty subjects (10 males and 10 females) between 18 and 22 years of age ingested a daily dose of SAIB at a level equivalent to 10 mg/kg bw/dy for a period of 14 days. The dose was taken as a bolus each morning. The following blood parameters were measured prior to treatment and at days 7 and 18 of the study: ASAT, ALAT, SAP, serum bilirubin, total protein, albumin, uric acid, BUN, erythrocyte sedimentation rate, sodium, potassium, phosphorous, total CO_2, cholesterol and glucose. There were no significant differences in any parameters in any individual (Hensley 1975).

In another 14-day study, 12 male and 12 female subjects were divided evenly by sex into 3 groups, receiving a carbonated drink only (controls), or a single daily dose of 7.0 or 20.0 mg SAIB/kg bw/day in a carbonated drink. In addition, four men received 20 mg SAIB/kg bw/day for 1 or 3 days only in a pilot experiment to provide early evaluation of possible alterations in normal hepatic function. The subjects were 21 to 42 years of age. Blood was collected prior to testing and on days 7 and 14 for haematological (platelets, total and differential WBC count, ESR, Hct and Hb) and clinical chemistry (total protein, albumin, A/G ratio, calcium, cholesterol, glucose, BUN, uric acid total bilirubin, SAP, ASAT, ALAT, and LDH) parameters. Standard urinalysis parameters were also recorded at these times. A 45-minute BSP retention test (5 mg/kg bw BSP) was also conducted on all subjects prior to treatment and after completion of treatment. Treatment with SAIB did not affect any of these parameters for any individual (Orr *et al*. 1976).

Twenty-seven adult subjects, 13 men and 14 women, between the ages of 18 to 55, received SAIB in an aqueous/orange juice emulsion daily for 14 days at a dose of 20 mg/kg bw. In the 7 days prior to treatment, each subject acted as his/her own control by ingesting an orange juice beverage and placebo emulsion. Blood samples were collected from each subject on days -6, 0, 7 and 14 of treatment for measurement of routine haematological and clinical chemistry parameters, including specific indicators of hepatobiliary function (SAP, ASAT, ALT, LDH, gamma-glutamyl transferase, total bilirubin, direct bilirubin, bile acids and serum proteins). No treatment-related changes were detected in any of these parameters over the 14-day dosing period (Chiang 1988).

3.   COMMENTS

Studies on the disposition of sucrose acetate isobutyrate in rats, dogs, and humans indicated that absorption from the gastrointestinal tract is delayed for several hours but that elimination is nearly complete by 4 to 5 days after ingestion. Extensive metabolism of sucrose acetate isobutyrate occurred in the gastrointestinal tract, mainly in the small intestine, characterized by its de-esterification by non-specific esterases to partially acylated esters and sucrose. Ingested sucrose acetate isobutyrate was partially absorbed from the gut and partially eliminated in the faeces. In all three species, the absorbed dose was largely catabolized to CO_2, and smaller amounts were excreted in the urine and bile.

The extent of absorption from the gastrointestinal tract was greater in humans and rats than in dogs in the dosage range of 1-10 mg/kg bw. However, at doses approaching 100 mg/kg bw/day in the rat, absorption of sucrose acetate isobutyrate was less extensive, resembling more the situation in the dog.

In studies with sucrose octaisobutyrate, the most lipophilic component of sucrose acetate isobutyrate, a dose of 200 mg/kg bw administered to rats, dogs, and monkeys was almost completely excreted in the faeces, although analysis of faecal metabolites indicated that the extent of hydrolysis in the gastrointestinal tract differed in the three species (rat > dog > monkey). In addition, the small amount of absorbed sucrose octaisobutyrate was preferentially excreted in the bile of dogs and in the expired air of rats. Chromatographic analysis of the urinary and biliary metabolites of sucrose acetate isobutyrate showed that dogs excreted more highly acylated sucrose molecules, whereas humans and rats excreted more polar sucrose esters. Consequently, the dog differs from the rat and human in its disposition of sucrose acetate isobutyrate in that it absorbs less of the total dose of sucrose acetate isobutyrate in the 1 - 10 mg/kg bw range, but it is capable of absorbing more highly acylated sucrose esters and compared with the rat, excretes a larger proportion of the absorbed dose in the bile. Data on the excretion of sucrose acetate isobutyrate in the bile of humans were not available for comparison.

The results of short-term (up to 1 year) toxicity studies in mice, rats, and monkeys were also available. The conclusions of an earlier 2-year study in rats were not considered to be reliable because of the small numbers of survivors at the end of the study. SAIB administered at dose levels of up to 10% in the diet for 12 weeks or 2 g/kg bw/day for 52 weeks had no toxicologically significant effect in the rat, nor was any effect evident in the liver as assessed by liver function tests, liver weights, and histopathology In the *Cynomolgus* monkey, oral doses of sucrose acetate isobutyrate of up to 2.4 g/kg bw/day had no apparent adverse effect. In humans, up to 20 mg SAIB/kg bw/day for 14 days was also without effect. In addition, special liver function tests conducted in rats, monkeys, and humans following oral administration of single or multiple exposures to sucrose acetate isobutyrate showed no effect on hepatobiliary excretion.

The available studies clearly showed the liver to be the target organ in the dog. Serum alkaline phosphatase levels were elevated and biliary excretory function was impaired. Liver enlargement was noted in the males and histopathological changes were apparent in the liver of both sexes. All of these changes were reversible within 3 weeks of removal of sucrose acetate isobutyrate from the diet. In addition, histochemical studies revealed increased enzyme activity in the bile canaliculi, but not in the hepatocytes. In special studies on liver function biliary excretion was reduced within 4-6 hours of oral administration of a single dose of sucrose acetate isobutyrate. The NOEL for this effect was 5 mg/kg bw/day. The authors of the report concluded that this represented a functional rather than a toxic effect of sucrose acetate isobutyrate. Although the effects on the liver of the dog were reversible, no study of longer than 12-13 weeks duration was available for evaluation. It was not known whether continuous exposure to sucrose acetate isobutyrate for a longer period of time would have resulted in the development of pathological lesions.

The carcinogenic potential of sucrose acetate isobutyrate has been investigated in mice and rats in long-term toxicity studies at doses of up to 2 and 5 g/kg bw/day, respectively, with negative results. Sucrose acetate isobutyrate was not genotoxic in *in vitro* point mutation, chromosomal aberration, or unscheduled DNA synthesis assays. A multigeneration reproduction/ teratologenicity study in rats and a teratology study in rabbits were also negative.

The NOELs from the long-term studies in mice and rats and from a 1-year study in monkeys were similar (5, 2, and 2.4 g/kg bw/day, respectively). However, the NOEL for the dog was much lower (5 mg/kg bw/day based on inhibition of biliary excretory function).

4.   EVALUATION

The Committee concluded that a 2-year study in dogs was no longer necessary since the effects of sucrose acetate isobutyrate and its constituent esters on the liver of the dog had been well characterized in liver function tests and 90-day toxicity studies, and a study of longer duration was unlikely to yield new information which would assist in setting an ADI.

Three studies in humans, involving a total of 71 volunteers, were available for consideration by the Committee. The results of these studies demonstrated that sucrose acetate isobutyrate had no effect on BSP clearance or indicator enzymes of cholestasis in humans when administered orally in a single daily dose (20 mg/kg bw) that dramatically reduced BSP clearance in the dog (25 mg/kg bw as a single dose). Humans, therefore, did not respond to sucrose acetate isobutyrate in the same way as dogs. The Committee agreed that the data suggested that the dog was an inappropriate species on which to base an ADI, but at the same time noted the absence of data on the mechanism by which cholestasis is induced in the dog.

Taking this into account, the Committee decided to use the NOEL of 2 g/kg bw/day for rats, the lowest obtained in a long-term toxicity study, to allocate a temporary ADI of 0-10 mg/kg bw, using a safety factor of 200. The submission of information that would clarify the disparate effects of sucrose acetate isobutyrate on hepatobiliary function in the dog compared with other species, in particular humans, is required for review by 1996.

5. REFERENCES

BLAIR, M. (1986). Exploratory four-week oral toxicity study with sucrose acetate isobutyrate in *Cynomolgus* monkeys. Unpub. Rept., study no 548-001, International Research and Development Corporation, Mattawan, Michigan, December 18. Submitted to WHO by Eastman Kodak Co., Rochester, NY, USA.

BLAIR, M. (1990). One year oral toxicity study with sucrose acetate isobutyrate in *Cynomolgus* monkeys. Unpub. Rept., study No. 548-002, International Research and Development Corporation, Mattawan, Michigan. Submitted to WHO by Eastman Kodak Co., Rochester, NY, USA.

BONIN, A.M. & BAKER, R.S.U. (1980). Mutagenicity testing of some approved food additives with the *Salmonella*/microsome assay. *Food Technology in Australia* 32(12), 608-611.

CHIANG, M. (1988). Determination of the effect of single daily ingestion of SAIB on the hepatobiliary function of normal human male and female volunteers. Unpub. Rept. No. 2657-001, Hazleton Laboratories Canada, Ltd. Submitted to WHO by Eastman Kodak Co., Rochester, NY, USA.

CIFONE, M.A. (1985). Evaluation of sucrose acetate isobutyrate special lot No. 84-8 in the rat primary hepatocyte unscheduled DNA synthesis assay. Unpub. Rept. No. 20991, Litton Bionetics Inc. Submitted to WHO by Eastman Kodak Co., Rochester, NY, USA.

DICKIE, B.C., RAO, G.N. & THOMSON, G.M. (1980a). Effect of sucrose acetate isobutyrate esters on liver excretory function in dogs. Unpub. Rept. No. 80004, Raltech Scientific Services. Submitted to WHO by Eastman Kodak Co., Rochester, NY, USA.

DICKIE, B.C., RAO, G.N. & THOMSON, G.M. (1980b). Preliminary study to determine the effect of sucrose hexaacetate diisobutyrate (SHADIB) and sucrose octaisobutyrate (SOIB) esters on liver excretory function in dogs. Unpub. Rept. No. 80503, Raltech Scientific Services. Submitted to WHO by Eastman Kodak Co., Rochester, NY, USA.

DICKIE, B.C., RAO, G.N. & THOMSON, G.M. (1980c). Effect of sucrose acetate isobutyrate and sucrose octaisobutyrate esters on liver excretory function in *Cynomolgus* monkeys. Unpub. Rept. No. 80540, Raltech Scientific Services. Submitted to WHO by Eastman Kodak Co., Rochester, NY, USA.

FASSETT, D.W. & REYNOLDS, R.C. (1962). The fate of sucrose acetate isobutyrate in the rat. Unpub. Rept. No. BCH 62-1, of Laboratory of Industrial Medicine, Eastman Kodak Company. Submitted to WHO by Eastman Kodak Co., Rochester, NY, USA.

FASSETT, D.W., ROUDABUSH, R.L. & TERHAAR, C.J. (1962). Sucrose acetate isobutyrate, low acetyl (SAIB) 95 day feeding study. Unpub. Rept., Eastman Kodak Company. Submitted to WHO by Eastman Kodak Co., Rochester, NY, USA.

FASSETT, D.W., ROUDABUSH, R.L. & TERHAAR, C.J. (1965). Reproduction study in rats fed sucrose acetate isobutyrate (61-115-2). Unpub. Rept. of Laboratory of Industrial Medicine, Eastman Kodak Company. Submitted to WHO by Eastman Kodak Co., Rochester, NY, USA.

HARPER, K.H., WHELDON, G.H., BENSON, H.G. & MAWDESLEY-THOMAS, L.E. (1966). Chronic toxicity and effect upon reproductive function of SAIB in the rat (Final Report). Huntingdon Research Lab. (HRC Report No. 1612/66/140). Submitted to WHO by Eastman Kodak Co., Rochester, NY, USA.

HENSLEY, W.J. (1975). A brief report on the use of sucrose acetate isobutyrate in human volunteers. Unpub. Rept. prepared for the Food Additives Sub-Committee of the National Health and Medical Research Council, Australia. Submitted to WHO by the Coca-Cola Co. and Eastman Kodak Co.

HINT, H. (1964). Short term toxicity of SAIB in rats. Report submitted to Aktiebolaget Fructus Fabriker, Stockholm, Sweden. Submitted to WHO by Eastman Kodak Co., Rochester, NY, USA.

IVETT, J.L. (1985). Mutagenicity evaluation of sucrose acetate isobutyrate special lot No. 84-8 in an *in vitro* cytogenetic assay measuring chromosome aberration frequencies in Chinese hamster ovary (CHO) cells. Final report, project No. 20990, Litton Bionetics Inc. Submitted to WHO by Eastman Kodak Co., Rochester, NY, USA.

JAGANNATH, D.R. & BRUSICK, D.J. (1978). Mutagenicity evaluation of 78-341 in the Ames *Salmonella*/microsome plate test (sucrose acetate isobutyrate). Unpub. Rept. No. 20938, Litton Bionetics Inc. Submitted to WHO by Eastman Kodak Co., Rochester, NY, USA.

KRASAVAGE, W.J (1973). A dominant lethal assay of sucrose acetate isobutyrate (SAIB) in the rat. Unpub. Rept. No. TOX-73-3, Eastman Kodak Company. Submitted to WHO by Eastman Kodak Co., Rochester, NY, USA.

KRASAVAGE, W.J. & TERHAAR, C.J. (1971a). Sucrose acetate isobutyrate, 70-339, a preliminary study of the reversibility of effects on liver weight and serum alkaline phosphatase in old beagle dogs. Unpub. Rept. No. Tox-70-8, Eastman Kodak Company. Submitted to WHO by Eastman Kodak Co., Rochester, NY, USA.

KRASAVAGE, W.J. & TERHAAR, C.J. (1971b). Sucrose acetate isobutyrate (70-339), a three part dietary feeding study in rats. Unpub. Rept., Eastman Kodak Company. Submitted to WHO by Eastman Kodak Co., Rochester, NY, USA.

KRASAVAGE, W.J. & TERHAAR, C.J. (1971c). Sucrose acetate isobutyrate (70-339), a subacute feeding study in beagle dogs. Unpub. Rept., TOX-7-7, Eastman Kodak Company. Submitted to WHO by Eastman Kodak Co., Rochester, NY, USA.

KRASAVAGE, W.J. & TERHAAR, C.J. (1972). Indocyanine green plasma clearance rates in rats fed high levels of sucrose acetate isobutyrate (SAIB, 70-339). Unpub. Rept. No. Tox-72-1, Eastman Kodak Company. Submitted to WHO by Eastman Kodak Co., Rochester, NY, USA.

KRASAVAGE, W.J., DIVINCENZO, G.D., ASTILL, B.D., ROUDABUSH, R.L. & TERHAAR, C.J. (1973). Biological effects of sucrose acetate isobutyrate in rodents and dogs, *J. Agr. Food Chem.*, **21**, 473-478.

LAWLOR, T.E. & VALENTINE, D.C. (1989). Mutagenicity test on sucrose acetate isobutyrate in the *Salmonella*/mammalian-microsome reverse mutation assay (Ames test) with confirmatory assay. Unpub. Rept. No. 10977-0-401, Hazleton Laboratories America, Inc. Submitted to WHO by Eastman Kodak Co., Rochester, NY, USA.

MACKENZIE, K.M. (1987). Short-term palatability study with sucrose acetate isobutyrate (SAIB) in mice. Unpub. Rept. No. 6194-103, Hazleton Laboratories America, Inc. Submitted to WHO by Eastman Kodak Co., Rochester, NY, USA.

MACKENZIE K.M. (1990a). One year chronic toxicity study with sucrose acetate isobutyrate (SAIB) in rats. Unpub. Rept., No. HLA 6194-100. Hazleton Laboratories America, Inc. Submitted to WHO by Eastman Kodak Co., Rochester, NY, USA.

MACKENZIE, K.M. (1990b). Two-year carcinogenicity study with sucrose acetate isobutyrate (SAIB) in rats. Unpub. Rept. No. 6194-101, Hazleton Laboratories America, Inc. Submitted to WHO by Eastman Kodak Co., Rochester, NY, USA.

MACKENZIE, K.M. (1990c). Carcinogenicity study with sucrose acetate isobutyrate (SAIB) in mice. Unpub. Rept., study No. 6194-104, Hazleton Laboratories America, Inc. Submitted to WHO by Eastman Kodak Co., Rochester, NY, USA.

MACKENZIE, K.M. (1990d). Three-generation reproduction and teratology study with sucrose acetate isobutyrate (SAIB) in rats. Unpub. Rept. No. 6194-105, Hazleton Laboratories America, Inc. Submitted to WHO by Eastman Kodak Co., Rochester, NY, USA.

MORGAREIDGE, K. (1965). Subacute (90-day) feeding studies with SAIB in dogs. Unpub. Rept. No. 86501, Food and Drug Research Laboratories. Submitted to WHO by Eastman Kodak Co., Rochester, NY, USA.

NOKER, P.E. (1982). Pharmacokinetics and metabolism studies of sucrose octa isobutyrate (SOIB) in rats. Report No. 4924-I, Southern Research Institute. Submitted to WHO by Eastman Kodak Co., Rochester, NY, USA.

NOKER, P.E. (1984a). A pharmacokinetic and metabolism study of sucrose octa isobutyrate (SOIB) in dogs. Unpub. Rept. No. 4924-III, Southern Research Institute. Submitted to WHO by Eastman Kodak Co., Rochester, NY, USA.

NOKER, P.E. (1984b). A pharmacokinetic and metabolism study of sucrose octa isobutyrate (SOIB) in monkeys. Unpub. Rept. No. 4924-IV, Southern Research Institute. Submitted to WHO by Eastman Kodak Co., Rochester, NY, USA.

NOKER, P.E., KALIN, J.R., MCCARTHY, D.J., EL DAREER, S.M. & CHAPPEL, C.I. (1986). Disposition of sucrose octa isobutyrate in rats, dogs and monkeys. *Food Chem. Toxicol.* **24**, 1287-1293.

ORR, J.M., MARIER, G. & CHAPPEL, C.I. (1976). Fourteen day feeding and tolerance study of sucrose acetate isobutyrate (SAIB) in human volunteers. Unpub. Rept. No. 1, project No. 4479, Bio-Research Laboratories Ltd. Submitted to WHO by Eastman Kodak Co., Rochester, NY, USA.

PHILLIPS, J.C., KINGSNORTH, J., ROWLAND, I., GANGOLLI, S.D. & LLOYD, A.G. (1976). Studies on the metabolism of sucrose acetate isobutyrate in the rat and in man. *Food. Cosmet. Toxicol.* **14**, 375-380.

PROCTER, B.G. & CHAPPEL, C.I. (1970a). An investigation of the effect of sucrose acetate isobutyrate on the liver of the rat. Unpub. Rept. No. 1110, Bio-Research Laboratories Ltd. Submitted to WHO by Eastman Kodak Co., Rochester, NY, USA.

PROCTER, B.G. & CHAPPEL, C.I. (1970b). Studies of the effect on bromsulfophthalein plasma clearance rate in the squirrel monkey *(Saimiri sciureus)*. Unpub. Rept. No. 1570, Bio-Research Laboratories, Ltd., Quebec, Canada. Submitted to WHO by the Canadian Soft Drink Association and Eastman Kodak Co., Rochester, NY, USA.

PROCTER, B.G. & CHAPPEL, C.I. (1971). Studies of the effect of sucrose acetate isobutyrate on bromsulfophthalein plasma clearance rate in the squirrel monkey *(Saimiri sciureus)*, in the albino rat and in the beagle dog. Unpub. Rept. No. 1370, Bio-Research Laboratories Ltd. Submitted to WHO by Eastman Kodak Co., Rochester, NY, USA.

PROCTER, B.G., DUSSAULT, P., RONA, G. & CHAPPEL, C.I. (1970). A study of the subacute oral toxicity of sucrose acetate isobutyrate (SAIB) in the Beagle dog. Unpub. Rept. No. 1, project No. 953, Bio-Research Laboratories, Ltd., Quebec, Canada. Submitted to WHO by the Canadian Soft Drink Association and Eastman Kodak Co., Rochester, NY, USA.

PROCTER, B.G., DUSSAULT, P., BURFORD, R.G., RONA, G. & CHAPPEL, C.I. (1971a). A subacute study of the effect of ingestion of sucrose acetate isobutyrate on the liver of the rat (a study of the subacute oral toxicity of sucrose acetate isobutyrate in the rat). Unpub. Rept. No. 966, Bio-Research Laboratories Ltd., Quebec, Canada. Submitted to WHO by the Canadian Soft Drink Association and Eastman Kodak Co., Rochester, NY, USA.

PROCTER, B.G., DUSSAULT, P., RONA, G. & CHAPPEL, C.I. (1971b). A study of the subacute oral toxicity of sucrose acetate isobutyrate (SAIB) in the beagle dog. Unpub. Rept. No. 2, project No. 953, Bio-Research Laboratories, Ltd., Quebec, Canada. Submitted to WHO by the Canadian Soft Drink Association and Eastman Kodak Co., Rochester, NY, USA.

PROCTER, B.G. DUSSAULT, P. & CHAPPEL, C.I. (1973). Biochemical effects of sucrose acetate isobutyrate (SAIB) on the liver, Proc. Soc. Expt. Biol. Med., 142, 595-599.

REYNOLDS, R.C. (1963). The in vivo absorption of sucrose acetate isobutyrate from the intestine of the rat. Unpub. Rept. No. BCH-63-5, Laboratory of Industrial Medicine, Eastman Kodak Company, Rochester, N.Y. 14652-3615. Submitted to WHO by Eastman Kodak Co., Rochester, NY, USA.

REYNOLDS, R.C. (1972a). Physiological fate of sucrose-^{14}C(U) acetate isobutyrate in rats: (1) After single oral doses in corn oil. Raw data report, BDH-72-5, Eastman Kodak Company. Submitted to WHO by Eastman Kodak Co., Rochester, NY, USA.

REYNOLDS, R.C. (1972b). Physiological fates of sucrose-^{14}C(U) acetate isobutyrate and sucrose-^{14}C(U) in rats: (2) After single oral doses in an aqueous emulsion. Raw data report, BCH-72-6, Eastman Kodak Company. Submitted to WHO by Eastman Kodak Co., Rochester, NY, USA.

REYNOLDS, R.C. & TRAVIS, M.G. (1972). Physiological fate of sucrose-^{14}C(U) acetate isobutyrate in dogs. Raw data report, BCH-72-4, Eastman Kodak Company. Submitted to WHO by Eastman Kodak Co., Rochester, NY, USA.

REYNOLDS, R.C. & ZIEGLER, D.A. (1977). Metabolites of sucrose acetate isobutyrate in the urine of rats, dogs and a man. Unpub. Rept. (BC-77-T2), Eastman Kodak Co. Submitted to WHO by Eastman Kodak Co., Rochester, NY, USA.

REYNOLDS, R.C., ASTILL, B.D. & FASSETT, D.W. (1971). The disposition of SAIB in mammals (rat, dog and man). Unpub. Rept. No. BCH-71-8. Laboratory of Industrial Medicine, Eastman Kodak Company. Submitted to WHO by Eastman Kodak Co, Rochester, N.Y. USA.

REYNOLDS, R.C., TRAVIS, M.G. & ELY, T.S. (1972). Physiological fate of sucrose-^{14}C(U) acetate isobutyrate and sucrose-^{14}C(U) in humans. Unpub. Rept. (BCH-72-1), Laboratory of Industrial Medicine, Eastman Kodak Co. Submitted to WHO by the Eastman Kodak Co, Rochester, NY, USA.

REYNOLDS, R.C., ASTILL, B.D., TERHAAR, C.J. & FASSETT, D.W. (1974). Fate and disposition of sucrose-U-^{14}C acetate isobutyrate in humans, rats and dogs. J. Agr. Food Chem., 22, 1084-1088.

REYNOLDS, R.C., KRASAVAGE, W.J., TRAVIS, M.G. & TERHAAR, C.J. (1975). Elimination of radioactivity in bile of rats and a dog fed sucrose-^{14}C(U) acetate isobutyrate. Unpub. Rept. No. BCH-75-6, Health and Safety Laboratory, Eastman Kodak Co., Rochester, N.Y. Submitted to WHO by Eastman Kodak Co., Rochester, NY, USA.

SCHARDEIN, J.L. (1988). Teratology study in rabbits with sucrose acetate isobutyrate (SAIB). International Research and Development Corporation. Unpub. Rept.. Submitted to WHO by Eastman Kodak Co., Rochester, NY, USA.

TIERNEY, W.J. & RINEHART, W.E. (1979). An acute oral tolerance study of sucrose acetate isobutyrate (SAIB) in monkeys. Unpub. Rept. No. 78-2187, Bio/dynamics Inc. Submitted to WHO by Eastman Kodak Co., Rochester, NY, USA.

TIERNEY, W.J. & RINEHART, W.E. (1980a). A range-finding study with sucrose acetate isobutyrate (SAIB) in monkeys. Unpub. Rept. No. 78-2188, Bio/dynamics Inc. Submitted to WHO by Eastman Kodak Co., Rochester, NY, USA.

TIERNEY, W.J. & RINEHART, W.E. (1980b). Evaluation of selected clinical chemistry parameters in monkeys following administration of sucrose acetate isobutyrate (SAIB) for 15 days. Unpub. Rept. No. 79-2431, Bio/dynamics Inc. Submitted to WHO by Eastman Kodak Co., Rochester, NY, USA.

YOUNG, R.R. (1985). Evaluation of sucrose acetate isobutyrate special lot No. 84-8 in the CHO/HGPRT forward mutation assay. Unpub. Rept. No. 22207, Litton Bionetics Inc. Submitted to WHO by Eastman Kodak Co., Rochester, NY, USA.

UREA

First draft prepared by
Dr P. Olsen
Institute of Toxicology, National Food Agency of Denmark
Ministry of Health, Søborg, Denmark

1. EXPLANATION

Urea is a white crystalline powder with a cooling saline taste (Merck, 1968). Urea occurs naturally in mammals and is an excretory end-product of amino acid metabolism. Urea is formed in the liver. Urea has not been evaluated previously by the Joint FAO/WHO Expert Committee on Food Additives.

Urea is used in sugar-free chewing gum to adjust the texture. A heavy user of chewing gum may consume approximately. Chewing gum may contain up to 3% urea, and intake from this source could be up to 300 mg urea/day. The Committee considered urea only for evaluation in relation to its use in chewing gum.

2. BIOLOGICAL DATA

2.1 Biochemical aspects

2.1.1 Absorption, distribution, and excretion

Urea has little or no nutritional value to monogastric mammals (Briggs, 1967). Ruminants are able to utilize urea as a source for food protein (Blood & Henderson, 1963). Urea present in the blood of ruminants appears to be actively transported across the rumen wall into the lumen and used as a nitrogen source (Schmidt-Nielsen, 1958).

A study in pregnant rats which were injected subcutaneously with urea dissolved in 0.9% NaCl solution showed that urea diffused readily through the placenta. The concentrations of urea in the maternal liver, thigh muscle and in the whole fetus were equal two hours after injection (Luck & Engle, 1929).

In dogs injected intraperitoneally with 3% urea solution, urea diffused throughout the body and was present in tissue fluid at concentrations equal to, or greater than, that present in the extracellular fluid (Grollman & Grollman, 1959).

The distribution of urea was determined in 4 young pigs given ^{15}N-labelled urea in the diet. Fifty-two per cent of the administered ^{15}N-labelled urea was excreted in the urine after 48 hours and 1.9% during the subsequent 48 hours. Faecal ^{15}N excretion over 96 hours accounted for only 1.3% of the amount administered. Less than 1% of the ^{15}N was found in the liver, muscle and blood cells, study concluded that this indicates incorporation of ^{15}N in body proteins. Only 60% of the administered ^{15}N was recovered (Grimson et al., 1971).

In another study, the distribution of ^{14}C-labelled urea after intraperitoneal injection was determined by radioactivity analysis and autoradiography techniques in the brain and spinal fluid of fasted cats. In the brain and cerebrospinal fluid the highest urea concentration was reached 6 hours following injection. Autoradiography showed dense areas in the cerebral and cerebellar cortex. White matter showed the least radioactivity (Schoolar et al., 1960).

Renal excretion of urea is rapid and chiefly by glomerular filtration (Sollmann, 1957). Renal tubular secretion (Sollmann, 1957) and reabsorption also occur (Mountcastle, 1974).

2.1.2   Biotransformation

Urea is an excretory end-product of amino acid metabolism in mammals. The formation of urea takes place in the liver. This is a cyclic process in which the initial step is the reaction between carbon dioxide and ammonia to yield carbamyl phosphate. Carbamyl phosphate reacts with ornithine to form citrulline which combines with aspartate to form argininosuccinate. This product is cleaved to fumarate and arginine. The terminal step is the hydrolysis of arginine, yielding urea and regenerating ornithine. This cycle of reactions involves several enzymes including carbamyl phosphate synthetase, ornithine carbamylase, argininosuccinate synthetase and arginine-lyase. The fetal liver was capable of synthesizing urea 28 days (in pigs), and 19 days (in rats) after gestation (Kennan & Cohen, 1959).

2.1.3   Effects on enzymes and other biochemical parameters

No information available.

2.2   Toxicological studies

2.2.1   Acute toxicity studies

The results of acute toxicity studies with urea are summarized in Table 1.

Table 1. Results of acute toxicity studies with urea.

Species	Sex	Rte	Dosage, mg/kg bw	LD/MLD	Reference
Dog	?	sc	3 000-9 000	LD	Abderhalden, 1935
Dog	?	iv	3 000	LD	Abderhalden, 1935
Rabbit	?	sc	1 000-2 000	LD	Abderhalden, 1935
Hamster	?	iv	4 000-8 000	LD	Abderhalden, 1935
Sheep(1)	?	po	160	LD	Satapathy & Panda, 1963
Cattle	M	po	511	MLD	Dinning et al., 1948
Cattle(1)	F	po	600	MLD	Stiles et al., 1970
Cattle(2)	M	po	1080	MLD	Stiles et al., 1970
Ponies	?	po	3461	LD	Hintz et al., 1970

(1): Not adapted to urea
(2): Adapted to urea

The clinical symptoms observed in cattle included ataxia, weakness, abdominal pain, dyspnoea, excessive salivation, frothing, violent struggling and bellowing. Acute urea toxicity in cattle may be due to ammonia formed by the rapid breakdown of urea by rumen microorganisms (Blood & Henderson, 1963).

The clinical signs of acute urea toxicity in ponies were typical of severe central nervous system derangement: incoordination, dilated pupils, sluggish pupillary response to light, depressed palpebral and corneal reflexes, slow respiratory rate, rapid and weak peripheral pulse, cold and clammy skin, and pressing of the head against fixed objects until falling at death (Hintz et al., 1970).

2.2.2   Short-term toxicity studies

2.2.2.1 Dogs

Twelve unilaterally nephrectomized dogs were injected subcutaneously with 10% urea solution (3 000-4 000 mg/kg bw) every 8 hours over a period of 45 days. Serum urea levels ranged from 600-700 mg/100 ml ½ hour after injection. Except for a mild drowsiness and increased diuresis urea did not induce any severe toxic symptoms (Balestri et al., 1971).

2.2.2.2 Ruminants

A gradual increase in the amount of urea in rations up to 1762 mg/kg bw/dy to steers over a period of 70 days did not cause distress (Dinning et al.,

1948). However, without adaptation to urea, doses of 166 mg/kg bw/dy and 232 mg/kg bw/dy urea caused sudden death in sheep and cattle, respectively (Satapathy & Panda, 1963). Tolerance to urea was reduced in starving ruminants and in ruminants on a low protein diet (Blood & Henderson, 1963).

2.2.3   Long-term toxicity/carcinogenicity studies

2.2.3.1 Mice

Three groups of 50 C57Bl/6 mice of each sex were administered either 0.45% ($\approx$ 674 mg/kg bw/day) 0.90% ($\approx$ 1350 mg/kg bw/day), or 4.5% ($\approx$ 6750 mg/kg bw/day) urea (no information on purity reported) in the diet for 1 year. The control group comprised 100 mice of each sex. The identity of urea was confirmed by melting point comparison. Biochemical and haematological parameters were not included in the study. No body weight depression was noted at terminal necropsy for mice of either sex at any dose levels. Survival of all treated groups were unaffected.

Among treated female mice there was a significant increased occurrence of malignant lymphomas in the middle dose-group. The incidence of malignant lymphomas was 10/92 in controls and 7/43, 10/38 (p=0.008) and 9/50 in the low-, middle-, and high-dose groups, respectively. The increased incidence of malignant lymphomas among middle-dose female mice was of questionable biological significance since the occurrence was not dose-related. Urea was non-carcinogenic in this study (Fleischman *et al.*, 1980).

2.2.3.2 Rats

Groups of 50 Fischer 344 rats of each sex were administered either 0, 0.45% ($\approx$ 225 mg/kg bw/day), 0.90% ($\approx$ 450 mg/kg bw/day) or 4.5% ($\approx$ 2 250 mg/kg bw/day) urea (no information on purity reported, identity of urea was confirmed by melting point comparison) in the diet for 1 year. Biochemical and haematological parameters were not included in the study. No body weight depression was noted at terminal necropsy for rats of either sex at any dose levels. The middle-dose male rats showed decreased survival (89%) relative to controls (95%)(statistics not reported). The survival of the other dose groups remained unaffected.

Among treated male rats, there was a significant increased linear trend (p=0.008), and a higher proportion of interstitial cell adenomas of testis in the high-dose group (p=0.004). The incidence of interstitial cell adenomas was 21/50 in the controls, and was 27/48, 25/48, and 35/50 in the low- middle- and high-dose groups, respectively. The statistically significant increased incidence of interstitial cell adenomas in male rats was of questionable biological significance since this tumour may occur in 100% of controls. Urea was non-carcinogenic in this study (Fleischman *et al.*, 1980).

2.2.3.3 **Ruminants**

A calf received 4.3% urea ($\approx$ 1290 mg/kg bw) in feed over a period of 12 months caused. Increased diuresis was observed throughout the experiment. Histologically, renal hyaline degeneration, tubular casts and several areas of liver necrosis were found (Hart *et al.*, 1939).

2.2.3   **Long-term toxicity/carcinogenicity studies**

No information available.

2.2.4   **Reproduction studies**

No information available.

2.2.5   **Special studies on genotoxicity**

The results of genotoxicity studies with urea are summarized in Table 1.

2.3   **Observations in humans**

2.3.1   **Blood values, distribution, metabolism, excretion and effects on other parameters.**

The absorption of urea was studied in 8 healthy fasting male volunteers by means of a colon perfusion technique. Only 5% of the urea perfused through the colon was absorbed. The authors concluded that the colon was relatively impermeable to urea (Wolpert *et al.*, 1971).

The mean concentrations of blood urea in healthy human subjects were 28.9 mg/100 ml (range 16-54 mg/100 ml) in 298 men and 21.7 mg/100 ml (range 12-47 mg/100 ml) in 278 woman. Urea levels tended to increase with age (Keating *et al.*, 1969).

Correlation between blood urea and the content of urea in parotid fluid has been found (Shannon & Prigmore, 1961).

The normal value of urea in saliva (unstimulated) was reported to be 3.3 mM/l (200 mg/l) with a range of 2.4-12.5 mM/l. Daily production of saliva varied from 500-1 500 ml (Geigy, 1981a).

Average daily urinary excretion of urea in adults was estimated to be 20.6 g. The urinary excretion of urea was proportional to protein intake and was increased on a high protein diet. Urea excretion was decreased during growth and pregnancy or due to action of insulin, growth hormone and testosterone (Geigy, 1981b).

Table 1. Results of genotoxicity tests for urea

Test System	Test Object	Concent. of urea	Result	Reference
In vitro bacterial mutagenicity assay	*S.typhimurium* TA98, TA100 TA1537	?	Neg.	Ishidate, et al., 1981
Mammalian cell mutation assay (1)	Mouse lymphoma TK locus assay	329-628 µM/l	Pos. (2)	Garberg, *et al.*, 1988
Chromosomal aberration assay (1)	Chinese hamster fibroblast cell	16 mg/ml	Pos. (2)	Ishidate & Odashima, 1977
Chromosomal aberration assay (1)	Chinese hamster fibroblast cell	13 mg/ml	Pos. (2)	Ishidate *et al.*, 1981
Chromosomal aberration assay	Human leucocytes	50 µM (4)	Pos. (3)	Oppenheim & Fishbein, 1965
In vivo Chromosomal aberration assay	Bone marrow cell	25 g/kg bw (5)	Pos.	Chaurasia & Sinha, 1987

(1) With and without metabolic activation.
(2) Only positive without metabolic activation; negative with metabolic activation.
(3) The authors considered the positive result as a non-specific effect of high-molarity urea solution on cell division.
(4) Concentration, probably per l.
(5) The applied oral dose appears unrealistically high, it exceeds lethal dose by several times.

Urea excretion was also diminished in cases of reduced urea formation due to liver diseases (Geigy, 1981b) and nephropathies (Mountcastle, 1974).

The enzyme system necessary for urea synthesis in human fetuses was functional when mesonephric glomeruli were present (Kennan *et al.*, 1959).

Urea has been shown to have a neutralizing effect on acidified plaque layers produced in the oral cavity after consumption of fermentable carbohydrates (Imfield, 1984 & 1985).

2.3.2 **Toxicity**

Four healthy male human subjects received an oral dose of 15 grams urea (≈ 250 mg/kg bw), blood urea rose from 30 mg/100 ml (mean level prior to treatment) to a mean level of 42 mg/100 ml (range: 40-46) within 15 to 60 minutes. The increased blood urea levels returned to normal after 3 hours. Fifteen patients with renal impairment, after similar oral treatment with 15 g urea, showed a rise in blood urea from 50 mg/100 ml (mean level prior to treatment; range: 26-220) to a mean level of 75 mg/100 ml (range: 38-299). The increased blood urea levels returned to the levels observed prior to treatment after more than 4 hours (Archer & Robb, 1925).

Six healthy subjects were given oral treatment of 2 000 to 3 000 mg/kg bw urea hourly for a period of 24 hours to induce azotaemia. Serum urea-nitrogen values ranged from 60-120 mg/100 ml (≈ blood urea of 128-257 mg/100 ml; [conversion factor for "blood urea" {serum urea} to "blood urea-nitrogen" = 2.14]) (Eknoyan et al., 1969).

No toxic effects were found in humans if the blood urea-nitrogen was below 45 mg/100 ml (≈ blood urea of 96 mg/100 ml). Loss of appetite, nausea and vomiting developed at about 70 mg/100 ml (≈ blood urea of 150 mg/100 ml) (Crawford & McIntosh 1925).

Signs of malaise, vomiting, weakness, lethargy, and bleeding were noted in patients with renal failure who were loaded with urea in the blood at levels of 300-600 mg/100 ml for 60 to 90 days. Blood urea concentrations below 300 mg/100 ml were well tolerated by the patients (Johnson et al., 1972).

80 patients were hospitalized after ingestion of urea fertilizer mistaken for table salt. The symptoms observed were nausea, persistent violent vomiting, excitement, and severe general convulsions. Complete recovery of all patients was observed within a few days (Steyn, 1961).

Six healthy human subjects were maintained at serum urea-nitrogen concentrations at 60 to 120 mg/100 ml (≈ blood urea of 128-257 mg/100 ml) over a period of 24 hours. Prolonged bleeding time and a drastic reduction of the blood platelet adhesiveness was observed in 5/6 subjects (Eknoyan et al., 1969).

Oxygen uptake in human blood platelets in vitro was reduced 7%, 14%, and 19% at urea levels of 100, 300, and 500 mg/100 ml, respectively (Schneider et al., 1967).

The relationship between plasma urea concentration and low birth weight in infants of non-toxaemic mothers was investigated. 16 infants with low birth weight had a statistically significantly higher mean plasma urea concentration of 23.2 mg/100 ml in comparison with a mean value of 18.6 mg/100 ml in 90 infants with normal birth weight (p < 0.02) (McKay & Kilpatrick, 1964).

Ingestion of 60 grams of urea per day (≈ 1 000 mg/kg bw/day), in divided doses, over a period of 3 1/4 days, resulted in prolonged clearance time of glucose in adults (Perkoff et al., 1958).

The irritant potential of urea dissolved in water was determined on human scarified skin. On the third day following daily application, a solution of 7.5% urea showed slight skin irritation, and a solution of 30% urea showed marked skin irritation. A solution of 30% urea did not affect normal skin (Frosch & Kligman, 1977).

Intra-amniotic injection of up to 300 ml 30% urea solution has been used to induce therapeutic abortion (Anteby et al., 1973).

2.3.3 Drug interactions

Treatment of 40 men suffering from sulfonamide-resistant gonorrhoea with urea (500 mg/kg bw/dy) for a period of 3 days enhanced the effect of sulfonamide in 52% of the patients. A combination of urea and sulfathiazole inhibited the growth of gonococci *in vitro*, although neither alone was effective (Schnitker & Lenhoff, 1944).

The inhibitory effect of sulfadiazine on the growth of *E.coli in vitro* was enhanced in combination with urea (Tsuchiya et al., 1942).

2.3.4 Use in human medicine

Urea has been used in human medicine as diuretic at doses of 15 to 60 grams/day. The mechanism of the diuretic effect originates from increased glomerular filtration due to osmotic action of urea (Sollmann, 1957).

In the oral therapy of sickle-cell anaemia, urea at doses of 667-2 000 mg/kg bw/day, in divided doses, was given for periods of 3 weeks to 9 months. Side effects included increased diuresis, thirst, gastrointestinal discomfort, nausea and vomiting (Bensinger et al., 1972).

3. COMMENTS

The Committee reviewed biochemical studies, short-term toxicity studies in dogs and ruminants, carcinogenicity studies in rats and mice, mutagenicity studies, and studies on effects in human volunteers. It noted that most of the available data were either inadequate or of little relevance for the evaluation of urea as a food additive. As urea is a naturally-occurring constituent of the body, the Committee carried out its evaluation in accordance with the principles relating to materials of this type outlined in Annex 1, reference 76.

4. EVALUATION

Since urea is a natural end-product of amino acid metabolism in humans, and that approximately 20 grams/day is excreted in the urine in adults (proportionately less in children) the Committee concluded that the use of urea at levels of up to 3% in chewing-gum was of no toxicological concern.

5. REFERENCES

ABDERHALDEN, E. (1935) Handbuch der biologischen Arbeitsmethoden, Urgan & Schwarzenberg, Berlin. vol IV p 1353

ANTEBY, S.O, SEGAL, S. & POLISHUK, W.E. (1973). Termination of midtrimester pregnancy by intra-amniotic injection of urea. *Obstetrics & Gynaecology*, **43**, 765-768.

ARCHER, H.E & ROBB, G.D. (1925). The tolerance of the body for urea in health and diseases. *Quart. J. Med.* **18**, 274-287.

BALESTRI, P.L., RINDI, P. & BIAGINI, M. (1971). Chronic urea intoxication in dogs. *Experimentia*, **27**, 811-812.

BENSINGER, T.A, MAHMOOD, L., CONRAD, M.E. & MCCURDY, P.R. (1972). The effect of oral urea administration on red cell survival in sickle cell disease. *Amer. J. Med. Sci.* **264**, 283-288.

BLOOD, D.C & HENDERSON, J.A. (1963). Veterinary Medicine. 2nd Edition, Balliere, Tyndall & Cassell, London. p.1077.

BRIGGS, H.M. (1967). Urea as a protein supplement. Pergamon Press, N.Y, p.12-14.

CHAURASIA, O.P & SINKA, S.P. (1987). Effects of urea on mitotic chromosomes of mice and onion. *Cytologia*, **52**, 877-882.

CRAWFORD, J.H & MCINTOSH (1925). Cited in: Sollman, A manual of pharmacology and its applications to therapeutics and toxicology Eighth Edition, 1957. Saunders Company, Philadelphia & London. p. 1051.

DINNING, J.S., BRIGGS, H.M., GALLUP, W.D., ORR, H.W. & BUTLER, R. (1948). The effect of orally administered urea on the ammonia and urea concentration in the blood of cattle and sheep, with observations on blood ammonia levels associated with symptoms of alkalosis. *Amer. J. Physiol.*, **153**, 41-46.

EKNOYAN, G., WACKSMAN, S.J., GLUECK, H.I. & WILL, J.J. (1969). Platelets function in renal failure. *New. Eng. J. Med.* **280**, 677-681.

FLEISCHMAN, R.W., HAYDEN, D.W., SMITH, E.R., WEISBURGER, J.H. AND WEISBURGER, E.K. (1980). Carcinogenesis bioassay of acetamide, hexanamide, adipamide, urea and p-tolyurea in mice and rats. *J. Environ. Path. Toxicol.*, **3**, 149-170.

FROSCH, P.J. & KLIGMAN, A.M. (1977). The chamber-scarification test for assessing irritancy of topically applied substances. In: Cutaneous toxicity. Proceedings of the 3rd Conference, 1976. Drill, V.A. & Lazar, P., eds. New York, Academic Press, 1977, 127-154.

GARBERG, P., ÅKERBLOM, E-L. & BOLCSFOLDI, G. (1988). Evaluation of a genotoxicity test measuring DNA-strand breaks in mouse lymphoma cells by alkaline unwinding and hydroxyapatite elution. *Mutation Res.*, **203**, 155-176.

GEIGY (1981a). Scientific Tables, Vol. 1, C.Lentner (Ed.). 8th Edition, CIBA-GEIGY Ltd., Basel, Switzerland, p.114.

GEIGY (1981b). Scientific Tables, Vol. 1, C.Lentner (Ed.). 8th Edition, CIBA-GEIGY Ltd., Basel, Switzerland, 62-63.

GOODRICH, R.D., MEISKE, J.C. & JACOBS, R.E. (1966). Cited in: Tracor-Jitco (1974). Scientific Literature Review on Generally Recognized as safe (GRAS) Food Ingredients - Urea. Report no.: FDABF-GRAS-272, National Technical Information Service, US Depart. of Commerce, August 1974.

GRIMSON, R.E., BOWLAND, J.P. & MILLIGAN, L.P. (1971). Use of nitrogen-15 labelled urea to study urea utilization by pigs. *Can. J. Anim. Sci.*, **51**, 103-110.

GROLLMAN, E.F. & GROLLMAN, A. (1959). Toxicity of urea and its role in the pathogenesis of uraemia. *J. Clin. Invest.*, **38**, 749-754.

HART, E.B, BOHSTEDT, G. DEOBALD, H.J. & WEGNER, M.I. (1939). Cited in: Osebold, W.J. (1947). Urea poisoning in cattle, *North American Veterinarian*, **28**, 89-91.

HINTZ, H.F., LOWE, J.E., CLIFFORD, A.J. & VISEK, W.J. (1970). Ammonia intoxication resulting from urea ingestion by ponies. *J. Amer. Vet. Med. Assoc.*, **157**, 963-966.

IMIELD, T. (1984). Telemetric evaluation of the neutralizing activity of two chewing gums produced by Fertin Laboratories. Unpublished report dated 11 December 1984. Submitted to WHO by Fertin Laboratories, Vejle, Denmark.

IMIELD, T. (1985). Telemetric evaluation of the neutralizing activity of two chewing gums produced by Fertin Laboratories. Unpublished report dated 24 July 1985. Submitted to WHO by Fertin Laboratories, Vejle, Denmark.

ISHIDATE Jr., M. & ODASHIMA, S. (1977). Chromosome tests with 134 compounds on Chinese hamster cells in vitro - A screening for chemical carcinogens. *Mutation Res.*, **48**, 337-354.

ISHIDATE Jr., M., SOFUNI, T. & YOSHIKAWA, K. (1981). Chromosome abberation tests in vitro as a primary screening tool for environmental mutagens and/or carcinogens. Gann, Monographs on cancer research, No.27, 95-108.

JOHNSON, W.J., HAGGE, H.H., WAGONER, R.D., DINAPOLI, R.P., & ROSEVEAR, J.W. (1972). Effects of urea loading in patients with advanced renal failure. *Mayo Clinic. Proc.*, **47**, 21-29.

KEATING, F.R., JONES, J.D., ELVEBACK.L.R., & RANDALL, R.V. (1969). The relation of age and sex to distribution of values of healthy adults of serum calcium, inorganic phosphorus, magnesium, alkaline phosphatase, total proteins, albumin, and blood urea. *J. Lab. Clin. Med.*, **73**, 825-834.

KENNAN, A.L. & COHEN, P.P. (1959). Biochemical studies of the developing mammalian fetus. *Dev. Biol.*, **1**, 511-525.

LUCK, J.M. & ENGLE, E.T. (1929). The permeability of the placenta of the rat to glycine, alanine and urea. *Amer. J. Physiol.*, **88**, 230-236.

MCKAY, E. & KILPATRICK, S.J. (1964). Maternal and infant plasma urea at delivery. *J. Obstet. Gynæcol. Brit. Commonwealth.* **71**, 449-452.

MERCK (1968). The Merck Index. An encyclopedia of chemicals and drugs. Merck and Co., Rahway, New Jersey, USA, p.1094.

MOUNTCASTLE, V.B. (1974). Medical physiology. Thirteenth Edition, p.1112. The C.V Mosby Company. Saint Louis, MO, USA.

OPPENHEIM, J.J. & FISHBEIN, W. (1965). Induction of chromosome breaks in cultured normal human leucocytes by potassium arsenite, hydroxyurea and related compounds. *Cancer Res.*, **25**, 980-985.

PERKOFF, G.T., THOMAS, C.L., NEWTON, J.D. SELLMAN, J.C. & TYLER, F.H. (1958). Mechanism of impaired glucose tolerance in anaemia and experimental hyperazotemia. *Diabetes*, **7**, 375-383.

SATAPATHY, N. & PANDA, B. (1963). Urea in ruminant nutrition. *Indian Vet. J.*, **40**, 228-236.

SAX, N.I. (1975). Dangerous properties of industrial materials. Fourth Edition. Van Nostrand Reinhold Compagny, New York, p.320.

SCHMIDT-NIELSEN, B. (1958). Urea excretion in mammals. *Physiological Reviews*, **38**, 139-168.

SCHNEIDER, W., SCHUMACHER, K. & GROSS, R. (1969). The influence of urea on energy metabolism of human blood platelets. *Thromb. Diath. Haemorr.*, **22**, 208-211.

SCHNITKER, M.A. & LENHOFF, C.D. (1944). Sulphonamide-resistant gonorrhoea treated with urea and sulphonamide by mouth. *J. Lab. Clin. Med.*, **29**, 889-898.

SCHOOLAR, J.C., BARLOW, C.F. & ROTH, L.J. (1960). The penetration of carbon-14 urea into cerebrospinal fluid and various areas of the cat brain. *J. Neuropath. Exptl. Neurol.*, **19**, 216-227.

SHANNON, I.L. & PRIGMORE, J.R. (1961). Effects of urea dosage on urea correlations in human parotid fluid and blood serum. *Arch. Oral Biol.*, **5**, 161-167.

SOLLMANN, T. (1957), A manual of pharmacology and its applications to therapeutics and toxicology. Eighth Edition. Saunders Company. Philadelphia & London. 1051-1052.

STEYN, D.G. (1961). An outbreak of urea poisoning among Bantu farm labourers in the Potgietersrust district, Transvaal. *S. Afr. Med. J.*, **35**, 721-722.

STILES, D.A., BARTLEY, E.E., MEYER, R.M., DEYOE, C.W. & PFOST, A.B. (1970). Food processing. VII. Effect of an expansion-processed mixture of grain and urea (Starea) on rumen metabolism in cattle and on urea toxicity. *J. Dairy Sci.*, **53**, 1436-1447.

TRACOR-JITCO (1974). Scientific literature reviews on Generally Recognized As Safe (GRAS) Food Ingredients - Urea. Report No.: FDABF-GRAS-272 from National Technical Information Service, USA.

TSUCHIYA, N.M., TENENBERG, D.J., CLACK, W.G. & STRAKOSCH, E.A. (1942). Antagonism of anti-sulfonamide effect of methionine, and enhancement of bacteriostatic action of sulfonamide by urea. *Proc. Soc. Exp. Biol. Med.*, **50**, 262-266.

WOLPERT, E., PHILLIPS, S.F. AND SUMMERSKILL, W.H.J. (1971). Transport of urea and ammonium production in the human colon. *Lancet*, **2**, 1387-1390.

CONTAMINANT

CHLOROPROPANOLS

First draft prepared by
Dr P. Olsen
Institute of Toxicology, National Food Agency of Denmark
Ministry of Health, Søborg, Denmark

1.   EXPLANATION

Certain chlorinated propanols occur as contaminants in hydrolyzed vegetable proteins. The two substances considered by the Committee at its present meeting were 3-chloro-1,2-propanediol and 1,3-dichloro-2-propanol, neither of which has previously been evaluated by the Committee. Processing of defatted vegetable proteins by traditional hydrochloric acid hydrolysis leads to the formation of significant amounts of 3-chloro-1,2-propanediol and 1,3-dichloro-2-propanol. However, manufacturing techniques have been improved, enabling the reduction of the level of 3-chloro-1,2-propanediol to less than 2 mg/kg and that of 1,3-dichloro-2-propanol to less than 0.02 mg/kg in hydrolyzed vegetable proteins.

Because this monograph covers the data considered by the Committee on both 3-chloro-1,2-propanediol and 1,3-dichloro-2-propanol, a modified form of the general monograph format has been used, presenting separately the biological data for each.

3-CHLORO-1,2-PROPANEDIOL

2.   BIOLOGICAL DATA

2.1   Biochemical aspects

2.1.1   Absorption, distribution, and excretion

3-chloro-1,2-propanediol was able to cross the blood-testis barrier, blood-brain barrier and was distributed widely in body fluids (Edwards *et al.* 1975). Accumulation of 3-chloro-1,2-propanediol was seen in the cauda epididymis of rats and to a lesser extent in mice through autoradiography (Crabo & Appelgren, 1972). This finding was disputed by Jones *et al.,* (1978), who did not observe any tissue-specific retention of radioactivity in rats injected intraperitoneally with 100 mg/kg bw [36]C-labelled 3-chloro-1,2-propanediol. Neither 3-chloro-1,2-propanediol nor the metabolite ß-chlorolactate was accumulated in the tissue (Jones *et al.,* 1978).

A single intraperitoneal injection of 100 mg/kg bw of ^{14}C-labelled 3-chloro-1,2-propanediol was given to male Wistar rats. After 24-hours 30% of the dose was exhaled as $^{14}CO_2$ and 8.5% was excreted unchanged in the urine (Jones, 1978). In another study in rats which were injected intraperitoneally with a single dose of 100 mg/kg bw ^{36}C-labelled 3-chloro-1,2-propanediol, 23% of the radioactivity was recovered in the urine as ß-chlorolactate (Jones et al., 1978).

2.1.2   Biotransformation

3-chloro-1,2-propanediol is detoxified by conjugation with glutathione yielding S-(2,3-dihydroxypropyl)cysteine and the corresponding mercapturic acid, N-acetyl-S-(2,3-dihydroxypropyl)cysteine (Jones, 1975). 3-chloro-1,2-propanediol undergoes oxidation to ß-chlorolactic acid and further to oxalic acid (Jones and Murcott, 1976). Formation of an intermediate metabolite, ß-chlorolactaldehyde may also take place as traces of this substance have been determined in the urine in rats (Jones et al., 1978). The intermediate formation of an epoxide has been postulated, but not proven (Jones, 1975).

2.1.3   Effects on enzymes and other biochemical parameters

The activity of all glycolytic enzymes in the epididymal and testicular tissue was reduced in rats given daily subcutaneous injection of 6.5 mg/kg bw/dy 3-chloro-1,2-propanediol for 9 days (Kaur & Guraya, 1981a).

Ram sperm incubated with 3-chloro-1,2-propanediol has shown that 3-chloro-1,2-propanediol inhibits the glycolysis of spermatozoa in vitro (Brown-Woodman et al., 1975), possibly a result of indirect inhibition of glyceraldehyde-3-phosphate dehydrogenase (Suter et al., 1975; Mohri et al., 1975). Decrease in the spermatozoa glycolytic enzymes was suggested to be a result of altered epididymal milieu (Kuar & Guraya, 1981b).

Rats receiving daily doses of 6.5 mg/kg bw 3-chloro-1,2-propanediol for a period of 9 days showed significantly decreased ($p < 0.05$) levels of RNA and protein in the testis and epididymis and the observations were closely related to a parallel increase in the concentration of proteinase and ribonuclease. The DNA content was unchanged (Kaur & Guraya, 1981c).

2.2   Toxicological studies

2.2.1   Acute toxicity studies

The oral LD_{50} of 3-chloro-1,2-propanediol was reported to be 152 mg/kg bw in rats (Ericsson & Baker, 1970).

2.2.2   Short-term toxicity studies

2.2.2.1 Rats

Groups of 8 male Fisher 344 rats were treated with a single subcutaneous injection of 75 mg/kg bw 3-chloro-1,2-propanediol and killed after 24 hours, 3, 8, 25, and 75 days, respectively. A slight but significant ($p < 0.05$) increase in liver weight was observed after 24 hours while this finding was not found at later sacrifices. Histologically the hepatocytes showed mild to moderate cytoplasmatic swelling in the periportal area (Kluwe et al., 1983).

Intraperitoneal injection of a single dose of 100 mg/kg bw 3-chloro-1,2-propanediol caused a increased diuresis for up to 15 days in male Sprague-Dawley rats. Higher doses (figure not reported) caused anuresis and death, and histological examination of the kidney showed acute glomerular nephritis. The type of kidney lesions was characteristic of oxalic acid poisoning and crystals characteristic of calcium oxalate were seen by microscopical examination of the urine. Oral treatment with 10 mg/kg bw/dy 3-chloro-1,2-propanediol for five consecutive days did not cause any increased diuresis in rats (Jones et al., 1978).

Another study showed that intraperitoneal injection of 100 and 120 mg/kg bw 3-chloro-1,2-propanediol caused severe proteinuria and glucosuria in male Wistar rats. Oliguria and anuria were observed and 4/9 animals died. The 5 surviving animals showed decreased appetite and body weight, proteinuria, dose-related diuresis and increased water intake (Morris and Williams, 1980).

Testing of (R)- and (S)-isomers of 3-chloro-1,2-propanediol, synthesized under laboratory condition, has shown that only the (R)-isomer induced a period of diuresis and glucosuria in rats (Porter and Jones, 1982).

Oxalic acid, a metabolite of 3-chloro-1,2-propanediol, appeared to play a important role in the development of kidney damage (Jones et al., 1979). Birefringent crystals characteristic of calcium oxalate present in tubules at the cortico-medullary junction were early (1 day) morphological changes seen in rats treated with a single subcutaneous injection of 75 mg/kg bw 3-chloro-1,2-propanediol. On day 75 focal tubular necrosis, regeneration, and tubular dilatation were observed in the kidney (Kluwe et al., 1983).

Groups of 20 Sprague-Dawley rats of each sex were given 0, 30, or 60 mg/kg bw/dy 3-chloro-1,2-propanediol by gavage 4 x 5 days over a period of 4 weeks. 10 animals/group and sex were sacrificed on day 2 and examined for clinical chemical parameters in the blood. On day 2, rats of the high-dose group showed elevated activity of serum glutamate-pyruvate-transaminase (males, $p < 0.05$; females, $p < 0.001$), and elevated levels of creatinine (females, $p < 0.001$), urea and glucose (females, $p < 0.05$). On day 25, treated rats exhibited elevated activity of glutamate-pyruvate-transaminase (males high-dose, $p < 0.001$; females low and high-

CHLOROPROPANOLS   270

dose, $p < 0.001$), and elevated serum urea in high-dose males ($p < 0.001$) and
females ($p < 0.05$). Statistically significant ($p < 0.05$ or lower) decreased values of
haemoglobin and haematocrit of treated male and female rats were observed.
Female rats in the high-dose group had decreased erythrocyte count ($p < 0.001$).
Treated rats showed lowered body weight gain, which at termination of the study
was statistically significant (statistics not reported). After 2 days of treatment the
relative organ weights of the kidney were elevated ($p < 0.001$), (males high-dose;
females low and high-dose). On day 25 treated rats had significantly elevated
relative weights of the kidney, liver, and testis (males high-dose) ($p < 0.01$ or
0.001). Histopathological examination revealed chronic progressive nephropathy
of 8 females in the high-dose group, mild tubular dilatation in the testis of 3 males
in the low-dose group and 7 in the high-dose group. One male in the high-dose
group had severe atrophy of both testes (Marchesini and Stalder, 1983).

  Groups of 20 Fisher 344 rats of each sex were administered 3-chloro-1,2-
propanediol in their drinking water at concentrations of 0, 100, 300, or 500 mg/l
over a period of 90 days. The exposure corresponded to average daily intake levels
of 9, 27 and 43 mg/kg bw 3-chloro-1,2-propanediol in males and 11, 31, and 46
mg/kg bw 3-chloro-1,2-propanediol in female rats. Ten animals of each sex/group
were sacrificed (interim sacrifice) after 30 days of treatment. Clinical chemical and
haematological parameters were determined. Histopathological examinations were
carried out on the high-dose and control groups.
  A slight anaemia ($p < 0.05$ or 0.001) was evident in the middle- and high-
dose females after 30 days and in rats of both sexes after 90 days of treatment
($p < 0.05$ or 0.01). However, no morphological evidence of impaired
haematopoiesis nor increased degradation of erythrocytes were observed. A dose-
dependent decrease ($p < 0.01$) in plasma creatinine of both sexes (middle and high-
dose groups) was seen after 30 days of treatment and at terminal sacrifice in all
treated groups ($p < 0.05$ or 0.01). Serum phosphate levels in high-dose male rats
were increased at interim ($p < 0.01$) and terminal sacrifice ($p < 0.05$). A statistically
significant ($p < 0.01$) dose-dependent increase in relative organ weights was found
for the kidney and liver, and the increase of the relative kidney weight was
significant at the lowest dose level. Histopathological examination of the high-dose
and control groups revealed a lower incidence of crystalline precipitations in the
kidneys of treated animals compared to the controls. In the livers of dosed rats,
single hepatocytes with 2-3 nuclei were noted in about half of the males after 90
days of treatment. In the epididymis an increased number of exfoliated
spermatozoids of treated male rats was observed (Marchesini et al., 1989).

2.2.2.2 Monkeys

  Three out of 6 monkeys given 30 mg/kg bw 3-chloro-1,2-propanediol
perorally/day for 6 weeks showed haematological abnormalities: anaemia,
leukopenia and severe thrombocytopenia (Kirton et al., 1970).

2.2.3 Long-term toxicity/carcinogenicity studies

2.2.3.1 Mice

A group of 50 female mice (CHR/Ha Swiss) was injected subcutaneously with 1 mg 3-chloro-1,2-propanediol/mouse/week over a period of 580 days. A second group of 50 mice was treated 3x/wk with 2 mg 3-chloro-1,2-propanediol (dissolved in acetone)/mouse by topical application. No changes were observed in the group treated by dermal application. After subcutaneous application, local sarcomas were found at the site of application in one dosed and one control mouse (Van Duuren *et al.*, 1974).

2.2.3.2 Rats

Three groups of 26 male and female Charles River CD rats received 0, 30, or 60 mg 3-chloro-1,2-propanediol by gavage twice weekly. After 10 weeks the doses were increased to 35 and 70 mg/kg bw. The animals were treated for 72 weeks and the study was terminated after 2 years. Three parathyroid adenomas were found in male rats at the high-dose level. However, this finding was not statistically significant when compared with the control group. The authors did not find the result conclusive indication that 3-chloro-1,2-propanediol is a parathyroid carcinogen. While the females showed no signs of toxicity, dosed male rats showed a higher mortality. All male rats at both dose levels showed severe testicular degeneration and atrophy (Weisburger *et al.,* 1981).

Four groups of Fisher F344 rats (50 animals/sex/group, SPF quality, 5-6 weeks old at start of the study, 11 days acclimatization period prior to study initiation) received either 0, 20, 100, or 500 ppm 3-chloro-1,2-propanediol (equivalent to a mean daily intake of 0, 1.1, 5.2, 28 mg/kg bw/day for males and 0, 1.4, 7.0, or 35 mg/kg bw/day for females) in their drinking water (tap water) for a period of 104 weeks. Feed and tap water were provided *ad libitum*. Feed was certified laboratory chow, feed contaminants were within acceptable range according to EPA, USA. Test substance was 3-chloro-1,2-propanediol, 98% pure, one batch used for the entire study. Stability: more than 4 days in water, test solution was prepared twice a week and tested once per group per week. Tap water contaminants: a mean concentration of 2.7 ppm 3-chloro-1,2-propanediol was determined (tested once/week). The report does not comment on presence of 3-chloro-1,2-propanediol in provided water.

Experimental animals were examined daily for signs of ill health or behavioural changes. Food consumption and body weight were recorded weekly from start to week 19 (feed consumption) and week 20 (body weight) of the study and thereafter monthly. From week 88 to the end of the study, the body weight was recorded weekly. Water consumption was recorded weekly from start to week 20 of the study, and thereafter fortnightly. Ophthalmological examination was performed regularly. Haematological examination and blood chemistry were performed on blood samples taken at day 722 to 737 from all surviving animals.

All animals found dead or animals killed "in extremis", as well as those killed at the end of the experiment, were subjected to complete necropsies and histopathological examination. The liver, spleen, pancreas, heart, adrenals, testis, epididymides and brain were weighed.

The body weights were significantly (P < 0.05) reduced in high-dose male and female rats following the first week of treatment. At termination the body weights were significantly reduced (P < 0.05 or lower) in intermediate-, and high-dose animals showing a reduction in body weights of 33% (males) and 35% (females) in high-dose rats. However, the mortality was unaffected by treatment, and at terminal sacrifice more than 42% of the group survived. The food and water intake were significantly (P < 0.05) reduced in high-dose male and female rats. No treatment-related clinical signs were noted. The results of the haematological and blood clinical chemical parameters varied considerably within the groups, however no consistent significant dose-related effects were observed. The reduced body weight in intermediate-, and high-dose rats made it difficult to interpret a possible effect of treatment on organ weights. However, the body weights were unaffected in low-dose rats, of which the males showed significant (P < 0.05) increased kidney weight (absolute only).

Dose-related increased (or decreased) incidence of hyperplasia/tumours were observed in the control, low- intermediate- and high-dose groups in the following organs: Kidney: tubular adenoma, males 0/50, 1/50, 1/50, 5/50, females 0/50, 1/50, 0/50, 9/50 (P < 0.05). Tubular hyperplasia, males 3/50, 6/50, 15/50, 34/50 (P < 0.05 in intermediate-, and high-dose when tubular adenoma and tubular hyperplasia were combined), females 2/50, 4/50, 20/50, 31/50 (P < 0.05). Testes: Leydig cell adenoma, 38/50, 43/50, 50/50 (P < 0.001), 47/50 (P < 0.05). Leydig cell adenocarcinoma, 0/50, 0/50, 0/50, 3/50 (P < 0.05). Nodular Leydig cell hyperplasia was present in a high proportion of controls and the incidence decreased significantly in a dose-dependent pattern. The incidence was 39/50, 27/50, 4/50, 0/50. When nodular Leydig cell hyperplasias, adenomas and carcinomas were combined for statistical analysis, there were no significant difference between groups. Mammary gland (males): fibroadenoma 0/50, 0/50, 2/50, 10/50 (P < 0.01). Adenoma 0/50, 0/50, 1/50, 1/50. Adenocarcinoma 0/50, 0/50, 1/50, 1/50. Preputial gland: adenoma 1/50, 2/50, 6/50 (P < 0.05), 5/50. Carcinoma 0/50, 0/50, 1/50, 2/50 (P < 0.05). When adenomas and carcinomas were combined for statistical analysis, the resulting increased incidence was significant for both intermediate-, and high-dose groups. Pancreas: There was a treatment-related decrease in the incidence of islet-cell hyperplasias, adenomas, and carcinomas in male rats. The incidences were for islet-cell hyperplasia 14/50, 8/50, 5/50, 1/50. Islet-cell adenoma 16/50, 9/50, 7/50, 0/50. Islet-cell carcinoma 8/50, 0/50, 2/50, 0/50. When hyperplasias and neoplastic lesions were combined for statistical analysis, the decrease in incidence was significant at all dose levels (P < 0.05 or lower). Chronic progressive nephropathy occurred in both sexes in all groups and the incidence increased with dose being significant at the intermediate-, and high-dose level (P < 0.05 or lower). Female rats were more severely affected than males. The figures were 36/50, 40/50, 45/50, 49/50 (males) and 24/50, 23/50, 42/50, 48/50 (females). Correlations (P < 0.001) between the severity of the nephropathy and the kidney tubular hyperplasia and kidney adenoma were found to be significant (P < 0.01).

A dose-dependent increase in epithelial single cell degeneration was observed in the epididymis. The incidence was significant at intermediate-, and high-dose level (P < 0.001).

The report concludes that treatment with 3-chloro-1,2-propanediol caused increases in renal and testicular Leydig cell tumours. Renal tumours developed in a dose-dependent fashion in both sexes and were considered secondary to the 3-chloro-1,2-propanediol treatment-related increase in chronic progressive nephropathy. The treatment-related increase and acceleration of Leydig cell tumours may be considered as hormone-mediated promotion. 3-chloro-1,2-propanediol treatment caused a dose-related increase in mammary and preputial gland tumours in the males. This effect may be considered as secondary to hormonal activity of large Leydig cell tumours (Sunahare et al, 1993).

2.2.4   Reproduction studies

3-Chloro-1,2-propanediol has been reported to exert an inhibitory activity on male fertility (Gunn et al., 1969; Helal, 1982) and the effect is reversible (Ericsson & Youngdale, 1970; Jones, 1983). The mechanism of the antifertility activity of 3-chloro-1,2-propanediol is not known in detail. However, it has been shown that the metabolites of 3-chloro-1,2-propanediol have an inhibitory activity on enzymes in spermatozoa glycolysis, resulting in a reduced motility of the spermatozoa (Jones, 1983). Inhibition of spermatozoa motility was suggested partly to be due to alkylation of spermatozoa cysteine by 3-chloro-1,2-propanediol (Kalla & Bansal, 1977). 3-Chloro-1,2-propanediol also affects several enzymes of epithelial cells in the testis and caput epididymis, resulting in decreased glycolysis (Gill & Guraya, 1980). It is suggested that only the 3-chloro-1,2-propanediol (S)-isomer, synthesized under laboratory condition, possesses a specific inhibitory action on glycolysis in boar sperm (Stevenson and Jones, 1984).

3-Chloro-1,2-propanediol has two specific effects on the reproductive tract of the male rat. These effects were dose-dependent and have been classified as the high-dose effect and the low-dose effect. The high-dose effect followed a single intraperitoneal injection of 75 mg/kg bw 3-chloro-1,2-propanediol. Bilateral retention cysts or spermatocele of the caput epididymis developed 5 to 7 days after treatment (Cooper & Jackson, 1973). Studies using electron microscopy have shown, that 3-chloro-1,2-propanediol, given by gavage at a level of 140 mg/kg bw, specifically affected the epithelia localized in the initial segment of epididymis in male rats 2 hours later. The cellular lesions were characterised by sloughing of the epithelium, which led to obstruction of the epididymal tract (Hoffer et al., 1973). The back-pressure of the testicular fluid caused oedema, inhibition of spermatogenesis and atrophy of the testis (Jones, 1983). Histological examination of testes from rats treated with daily injection of 40 mg/kg bw 3-chloro-1,2-propanediol for 20 days revealed total inhibition of the spermiogenesis by presence of degeneration and disappearance of the spermiogonia from the tubules.

Proliferation of the epithelial cells of the ducts in the cauda epididymis was observed and several blood vessels showed thickened walls (Samojlik and Chang 1970).

The low-dose effect was directed towards mature sperm contained in the cauda epididymis. The effect, which was evident after a few days following oral treatment of rats with levels of 5-10 mg/kg bw 3-chloro-1,2-propanediol/dy, rendered the spermatozoa incapable of fertilization without causing any visible changes in their morphology (Jones 1983).   Male rats treated with daily subcutaneous injections of 15 or 40 mg/kg bw 3-chloro-1,2-propanediol showed infertility 6 and 3 days after commencement of treatment, respectively.   If the treatment with 15 mg/kg bw 3-chloro-1,2-propanediol was continued for 30 days recovery of fertility was observed 18 days after cessation of the treatment (Samojlik and Chang, 1970).   The lowest doses shown to cause infertility of male rats, determined by mating studies, were observed at the following daily orally treatment of male rats with 3-chloro-1,2-propanediol: 6.5 mg/kg bw for 10 days (Gunn *et al.,* 1969); 5 mg/kg bw for 14 days (Coppola, 1969); 2.5 mg/kg bw at "continuous" treatment (Erickson & Bennett, 1971); (subcutaneous injection): 8 mg/kg bw for 3 days (Black *et al.,* 1975); 8 mg/kg bw for 4 days (Turner, 1971).

Groups of 5 albino male rats treated perorally for 10 to 12 days with either 0.5, 1.0, 2.0, 4.0, or 6.0 mg/kg bw 3-chloro-1,2-propanediol showed 2.5%, 20%, 45%, 85% and 100% sterility (sterility was based upon histological degree of spermiogenesis), respectively (Helal, 1982).

The following abstract has been compiled from a summary report: groups of 5 Wistar male rats were dosed with 0 (distilled water), 0.1, 0.5, 1, 2, 3, 4, 5, or 10 mg/kg bw/dy 3-chloro-1,2-propanediol by gavage for 7 days prior to, and during mating.   Each male rat was mated with a total of 5 virgin females which were sacrificed on day 14 of gestation and examined for pregnancy status.   3-Chloro-1,2-propanediol induced no adverse effect on male fertility at a dose level of 3 mg/kg bw/dy and lower as shown by the pregnancy rate, total implantations and number of live embryos. However, the pre-implantation loss was significantly greater (p=0.05) for female rats mated with males given 3 mg/kg bw/dy 3-chloro-1,2-propanediol when compared to controls.   The NOEL was 2 mg/kg bw/dy (Parish, 1989).

Antifertility activity of 3-chloro-1,2-propanediol in other species than rat has been reported in males of hamster, gerbil, guinea pig, dog, ram and rhesus monkey *in vivo* (Jones, 1983). 3-chloro-1,2-propanediol was reported to have no antifertility activity in the mouse, quail or rabbit (Jones, 1978).

Groups of 10 female rats were injected subcutaneously with 0 or 10 mg 3-chloro-1,2-propanediol ($\approx$ 25 mg/kg bw) every second day for a period of 30 days. Significant (p < 0.01) decrease was noted in the relative organ weights of the ovary, uterus and vagina of treated females compared to the controls.   Histological examination revealed the following changes of the treated female rats: the ovary appeared small in size and showed wide spread follicular atresia and degeneration of corpora lutea; in the uterus the gland was regressed and the lumen was lined with columnar epithelium; atrophic changes were observed in the vaginal epithelium. The protein and RNA content in the uterus and vagina were significantly ($p < 0.01$) reduced in the treated females compared to controls. The authors suggested a luteolytic and possibly antioestrogenic effect of 3-chloro-1,2-propanediol in female rats (Lohika and Arya, 1979).

2.2.8 Special studies on genotoxicity

The results of genotoxicity studies with 3-chloro-1,2-propanediol are summarized in Table 1.

Table 1. Results of genotoxicity tests on 3-chloro-1,2-propanediol

Test system	Test object	Concentration of 3-chloro-1,2-propanediol	+/-	Reference
In vitro bacterial mutagenicity assay (1)	*S.typhimurium* TA1535, TA1537, TA1538, TA98	2-200 μmol/plate	+ (2)	Silhankova *et al.*, 1982
	S.typhimurium TA100	10-1 000μmol/plate	+	Stolzenberg & Hine, 1980
	E.coli TM930	2-200 μmol/plate	-	Silhankova *et al.*, 1982
Forward-mutation assay on yeast(1)	*Schizosaccharomyces plombe*	100-300 mM	+	Rossi *et al.*, 1983
Mammalian cell mutation assay (1)	Mouse lymphoma TK locus assay	2-9 mg/ml	+ (5)	Henderson *et al.*, 1987
Mammalian cell mutation assay (1)	HeLa cell	(6)	-	Painter & Howard, 1982
Mammalian cell mutation assay	Mouse fibroblast M2-clone	0.1-2 mg/ml	+	Piasecki *et al.*, 1990
Sister chromatid exchange assay(1)	Chinese hamster V79 cells	700-2800 μg/ml	+	May, 1991
Mammalian cell HPRT-test (1)	Chinese hamster V79 cells	0.3-70mM	? (4)	Görlitz, 1991
In vivo dominant lethal assay	ICR/Ha Swiss mice	(3)	-	Epstein *et al.*, 1972
Micronucleus test	OF₁ mice	40-120 mg/kg bw	-	Jaccaud & Aeschbacher, 1989

(1) With and without metabolic activation. (2) No frame shift mutations in strains TA1537, TA1538 or TA98. (3) Single intraperitoneal injection of 125 mg/kg bw 3-chloro-1,2-propanediol or peroral treatment of 20 mg/kg bw 3-chloro-1,2-propanediol for five days. (4) Weak mutagenic effect only at toxic dose level (50mM). (5) Positive only after metabolic activation. (6) Not reported.

2.3   Observations in humans

A synergistic effect of 3-chloro-1,2-propanediol and copper ions in decreasing the motility of human spermatozoa was observed *in vitro* (Kalla & Singh, 1981). When 3-chloro-1,2-propanediol was incubated with ejaculated human sperm the motility of the spermatozoa was inhibited and their metabolic activity was reduced, as measured by glucose, oxygen uptake and lactate production (Homonnai *et al.*, 1975).

1,3-DICHLORO-2-PROPANOL

2.   Biological data

2.1   Biochemical aspects

2.1.1   Absorption, distribution, and excretion

No information was available.

2.1.2   Biotransformation

ß-Chlorolactate (approx. 5% of dose), N,N'-bis-acetyl-S,S'-(1,3-bis-cysteinyl)propan-2-ol (approx. 1% of dose), and N-acetyl-S-(2,3-dihydroxypropyl)cysteine were identified in the urine of rats treated orally with 50 mg/kg bw/dy 1,3-dichloro-2-propanol for 5 days. The authors proposed that epoxyhalopropane (*epi*-chlorohydrin) is formed as an intermediate, which may either undergo conjugation with glutathione to form mercapturic acid or be hydrolyzed to 3-chloro-1,2-propanediol. The latter undergoes oxidation to ß-chlorolactate which is further oxidized to oxalic acid. Formation of other epoxides was postulated. However, the formation of epoxides from alpha-chlorohydrins only takes place at high pH-values and is unlikely to occur under physiological conditions (Jones and Fakhouri, 1979).

2.2   Toxicological studies

2.2.1   Acute toxicity studies

The oral LD_{50} of 1,3-dichloro-2-propanol was reported to be 122 mg/kg bw in rats, while by intraperitoneal application the LD_{50} was 106 mg/kg bw (Pallade *et al.*, 1963). In rabbits the LD_{50} was 800 mg/kg bw following dermal application (Smyth *et al.*, 1962). In mice the LC_{50} over a period of 1-15 days was 1.7-3.2 mg/l air (Pallade *et al.*, 1963). When tested on rabbit eyes 1,3-dichloro-2-propanol caused irritation and moderately severe damage (Grant, 1974).

2.2.2   Short-term toxicity studies

2.2.2.1   Rats

The following summary was written from an abstract cited in *The Toxicologist*. A critical evaluation of the findings from this abstract has not been possible. 1,3-dichloro-2-propanol was evaluated for subchronic toxicity in Sprague-Dawley rats (10/sex/dose group) treated with dose levels of 0, 0.1, 1, 10, or 100 mg/kg bw/dy 1,3-dichloro-2-propanol by gavage in distilled water 5 days/week for 13 weeks. Decreases in bw gain, feed consumption and haematologic parameters, increases in liver and kidney weights, alterations in serum chemistry and urinary parameters, gross pathologic changes in the stomach and histopathologic changes in the stomach, kidney, liver and nasal tissue were observed at 100 mg/kg/day in males and females. The changes in serum chemistry were considered secondary to renal and hepatic changes observed in high-dose animals. At 10 mg/kg, increased liver weights in males and females and histopathologic changes in the stomach, kidneys and liver in males were observed. The treatment related-effects observed at 10 mg/kg were less frequent and/or less severe than the effects observed at 100 mg/kg. No effects were observed at 0.1 or 1 mg/kg in males or females (Jersey *et al.*, 1991).

2.2.3   Long-term toxicity/carcinogenicity studies

2.2.3.1   Rats

In a combined long-term toxicity/carcinogenicity study, 4 groups of 80 male and 80 female rats (Wistar KFM/Han, initial age of 4 weeks; 10 days acclimatization prior to test), received 1,3-dichloro-2-propanol [purity: 99%; stability confirmed by sponsor at six-month intervals] in their drinking water over a period of up to 104 weeks. 1,3-dichloro-2-propanol concentrations in the drinking water (daily preparation of 1,3-dichloro-2-propanol/water mixture, regular determination of 1,3-dichloro-2-propanol stability, concentration and homogeneity) were 0, 27, 80, or 240 mg/l corresponding to intakes of 0, 2.1, 6.3, and 19.3 mg/kg bw/day for male rats and 0, 3.4, 9.6, and 30 mg/kg bw/day for female rats. The diet [pelleted; regular determination of contaminants showed presence of low, biologically insignificant levels of aflatoxin, estrogen, pesticides and heavy metals] was provided *ad libitum*. Interim kill was performed on 10 rats of each sex and group after 26, 52, and 78 weeks of treatment.

Haematologically, female rats in the high-dose group, in particular, showed statistically significantly ($p < 0.05$) decreased haemoglobin concentration and haematocrit (26 and 104 weeks), and red blood cell count (104 weeks). Clinical biochemical and urine analysis findings suggested hepatotoxicity primarily in high-dose females. Statistically significant ($p < 0.05$) increased activity of aspartate- and alanine aminotransferase (78 and 104 weeks), alkaline phosphatase (104 weeks), and gamma-glutamyltransferase (104 weeks) were observed in female rats. Statistically significant ($p < 0.05$) increases in urinary levels of protein and amylase were noted in high-dose female rats after 52, 78, and 104 weeks of treatment. Increased mortality was observed in high-dose males (32/50) and females (27/50) compared to that in the controls (males 18/50; females 13/50), (statistics not reported). The mortality of the low-dose group was: 11/50 (males), 9/50 (females); of the intermediate-dose group was: 16/50 (males), 14/50 (females).

There were no treatment-related signs of toxicity nor changes in food and water consumption. However, statistically significant ($p < 0.05$ or lower) reductions in mean body weights were observed in high-dose males after 74 weeks and in high-dose females after 78 weeks. A dose-related increase in the relative organ weights was observed in a number of organs, in particular, the liver and kidney. After 26 weeks: liver of males and females in all treated groups ($p < 0.05$); kidney of males at intermediate- and high-dose ($p < 0.05$), and females at high-dose ($p < 0.05$). After 52 weeks: livers of males and females in intermediate- and high-dose groups ($p < 0.05$); kidney of females at high-dose ($p < 0.05$). After 78 weeks: liver and kidney of males and females at high-dose ($p < 0.01$). After 104 weeks: liver, kidney and brain of males and females at high-dose ($p < 0.01$). Histopathological examination revealed occurrence of several tumours in various organs. Among these tumours dose-related neoplastic lesions in middle- and high-dose male and female rats were seen. Statistically significant positive trends were found for hepatocellular adenoma (females, $p < 0.001$); hepatocellular carcinoma (males and females, $p < 0.001$); hepatic hemangiosarcoma (males, $p < 0.01$ and females, $p < 0.05$); renal tubular adenoma (males, $p < 0.001$); renal tubular carcinoma (males, $p < 0.05$); lingual papilloma (males and females, $p < 0.001$); lingual papillary carcinoma (males, $p < 0.001$ and females, $p < 0.01$); thyroid follicular adenoma (females, $p < 0.05$); thyroid follicular carcinoma (males, $p < 0.01$). These neoplastic lesions occurred in treated animals after 26 weeks (hepatocellular adenoma), 52 weeks (hepatocellular adenoma and carcinoma, lingual papilloma and carcinoma), and 78 weeks (hepatocellular carcinoma, renal tubular adenoma, lingual papilloma and carcinoma, thyroid follicular adenoma). In addition to the above-mentioned tumours, one stomach papilloma was found in one high-dose female rat after 78 weeks and at terminal sacrifice one stomach carcinoma (low-dose, female), carcinomas in the oral cavity [intermediate-dose (one, female) and high-dose (two, males)].

The incidence of the above-mentioned neoplastic lesions in control rats was: two hepatocellular adenomas (male and female) and one thyroid follicular adenoma (female). Among non-neoplastic lesions the liver showed dose-dependent increase in incidence of fatty change, eosinophilic foci, glycogen free foci, Kupffer cell haemosiderin storage, and peliosis. Follicular hyperplasia was evident in thyroid glands of high-dose males. These results strongly suggest an oncogenic effect of 1,3-dichloro-2-propanol on liver, kidney, oral epithelia/tongue and thyroid gland in rats at the intermediate- and high-dose level. The significance of the sinusoidal peliosis observed in all treated groups was not clear. However, peliosis has been suggested to represent a pre-neoplastic stage of vascular hepatic neoplasia (Wayss *et al.,* 1979).

The increased incidence of hepatic fatty change and haemosiderin-storing Kupffer cells in the liver in animals in the intermediate- and high-dose groups were suggested to reflect a metabolic disturbance of the liver caused by 1,3-dichloro-2-propanol (RCC, 1986).

2.2.4   Reproduction studies

2.2.4.1 Rats

The following summary has been obtained from an abstract cited in Hazardous Substances Data Base. A critical evaluation of material from this abstract has not been possible: Groups of 20, 10 or 10 male Wistar rats were dosed with either water (controls), 15, or 60 mg/kg bw/dy 1,3-dichloro-2-propanol by gavage for 14 days, respectively. Treated rats showed appearance of spermatocele or sperm granuloma formation in the epididymides (Tunstall Laboratories, 1979).

2.2.8   Special studies on genotoxicity

Table 2. Results of genotoxicity tests on 1,3-dichloro-2-propanol

Test system	Test object	Concentration 1,3-dichloro-2-propanol	+/-	Reference
In vitro Bacterial mutagenicity assay (1)	*S.typhimurium* TA1535, TA1537, TA1538, TA98	2-200 μmol/ plate	+ (2)	Silhankova, *et al.*, 1982
	S.typhimurium TA100	0.1-10μmol/plate	+	Stolzenberg & Hine, 1980
	S.typhimurium TA100, TA1535	3-300μmol/plate	+	Nakamura *et al.*, 1979
	E.coli, TM930	2-200μmol/plate	+ (3)	Silhankova *et al.*, 1982
Mammalian cell mutation assay(1)	Mouse lymphoma TK locus assay	2-9 mg/ml	+	Henderson *et al.*, 1987
Sister chromatid exchange assay(1)	Chinese hamster V79 cells	0.12-3.3 mM	+ (5)	Von der Hude *et al.*, 1987
Mammalian cell mutation assay(6)	HeLa cell	2.5×10^3 M (4)	+	Painter & Howard, 1982
Mammalian cell mutation assay	Mouse fibroblast M2-clone	0.1-1 mg/ml	+	Piasecki *et al.*, 1990

(1) with and without metabolic activation
(2) no frame shift mutations in strains TA1537, TA1538 or TA98
(3) only positive after metabolic activation
(4) effective concentration
(5) almost inactivated with metabolic activation
(6) only tested with metabolic activation

Investigations on the genotoxic mechanisms of 1,3-dichloro-2-propanol (Hahn *et al.*, 1991), indicate that the genotoxic effect of 1,3-dichloro-2-propanol depends on the chemical formation of epichlorohydrin, which has mutagenic activity (Rossi *et al.*, 1983).

2.3   Observations in humans

Severe irritation of the throat and stomach has been described as a likely effect after ingestion of 1,3-dichloro-2-propanol (Gosselin *et al.*, 1976).

3.   COMMENTS

3-Chloro-1,2-propanediol

3-Chloro-1,2-propanediol has been shown to increase the relative kidney weights of rats treated for 4 weeks (30 mg/kg bw/dy by gavage), or 3 months (9 mg/kg bw/dy in the drinking water) and absolute kidney weights when treated for 104 weeks (1.1 mg/kg bw/dy in the drinking water). A single subcutaneous injection of 75 mg 3-chloro-1,2-propanediol/kg bw to rats caused renal tubular necrosis and dilatation. A no-effect level for the effect on the kidney was not observed.

In monkeys 3-chloro-1,2-propanediol induced anaemia, leucopenia, and thrombocytopenia following ingestion of 30 mg/kg bw/dy for 6 weeks.

Data presented to the Committee clearly demonstrated that 3-chloro-1,2-propanediol possesses an inhibitory effect on male fertility in rats and that the effect is reversible. This effect is caused by an inhibition of glycolytic enzymes in the epididymis, testicular tissue, and in spermatozoa, resulting in reduced motility of the spermatozoa. No visible morphological changes of the spermatozoa or epididymis were seen at dose levels of 5-10 mg 3-chloro-1,2-propanediol/kg bw/dy, while a single intraperitoneal injection of 75 mg/kg bw caused development of retention cysts or spermatocele of the caput epididymis in rats. In a reproduction study the NOEL for male rat fertility was 2 mg/kg bw/dy when the rats were treated orally with 3-chloro-1,2-propanediol for 7 days and during the mating period.

3-Chloro-1,2-propanediol was genotoxic in most *in vitro* assays, while it was negative in *in vivo* assays. In addition, 3-chloro-1,2-propanediol induced malignant transformation of mouse M2-fibroblasts in culture.

The results of a recently-completed long-term toxicity/carcinogenicity study in rats treated at dose levels of 1.1, 5.2 or 28 mg 3-chloro-1,2-propanediol/kg bw/dy in drinking-water for 104 weeks indicated a carcinogenic effect. Occurrence of treatment-related increased incidences of tumours in the kidneys of both sexes and testis, mammary and preputial gland of male rats were reported. Although it has been suggested that the occurrence of these tumours might be secondary to either a sustained organ toxicity (kidney) or hormonal disturbances (testis and mammary gland), information was not available to the Committee to support this assumption. The Committee noted that the drinking-water of the control animals contained low levels of 3-chloro-1,2-propanediol. The presence of 3-chloro-1,2-

propanediol in the drinking-water may have confounded the quantitative evaluation of the dose-response relationships for carcinogenicity. In addition, significantly increased kidney weights were observed in male rats at the lowest dose level.

1,3-dichloro-2-propanol.

The Committee reviewed studies on biotransformation, acute toxicity and long-term toxicity/carcinogenicity in rats, and *in vitro* genotoxicity of 1,3-dichloro-2-propanol.

The results of a long-term toxicity/carcinogenicity study in rats treated at dose levels of 2.1, 6.3, or 19 mg 1,3-dichloro-2-propanol/kg bw/dy in the drinking-water for 104 weeks indicated a carcinogenic effect of 1,3-dichloro-2-propanol. Induction of benign and malignant tumours of the liver, kidney, thyroid gland, and oral epithelia/tongue was observed in rats at the mid- and high-dose levels.

1,3-Dichloro-2-propanol was active in a range of genotoxicity screening assays, including tests for chromosomal effects in mammalian cells in culture and tests for gene mutations in bacteria. In addition, 3-chloro-1,2-propanediol induced malignant transformation of mouse M2-fibroblasts in culture.

The Committee was not presented with results from studies on absorption, distribution or excretion of 1,3-dichloro-2-propanol.

The Committee noted that different rat strains were used in the long-term toxicity/carcinogenicity studies on 3-chloro-1,2-propanediol and on 1,3-dichloro-2-propanol, which precluded a direct comparison between these two compounds in regard to their carcinogenicity.

4.   EVALUATION

The Committee concluded that 3-chloro-1,2-propanediol and 1,3-dichloro-2-propanol are undesirable contaminants in food and expressed the opinion that their levels in hydrolyzed vegetable proteins should be reduced to the lowest technologically achievable.

5.   REFERENCES

BLACK, D.J., GLOVER, T.D., SHENTON, J.C. & BOYD, G.P. (1975). The effects of α-chlorohydrin on the composition of rat and rabbit epididymal plasma: a possible explanation of species difference. *J. Reprod. Fertil.* **45**, 117-128.

BROWN-WOODMAN, P.D., WHITE, I.G. & SALAMON, S. (1975). Effects of α-chlorohydrin on the fertility of rams and the metabolism of spermatozoa *in vitro*. *J. Reprod. Fertil.* **43**, 381.

COOPER, E.R.A. & JACKSON, H. (1973). Chemically induced sperm retention cysts in the rat. *J. Reprod. Fertil.* **34**, 445-449.

COPPOLA, J.A. (1969). An extragonadal male antifertility agent. *Life Sciences*, **8**, 43-48.

CRABO, B. & APPELGREN, L.E. (1972). Distribution of ^{14}C-α-chlorohydrin in mice and rats. *J. Reprod. Fert.* **30**, 161-163.

EDWARDS, E.M., JONES, A.R. & WAITES, G.M.H. (1975). The entry of α-chlorohydrin into body fluids of male rats and its effect upon incorporation of glycerol into lipids. *J. Reprod. Fert.* **43**, 225-232.

EPSTEIN, S.S., ARNOLD, E., ANDREA, J., BASS, W. & BISHOP, Y. (1972). Detection of chemical mutagens by the dominant lethal assay in the mouse. *Toxicol. Appl. Pharmacol.* **23**, 288-325.

ERICKSON, G.I. & BENNETT, J.P. (1971). Mechanism of antifertility activity of minimal dose level of α-chlorohydrin in the male rat. *Biol. Reprod.* **5**, 98.

ERICSSON, R.J. & BAKER, V.F. (1970). Male antifertility compounds: biological properties of U-5897 and U-15, 646. *J. Reprod. Fert.* **21**, 267-373.

ERICSSON, R.J. & YOUNGDALE., G.A. (1970). Male antifertility compounds: structure and activity relationships of U-5897, U-15, 646 and related substances. *J. Reprod. Fert.* **21**, 263-266.

GILL, S.K. & GURAYA, S.S. (1980). Effects of low doses of α-chlorohydrin on phosphatase, ß-glucosidase, ß-glucuronidase & hyaluronidase of rat testis & epididymis. *Ind. J. Exp. Biol.* **18**, 1351-1352.

GOSSELIN, R.E. (1976). Clinical Toxicology of Commercial Products. 4th Edition, p.119. The Williams & Wilkins Co., Baltimore, MD, USA.

GRANT, W.M. (1974). Toxicology of the eye. 2nd Edition, p. 374. Charles C. Thomas, Springfield, IL, USA

GUNN, S.A., GOULD, T.C. & ANDERSON, W.A.D. (1969). Possible mechanism of posttesticular antifertility action of 3-chloro-1, 2-propanediol. *Proc. Soc. Exptl. Biol. Med.* **132**, 656-659.

GÖRLITZ, B.D. (1991). In vitro mammalian cell HPRT-test with 3-chloro-1, 2-propanediol. Unpublished report No. G91/3 from Fraunhofer-Institute für Toxicologie und Aerosolforschung, Hannover, Germany.

HAHN, H., EDER, E. & DEININGER, C. (1991). Genotoxicity of 1, 3-dichloro-2-propanol in the SOS chromotest and in the Ames test. Elucidation of the genotoxic mechanism. *Chem.-Biol. Interactions.* **80**, 73-88.

HELAL, T.Y. (1982). Chemosterilant and rodenticidal effects of 3-chloro-1, 2-propanediol (Epibloc) against the albino laboratory rat and the Nile field rat. *Internat. Pest Control.* **24**, 20-23.

HENDERSON, L.M., BOSWORTH, H.J., RANSOME, S.J., BANKS, S.J., BRABBS, C.E. & TINNER, A.J. (1987). An assessment of the mutagenic potential of 1, 3-dichloro-2-propanol, 3-chloro-1, 2-propanediol and a cocktail of chloropropanols using the mouse lymphoma TK locus assay. Unpublished report No. ULR 130 ABC/861423 from Huntingdon Research Centre Ltd. Huntingdon, Cambridgeshire, England.

HOFFER, A.P., HAMILTON, D.W., & FAWCETT, D.W. (1973). The ultrastructural pathology of the rat epididymis and after administration of α-chlohydrin (U-5897). 1 Effects of a single high dose. *Anat. Rec.* **175**, 203-230.

HOMONNAI, Z.T., PAZ, G., SOFER, A. YEDWAB, G.A. & KRAICER, P.F. (1975). A direct effect of α-chlorohydrin on motility and metabolism of ejaculated human spermatozoa. *Contraception* **12**, 579-589.

JACCAUD, E. & AESCHBACHER, H.U. (1989). Evaluation of 3-chloro-1, 2-propanediol (3MCPD) in the bone marrow and colonic micronucleus mutagenicity tests in mice. Unpublished report No. 1265 from Nestec Ltd. Research Centre, Nestlé.

JERSEY, G.C., BRESLIN, W.J. & ZIELKE, G.J. (1991). Subchronic toxicity of 1, 3-dichloro-2-propanol in the rat. *The Toxicologist*, **11**, 353.

JONES, A.R. (1975) The metabolism of 3-chloro-, 3-bromo- and 3-iodopropan-1, 2-diol in rats and mice. *Xenobiotica*, **5**, 155-165.

JONES, A.R. (1978). The antifertility actions of α-chlorohydrin in the male. *Life Sciences*, **23**, 1625-1646.

JONES, A.R. (1983). Antifertility actions of α-chlorohydrin in the male. *Aust. J. Biol. Sci.* **36**, 333-350.

JONES, A.R. & FAKHOURI, G. (1979). Epoxides as obligatory intermediates in the metabolism of α-halohydrins. *Xenobiotica*. **9**, 595-599.

JONES, A.R. & MURCOTT, C. (1976). The oxidative metabolism of α-chlorohydrin and the chemical induction of spermatocoele. *Experientia*, **32**, 1135-1136.

JONES, A.R., GADEL, P. & MURCOTT, C. (1979). The renal toxicity of the rodenticide α-chlorohydrin in the rat. *Naturwissenschaften*, **66**, 425.

JONES, A.R., MILTON, D.H. & MURCOTT, C. (1978). The oxidative metabolism of α-chlorohydrin in the male rat and the formation of spermatocele. *Xenobiotica,* **8**, 573-582.

KALLA, N.R. & BANSAL, M.P. (1977). *In vivo* and *in vitro* alkylation of testicular cysteine by α-chlorohydrin administration. *Ind. J. Exp. Biol.* **15**, 232-233.

KALLA, N.R. & SINGH, B. (1981). Synergistic effect of alpha-chlorohydrin on the influence of copper ions on human spermatozoa. *Int. J. Fertil.* **26**, 65-67.

KAUR, S. & GURAYA, S.S. (1981a). Effects of low doses of alpha-chlorohydrin on the enzymes of glycolytic and phosphogluconate pathways in the rat testis and epididymis. *Int. J. Andrology*, **4**, 196-207.

KAUR, S. & GURAYA, S.S. (1981b). Effects of low doses of alpha-chlorohydrin on the dehydrogenase and oxidase of rat epididymal epithelium and sperms: A correlative histochemical and biochemical study. *Andrologia*. **13**, 225-231.

KAUR, S. & GURAYA, S.S. (1981c). Biochemical observations on the protein and nucleic acid metabolism of the rat testis and the epididymis after treatment with low doses of alpha-chlorohydrin. *Int. J. Fertil.* **26**, 8-13.

KIRTON, K.T., ERICKSON, R.J., RAY, J.A. & PORBES, A.D. (1970). Male antifertility compounds: efficacy of N-5897 in primates (*Macaca mulatta*). *J. Reprod. Fert.* **21**, 275-278.

KLUWE, W.M., GUPTA, B.N. & LAMB IV, J.C. (1983) The Comparative effects of 1, 2-dibromo-3-chloropropane (DBCP) and its metabolites, 3-chloro-1, 2-propaneoxide (Epichlorohydrin), 3-chloro-1, 2-propanediol (alpha-chlorohydrin), and oxalic acid, on the urogenital system of male rats. *Toxicol. Appl. Pharmacol.* **70**, 67-86.

LOHIKA, N.K. & ARYA, M. (1979). Antifertility activity of α-chlorohydrin (3-chloro-1, 2-propanediol, U-5897) on the female rats. *Acta Eur. Fertil.* **10**, 23-28.

MARCHESINI, M. & STALDER, R. (1983). Toxicity of 3-chloro-1, 2-propanediol in a 4 weeks gavage study on rats. Part I. Unpublished report. No. LA 70/1082 from Société d'Assistance Technique Pour Produits Nestlé S.A.

MARCHESINI, M., STALDER, R. & PERRIN, I. (1989). Subchronic toxicity of 3-chloro-1, 2-propanediol, 90 days administration in drinking water of Fischer F 344 rats. Unpublished report No. 1264 from Nestec Ltd. Research Centre, Nestlé.

MAY, C. (1991). In vitro sister chromatid exchange assay in mammalian cells. Unpublished report No. 91/4 CM from Fraunhofer-Institute für Toxicologie und Aerosolforschung, Hannover, Germany.

MOHRI, H., SUTER, D.A.J., BROWN-WOODMANN, P.D.C., WHITE, J.G. & RIDLEY, D.D. (1975). Identification of the biochemical lesion produced by α-chlorohydrin in spermatozoa. *Nature*. **255**, 75-77.

MORRIS, J.D. & WILLIAMS, L.M. (1980). Some preliminary observations of the nephrotoxicity of the male antifertility drug ($\pm$) α-chlorohydrin. *J. Pharm. Pharmacol.* **32**, 35-38.

NAKAMURA, A., NORIYUKITATENO, KOJIMA, S., KANIWA, M-A. & KAWAMURA, T. (1979). The mutagenicity of halogenated alkanols and their phosphoric acid esters for *Salmonella typhimurium*. *Mutation Res.* **66**, 373-380.

PAINTER, R.B. & HOWARD, R (1982). The HeLa DNA synthesis inhibition test as a rapid screen for mutagenic carcinogens. *Mutation Res.* **92**, 427-437.

PALLADE, S., GOLDSTEIN, J., SERBAN, P., ANITESCU, C. & GABRIELESCU, E. (1963). 14th International Congress of Occupational Health, Madrid. *Chem. Abstr.* 1966, **64**, 8835g.

PARISH, W.E. (1989). Effect of 3-chloropropane-1, 2-diol on rat fertility. Summary Report. Unpublished report No. D 89/005, from Unilever Research, Sharnbrook, Bedford, England.

PIASECKI, A., RUGE, A. & MARQUARDT, H. (1990). Malignant transformation of mouse M2-fibroblasts by glycerol chlorohydrines contained in protein hydrolysate and commercial food. *Arzneim.-Forsch/Drug Res.* **40**, 1054-1055.

PORTER, K.G. & JONES, A.R. (1982). The effect of the isomers of α-chlorohydrin and racemic ß-chlorolactate on the rat kidney. *Chem.-Biol. Interactions.* **41**, 95-104.

RCC (1986). 104-week chronic toxicity and oncogenicity study with 1, 3-dichlor-propan-2-ol in the rat. Unpublished report No. 017820 from Research & Consulting Company AG, Itingen, Switzerland.

ROSSI, A.M., MIGLIORE, L., LASCIALFARI, D., SBRANA, I., LOPRIENO, N., TORTORETO, M., BIDOLI, F. & PANTAROTTO, C. (1983). Genotoxicity, metabolism and blood kinetics of epichlorohydrin in mice. *Mutation Res.* **118**, 213-226.

SAMOJLIK, E. & CHANG, M.C. (1970). Antifertility activity of 3-chloro-1, 2-propanediol (U-5897) on male rats. *Biol. Reprod.* **2**, 299-304.

SILHANKOVÀ, L., SMID, F., CERNÀ, M., DAVIDEK, J. & VELISEK, J. (1982). Mutagenicity of glycerol chlorohydrines and of their esters with higher fatty acids present in protein hydrolysate. *Mutat. Res.* **103**, 77-81.

SMYTH, H.F., CARPENTER, C.P., WEIL, C.S., POZZANI, U.C. & STRIEGEL, J.A. (1962). Range-finding toxicity data: List VI. *Amer. Ind. Hyg. Ass. J.* **23**, 95-107.

STEVENSON, D. & JONES, A.R. (1984). The action of (R)- and (S)-α-chlorohydrin and their metabolites on the metabolism of boar sperm. *Int. J. Androl.* **7**, 79-86.

STOLZENBERG, S.J. & HINE, C.H. (1980). Mutagenicity of 2- and 3-carbon halogenated compounds in the salmonella/mammalian-microsome test. *Environ. Mutagenesis.* **2**, 59-66.

SUNAHARE, G., PERRIN, I. AND MARCHESINI, M. (1993). Carcinogenicity study on 3-monochloropropane-1,2-diol (3-MCPD) administered in drinking water to Fischer 344 rats. Report No. RE-SR93003 submitted to WHO by Nestec Ltd., Research & Development, Switzerland.

SUTER, D.A.I., BROWN-WOODMAN, P.D.C., MHORI, H. & WHITE, G.I. (1975). The molecular site of action of the anti-fertility agent, α-chlorohydrin, in ram spermatozoa. *J. Reprod. Fertil.* **43**, 382-383.

TUNSTALL LABORATORIES. (1979). Shell Oil Company. Toxicity of fine chemicals: Preliminary studies for the detection of testicular changes in rats. Unpublished report. EPA document No. 878216424 (cited in Hazardous Substances Data Bank).

TURNER, M.A. (1971). Effects of α-chlorohydrin upon the fertility of spermatozoa of the cauda epididymides of the rat. *J. Reprod. Fert.* **24**, 267-269.

VAN DUUREN, B.L., GOLDSCHMIDT, B.M., KATZ, C., SEIDMAN, J. & PAUL, J.S. (1974). Carcinogenic activity of alkylating agents. *J. Natl. Cancer Inst.* **53**, 695-700.

VELISEK, J., DAVIDEK, J., HAJSLOVA, J. KUBELKA, V. BARTOSOVA, J. TUCKOVA, A., HAJSLOVA, J. & JANICEK, G. (1979). Formation of volatile chlorohydrins from glycerol (triacetin, tributyrin) and hydrochloric acid. *Lebensmitt.-Wiss.u.Technol.* **12**, 234-236.

VON DER HUDE, W., SCHEUTWINKEL, M., GRAMLICH, U., FIßLER, B. & BASLER, A. (1987). Genotoxicity of three-carbon compounds evaluated in the SCE test in vitro. *Environ. Mutagen.*, **9**, 401-410.

WAYSS, K., BANNASCH, P., MATTERN, J. & VOLM, M. (1979). Vascular liver tumours induced in Mastomys (Praomys). Natalensis by single or two fold administration of dimethylnitrosamine. *J. Nat. Canc. Inst.* **62**, 1199-1207.

WEISBURGER, E.K., ULLAND, B.M., NAM, J., GART, J.J. & WEISBURGER, J.H. (1981). Carcinogenicity tests of certain environmental and industrial chemicals. *J. Natl. Cancer Inst.* **67**, 75-88.

ANNEXES

ANNEX 1

Reports and other documents resulting from previous meetings of the Joint FAO/WHO Expert Committee on Food Additives

1. **General principles governing the use of food additives** (First report of the Joint FAO/WHO Expert Committee on Food Additives). FAO Nutrition Meetings Report Series, No. 15, 1958; WHO Technical Report Series, No. 129, 1957 (out of print).

2. **Procedures for the testing of intentional food additives to establish their safety for use** (Second report of the Joint FAO/WHO Expert Committee on Food Additives). FAO Nutrition Meetings Report Series, No. 17, 1958; WHO Technical Report Series, No. 144, 1958 (out of print).

3. **Specifications for identity and purity of food additives (antimicrobial preservatives and antioxidants)** (Third report of the Joint FAO/WHO Expert Committee on Food Additives). These specifications were subsequently revised and published as **Specifications for identity and purity of food additives, Vol. I. Antimicrobial preservatives and antioxidants**, Rome, Food and Agriculture Organization of the United Nations, 1962 (out of print).

4. **Specifications for identity and purity of food additives (food colours)** (Fourth report of the Joint FAO/WHO Expert Committee on Food Additives). These specifications were subsequently revised and published as **Specifications for identity and purity of food additives, Vol. II. Food colours**, Rome, Food and Agriculture Organization of the United Nations, 1963 (out of print).

5. **Evaluation of the carcinogenic hazards of food additives** (Fifth report of the Joint FAO/WHO Expert Committee on Food Additives). FAO Nutrition Meetings Report Series, No. 29, 1961; WHO Technical Report Series, No. 220, 1961 (out of print).

6. **Evaluation of the toxicity of a number of antimicrobials and antioxidants** (Sixth report of the Joint FAO/WHO Expert Committee on Food Additives). FAO Nutrition Meetings Report Series, No. 31, 1962; WHO Technical Report Series, No. 228, 1962 (out of print).

7. **Specifications for the identity and purity of food additives and their toxicological evaluation: emulsifiers, stabilizers, bleaching and maturing agents** (Seventh report of the Joint FAO/WHO Expert Committee on Food Additives). FAO Nutrition Meetings Series, No. 35, 1964; WHO Technical Report Series, No. 281, 1964 (out of print).

8. **Specifications for the identity and purity of food additives and their toxicological evaluation: food colours and some antimicrobials and antioxidants** (Eighth report of the Joint FAO/WHO Expert Committee on Food Additives). FAO Nutrition Meetings Series, No. 38, 1965; WHO Technical Report Series, No. 309, 1965 (out of print).

9. **Specifications for identity and purity and toxicological evaluation of some antimicrobials and antioxidants.** FAO Nutrition Meetings Report Series, No. 38A, 1965; WHO/Food Add/24.65 (out of print).

10. **Specifications for identity and purity and toxicological evaluation of food colours.** FAO Nutrition Meetings Report Series, No. 38B, 1966; WHO/Food Add/66.25.

11. **Specifications for the identity and purity of food additives and their toxicological evaluation: some antimicrobials, antioxidants, emulsifiers, stabilizers, flour-treatment agents, acids, and bases** (Ninth report of the Joint FAO/WHO Expert Committee on Food Additives). FAO Nutrition Meetings Series, No. 40, 1966; WHO Technical Report Series, No. 339, 1966 (out of print).

12. **Toxicological evaluation of some antimicrobials, antioxidants, emulsifiers, stabilizers, flour-treatment agents, acids, and bases.** FAO Nutrition Meetings Report Series, No. 40A, B, C; WHO/Food Add/67.29.

13. **Specifications for the identity and purity of food additives and their toxicological evaluation: some emulsifiers and stabilizers and certain other substances** (Tenth report of the Joint FAO/WHO Expert Committee on Food Additives). FAO Nutrition Meetings Series, No. 43, 1967; WHO Technical Report Series, No. 373, 1967.

14. Specifications for the identity and purity of food additives and their toxicological evaluation: some flavouring substances and non-nutritive sweetening agents (Eleventh report of the Joint FAO/WHO Expert Committee on Food Additives). FAO Nutrition Meetings Series, No. 44, 1968; WHO Technical Report Series, No. 383, 1968.

15. Toxicological evaluation of some flavouring substances and non-nutritive sweetening agents. FAO Nutrition Meetings Report Series, No. 44A, 1968; WHO/Food Add/68.33.

16. Specifications and criteria for identity and purity of some flavouring substances and non-nutritive sweetening agents. FAO Nutrition Meetings Report Series, No. 44B, 1969; WHO/Food Add/69.31.

17. Specifications for the identity and purity of food additives and their toxicological evaluation: some antibiotics (Twelfth report of the Joint FAO/WHO Expert Committee on Food Additives). FAO Nutrition Meetings Series, No. 45, 1969; WHO Technical Report Series, No. 430, 1969.

18. Specifications for the identity and purity of some antibiotics. FAO Nutrition Meetings Series, No. 45A, 1969; WHO/Food Add/69.34.

19. Specifications for the identity and purity of food additives and their toxicological evaluation: some food colours, emulsifiers, stabilizers, anticaking agents, and certain other substances (Thirteenth report of the Joint FAO/WHO Expert Committee on Food Additives). FAO Nutrition Meetings Series, No. 46, 1970; WHO Technical Report Series, No. 445, 1970.

20. Toxicological evaluation of some food colours, emulsifiers, stabilizers, anticaking agents, and certain other substances. FAO Nutrition Meetings Report Series, No. 46A, 1970; WHO/Food Add/70.36.

21. Specifications for the identity and purity of some food colours, emulsifiers, stabilizers, anticaking agents, and certain other food additives. FAO Nutrition Meetings Report Series, No. 46B, 1970; WHO/Food Add/70.37.

22. Evaluation of food additives: specifications for the identity and purity of food additives and their toxicological evaluation: some extraction solvents and certain other substances; and a review of the technological efficacy of some antimicrobial agents. (Fourteenth report of the Joint FAO/WHO Expert Committee on Food Additives). FAO Nutrition Meetings Series, No. 48, 1971; WHO Technical Report Series, No. 462, 1971.

23. Toxicological evaluation of some extraction solvents and certain other substances. FAO Nutrition Meetings Report Series, No. 48A, 1971; WHO/Food Add/70.39.

24. Specifications for the identity and purity of some extraction solvents and certain other substances. FAO Nutrition Meetings Report Series, No. 48B, 1971; WHO/Food Add/70.40.

25. A review of the technological efficacy of some antimicrobial agents. FAO Nutrition Meetings Report Series, No. 48C, 1971; WHO/Food Add/70.41

26. Evaluation of food additives: some enzymes, modified starches, and certain other substances: Toxicological evaluations and specifications and a review of the technological efficacy of some antioxidants (Fifteenth report of the Joint FAO/WHO Expert Committee on Food Additives). FAO Nutrition Meetings Series, No. 50, 1972; WHO Technical Report Series, No. 488, 1972.

27. Toxicological evaluation of some enzymes, modified starches, and certain other substances. FAO Nutrition Meetings Report Series, No. 50A, 1972; WHO Food Additives Series, No. 1, 1972.

28. Specifications for the identity and purity of some enzymes and certain other substances. FAO Nutrition Meetings Report Series, No. 50B, 1972; WHO Food Additives Series, No. 2, 1972.

29. A review of the technological efficacy of some antioxidants and synergists. FAO Nutrition Meetings Report Series, No. 50C, 1972; WHO Food Additives Series, No. 3, 1972.

30. Evaluation of certain food additives and the contaminants mercury, lead, and cadmium (Sixteenth report of the Joint FAO/WHO Expert Committee on Food Additives). FAO Nutrition Meetings Series, No. 51, 1972; WHO Technical Report Series, No. 505, 1972, and corrigendum.

31. Evaluation of mercury, lead, cadmium and the food additives amaranth, diethylpyrocarbamate, and octyl gallate. FAO Nutrition Meetings Report Series, No. 51A, 1972; WHO Food Additives Series, No. 4, 1972.
32. Toxicological evaluation of certain food additives with a review of general principles and of specifications (Seventeenth report of the Joint FAO/WHO Expert Committee on Food Additives). FAO Nutrition Meetings Series, No. 53, 1974; WHO Technical Report Series, No. 539, 1974, and corrigendum (out of print).
33. Toxicological evaluation of certain food additives including anticaking agents, antimicrobials, antioxidants, emulsifiers, and thickening agents. FAO Nutrition Meetings Report Series, No. 53A, 1974; WHO Food Additives Series, No. 5, 1974.
34. Specifications for identity and purity of thickening agents, anticaking agents, antimicrobials, antioxidants and emulsifiers. FAO Food and Nutrition Paper, No. 4, 1978.
35. Evaluation of certain food additives (Eighteenth report of the Joint FAO/WHO Expert Committee on Food Additives). FAO Nutrition Meetings Series, No. 54, 1974; WHO Technical Report Series, No. 557, 1974, and corrigendum.
36. Toxicological evaluation of some food colours, enzymes, flavour enhancers, thickening agents, and certain other food additives. FAO Nutrition Meetings Report Series, No. 54A, 1975; WHO Food Additives Series, No. 6, 1975.
37. Specifications for the identity and purity of some food colours, enhancers, thickening agents, and certain food additives. FAO Nutrition Meetings Report Series, No. 54B, 1975; WHO Food Additives Series, No. 7, 1975.
38. Evaluation of certain food additives: some food colours, thickening agents, smoke condensates, and certain other substances. (Nineteenth report of the Joint FAO/WHO Expert Committee on Food Additives). FAO Nutrition Meetings Series, No. 55, 1975; WHO Technical Report Series, No. 576, 1975.
39. Toxicological evaluation of some food colours, thickening agents, and certain other substances. FAO Nutrition Meetings Report Series, No. 55A, 1975; WHO Food Additives Series, No. 8, 1975.
40. Specifications for the identity and purity of certain food additives. FAO Nutrition Meetings Report Series, No. 55B, 1976; WHO Food Additives Series, No. 9, 1976.
41. Evaluation of certain food additives (Twentieth report of the Joint FAO/WHO Expert Committee on Food Additives). FAO Food and Nutrition Meetings Series, No. 1., 1976; WHO Technical Report Series, No. 599, 1976.
42. Toxicological evaluation of certain food additives. WHO Food Additives Series, No. 10, 1976.
43. Specifications for the identity and purity of some food additives. FAO Food and Nutrition Series, No. 1B, 1977; WHO Food Additives Series, No. 11, 1977.
44. Evaluation of certain food additives (Twenty-first report of the Joint FAO/WHO Expert Committee on Food Additives). WHO Technical Report Series, No. 617, 1978.
45. Summary of toxicological data of certain food additives. WHO Food Additives Series, No. 12, 1977.
46. Specifications for identity and purity of some food additives, including antioxidant, food colours, thickeners, and others. FAO Nutrition Meetings Report Series, No. 57, 1977.
47. Evaluation of certain food additives and contaminants (Twenty-second report of the Joint FAO/WHO Expert Committee on Food Additives). WHO Technical Report Series, No. 631, 1978.
48. Summary of toxicological data of certain food additives and contaminants. WHO Food Additives Series, No. 13, 1978.
49. Specifications for the identity and purity of certain food additives. FAO Food and Nutrition Paper, No. 7, 1978.
50. Evaluation of certain food additives (Twenty-third report of the Joint FAO/WHO Expert Committee on Food Additives). WHO Technical Report Series, No. 648, 1980, and corrigenda.
51. Toxicological evaluation of certain food additives. WHO Food Additives Series, No. 14, 1980.

52. **Specifications for identity and purity of food colours, flavouring agents, and other food additives.** FAO Food and Nutrition Paper, No. 12, 1979.

53. **Evaluation of certain food additives** (Twenty-fourth report of the Joint FAO/WHO Expert Committee on Food Additives). WHO Technical Report Series, No. 653, 1980.

54. **Toxicological evaluation of certain food additives.** WHO Food Additives Series, No. 15, 1980.

55. **Specifications for identity and purity of food additives (sweetening agents, emulsifying agents, and other food additives).** FAO Food and Nutrition Paper, No. 17, 1980.

56. **Evaluation of certain food additives** (Twenty-fifth report of the Joint FAO/WHO Expert Committee on Food Additives). WHO Technical Report Series, No. 669, 1981.

57. **Toxicological evaluation of certain food additives.** WHO Food Additives Series, No. 16, 1981.

58. **Specifications for identity and purity of food additives (carrier solvents, emulsifiers and stabilizers, enzyme preparations, flavouring agents, food colours, sweetening agents, and other food additives).** FAO Food and Nutrition Paper, No. 19, 1981.

59. **Evaluation of certain food additives and contaminants** (Twenty-sixth report of the Joint FAO/WHO Expert Committee on Food Additives). WHO Technical Report Series, No. 683, 1982.

60. **Toxicological evaluation of certain food additives.** WHO Food Additives Series, No. 17, 1982.

61. **Specifications for the identity and purity of certain food additives.** FAO Food and Nutrition Paper, No. 25, 1982.

62. **Evaluation of certain food additives and contaminants** (Twenty-seventh report of the Joint FAO/WHO Expert Committee on Food Additives). WHO Technical Report Series, No. 696, 1983, and corrigenda.

63. **Toxicological evaluation of certain food additives and contaminants.** WHO Food Additives Series, No. 18, 1983.

64. **Specifications for the identity and purity of certain food additives.** FAO Food and Nutrition Paper, No. 28, 1983.

65. **Guide to specifications--General notices, general methods, identification tests, test solutions, and other reference materials.** FAO Food and Nutrition Paper, No. 5, Rev. 1, 1983.

66. **Evaluation of certain food additives and contaminants** (Twenty-eight report of the Joint FAO/WHO Expert Committee on Food Additives). WHO Technical Report Series, No. 710, 1984, and corrigendum.

67. **Toxicological evaluation of certain food additives and contaminants.** WHO Food Additives Series, No. 19, 1984.

68. **Specifications for the identity and purity of food colours.** FAO Food and Nutrition Paper, No. 31/1, 1984.

69. **Specifications for the identity and purity of food additives.** FAO Food and nutrition Paper, No. 31/2, 1984.

70. **Evaluation of certain food additives and contaminants** (Twenty-ninth report of the Joint FAO/WHO Expert Committee on Food Additives). WHO Technical Report Series, No. 733, 1986, and corrigendum.

71. **Specifications for the identity and purity of certain food additives.** FAO Food and nutrition Paper, No. 34, 1986.

72. **Toxicological evaluation of certain food additives and contaminants.** WHO Food Additives Series, No. 20. Cambridge University Press, 1987.

73. **Evaluation of certain food additives and contaminants** (Thirtieth report of the Joint FAO/WHO Expert Committee on Food Additives). WHO Technical Report Series, No. 751, 1987.

74. **Toxicological evaluation of certain food additives and contaminants.** WHO Food Additives Series, No. 21. Cambridge University Press, 1987.

75. **Specifications for the identity and purity of certain food additives.** FAO Food and Nutrition Paper, No. 37, 1987.

76. **Principles for the safety assessment of food additives and contaminants in food.** WHO Environmental Health Criteria, No. 70. Geneva, World Health Organization, 1987.

77. **Evaluation of certain food additives and contaminants** (Thirty-first report of the Joint FAO/WHO Expert Committee on Food Additives). WHO Technical Report Series, No. 759, 1987 and corrigendum.

78. **Toxicological evaluation of certain food additives.** WHO Food Additives Series, No. 22. Cambridge University Press, 1988.

79. **Specifications for the identity and purity of certain food additives.** FAO Food and Nutrition Paper, No. 38, 1988.

80. **Evaluation of certain veterinary drug residues in food** (Thirty-second report of the Joint FAO/WHO Expert Committee on Food Additives). WHO Technical Report Series, No. 763, 1988.

81. **Toxicological evaluation of certain veterinary drug residues in food.** WHO Food Additives Series, No. 23. Cambridge University Press, 1988.

82. **Residues of some veterinary drugs in animals and foods.** FAO Food and Nutrition paper, No. 41, 1988.

83. **Evaluation of certain food additives and contaminants** (Thirty-third report of the Joint FAO/WHO Expert Committee on Food Additives). WHO Technical Report Series, No. 776, 1989.

84. **Toxicological evaluation of certain food additives and contaminants.** WHO Food Additives Series, No. 24. Cambridge University Press, 1989.

85. **Evaluation of certain veterinary drug residues in food** (Thirty-fourth report of the Joint FAO/WHO Expert Committee on Food Additives). WHO Technical Report Series, No. 788, 1989.

86. **Toxicological evaluation of certain veterinary drug residues in food.** WHO Food Additives Series, No. 25, 1990.

87. **Residues of some veterinary drugs in animals and foods.** FAO Food and Nutrition Paper, No. 41/2, 1990.

88. **Evaluation of certain food additives and contaminants** (Thirty-fifth report of the Joint FAO/WHO Expert Committee on Food Additives). WHO Technical Report Series, No. 789, 1990, and corrigenda.

89. **Toxicological evaluation of certain food additives and contaminants.** WHO Food Additives Series, No. 26, 1990.

90. **Specifications for identity and purity of certain food additives.** FAO Food and Nutrition Paper, No. 49, 1990.

91. **Evaluation of certain veterinary drug residues in food** (Thirty-sixth report of the Joint FAO/WHO Expert Committee on Food Additives). WHO Technical Report Series, No. 799, 1990.

92. **Toxicological evaluation of certain veterinary drug residues in food.** WHO Food Additives Series, No. 27, 1991.

93. **Residues of some veterinary drugs in animals and foods.** FAO Food and Nutrition Paper, No. 41/3, 1991.

94. **Evaluation of certain food additives and contaminants** (Thirty-seventh report of the Joint FAO/WHO Expert Committee on Food Additives). WHO Technical Report Series, No. 806, 1991.

95. **Toxicological evaluation of certain food additives and contaminants.** WHO Food Additives Series, No. 28, 1991.

96. **Compendium of food additive specifications** (Joint FAO/WHO Expert Committee on Food Additives (JECFA)). Combined specifications from 1st through 37th meetings, 1956-1990. FAO, 1992 (2 volumes).

97. **Evaluation of certain veterinary drug residues in food.** (Thirty-eighth report of the Joint FAO/WHO Expert Committee on Food Additives). WHO Technical Report Series, No. 815, 1991.

98. **Toxicological evaluation of certain veterinary drug residues in food.** WHO Food Additives Series, No. 29, 1991.

99. **Residues of some veterinary drugs in animals and foods.** FAO Food and Nutrition Paper, No. 41/4, 1991.

100. **Guide to specifications - General notices, general analytical techniques, identification tests, test solutions, and other reference materials.** FAO Food and Nutrition Paper, No. 5, Rev. 2, 1991.

101. **Evaluation of certain food additives and naturally occurring toxicants.** (Thirty-ninth report of the Joint FAO/WHO Expert Committee on Food Additives). WHO Technical Report Series, No. 828, 1992.

102. **Toxicological evaluation of certain food additives and naturally occurring contaminants.** WHO Food Additives Series, No. 30, 1993.

103. **Compendium of food additive specifications, Addendum 1** (Joint FAO/WHO Expert Committee on Food Additives (JECFA)). FAO Food and Nutrition Paper, No. 52, 1992.

104. **Evaluation of certain veterinary drug residues in food.** (Fortieth report of the Joint FAO/WHO Expert Committee on Food Additives). WHO Technical Report Series, No. 832, 1992.

105. **Toxicological evaluation of certain veterinary drug residues in food.** WHO Food Additives Series, No. 31, 1993.

106. **Residues of some veterinary drugs in animals and foods.** FAO Food and Nutrition Paper, No. 41/5, 1993.

107. **Evaluation of certain food additives and contaminants** (Forty-first report of the Joint FAO/WHO Expert Committee on Food Additives). WHO Technical Report Series, in preparation.

ANNEX 2

ABBREVIATIONS USED IN THE MONOGRAPHS

AAF	2-acetylaminofluorene	EHEN	N-ethyl-N-hydroxy ethylnitrosamine
ADI	acceptable daily intake	EPA	Environmental Protection
A/G	albumin/globulin ratio		Agency (U.S.)
AIIBP	Association Internationale de	Er	erythrocytes
	L'Industrie des Bouillons et	EROD	hepatic ethoxy-resorufin-O-
	Potages		deethylase
Alk-P-ase	alkaline phosphatase	ESR	erythrocyte sedimentation rate
ALAT	alanine aminotransferase		
AMP	adenosine monophosphate	F	female
ANFT	2-amino-(5-nitro-furyl)thiazole	F_1	filial generation, first
ASAT	aspartate aminotransferase	F_2	filial generation, second
ATP	adenosine triphosphate	FANFT	N-[-(5-nitro-2-furyl)-
AUC	area under curve		thiazolyl]formamide
		FAO	Food and Agriculture
BBN	N-butyl-N-(-hydroxy-		Organization of the United
	butyl)nitrosamine		Nations
BHA	butylated hydroxyanisole	FBG	fasting blood glucose
BHT	butylated hydroxytoluene	FEMA	Flavor and Extract
BSP	bromosulfophthalein		Manufacturers' Association
BUN	blood urea nitrogen		of the United States
bw	body weight	FEP	free erythrocyte protoporphyrin
C	control group		
CFR	Code of Federal Regulations	GHB	glycosylated haemoglobin
	(USA)	GI	gastrointestinal
CGT	cyclodextrin glycosyl transferase	GIP	gastric inhibitory polypeptide
CHO	Chinese hamster ovary	GMP	Disodium 5'-guanylate (guanylic
CMC	carboxymethylcellulose		acid, disodium salt)
Comm	Community	G6Pase	glucose-6-phosphatase
cP	centipoise (viscosity measure)	GRAS	food chemicals generally
			recognized as safe
d	day		
D_{20}	dose at which structural	h	hour
	aberrations were detected in	H	high dose
	20% of the metaphases	Hb	haemoglobin
	observed	HDL	high-density lipoprotein
DBCP	1,2 dibromo-3-chloropropane	HDL-C	high-density lipoprotein
DEHP	di-[2-ethylhexyl]phthalate		cholesterol
derm	dermal	HeLa	Helen Lane
DiEHA	ethylhexanedioic acid	HHS	Department of Health and
Diff	differential leucocytes		Human Services (USA)
DMBA	7,12 dimethyl-1,2-	HPF	high polyunsaturated fat
	benzanthracene	HPLC	high performance liquid
DMH	1,2-dimethylhydrazine		chromatography
DNA	deoxyribonucleic acid	HSF	high saturated fat
Ds	*Dunaliella salina*	Hct	haematocrit
dy	day		
EA	2-ethylhexanoic acid	IARC	International Agency for
EC_{50}	effective concentration, median		Research on Cancer
EDA	ethylene diamine	IBT	Industrial Bio-Test Labs., Inc.
ED_{50}	effective dose, median	ICG	indocyanine green
EEC	European Economic Community	ID_{50}	inhibitory dose, 50%
EHA	ethylhexanoic acid	ID	iron deficiency
EH	2-Ethylhexanol	IDA	iron deficiency anaemia

im	intramuscular	5-OH EHA	5-hydroxyethylhexanoic acid
IMP	disodium 5'-inosinate		
inh	inhalation	PAS	periodic acid Shiff
IPCS	International Programme on	PBG	2-hour post-prandial blood
	Chemical Safety		glucose
ip	intraperitoneal	pc	percutaneous
IRDC	International Research and	PCV	packed red cell volume
	Development Corporation	PG	propyl gallate
iv	intravenous	PGA	propylene glycol alginate
		PN	papillary or nodular hyperplasia
JECFA	Joint FAO/WHO Expert	PNG	Phillipines natural grade
	Committee on Food		[carrageenan]
	Additives	po	by mouth
		ppm	parts per million
KM	konjac flour, konjac mannan	PSP	phenosulfophthalein
		RNA	ribonucleic acid
L	low dose	RTP	Research Triangle Park, NC
LD$_{50}$	lethal dose, median		(USA)
LDH	lactate dehydrogenase		
LDL-C	low-density lipoprotein	SAIB	sucrose acetate isobutyrate
	cholesterol	SAP	serum alkaline phosphatase
LD$_{LO}$	lethal dose, lowest	% Sat	% Saturation of Transferrin
Leu	leucocytes	s.c.	subcutaneous(ly)
LF	low fat	SCF	soya-bean cotyledon fiber
		SER	smooth endoplasmic reticulum
m	male	SHADIB	sucrose hexaacetate diisobutyrate
MCHC	mean corpuscular haemoglobin	SLRL	sex-linked recessive lethal
	concentration	SOIB	sucrose octaisobutyrate
3-MCPD	3-chloro-1,2-propanediol (3-		
	monochloropropane-1,2-	t$_{1/2}$	half-life
	diol)	TBHQ	tertiary butylhydroquinone
MCV	mean cell volume	TC	total cholesterol
MEHP	mono-[2-ethylhexyl]phthalate	TG	triglyceride
MFO	mixed function oxidase	TR	frequency of cells with exchange
mg	milligram		type aberrations per unit
min	minute		dose (mg/ml)
MNNG	N-methyl-N-nitrosoguanidine		
MNU	methyl-N-nitrosourea	USEPA	United States Environmental
MRI	Midwest Research Institute		Protection Agency
MSG	monosodium glutamate		
MTD	maximum tolerated dose	v/v	volume/volume
mU	1/1000 International Unit		
	insulin, 1 IU=0.04167 mg	WBC	white blood cell
	of international standard	WHO	World Health Organization
	preparation		
NaFeEDTA	sodium iron EDTA		
NBR	NCI-Black-Reiter (rats)		
NEL	no-effect-level		
NOAEL	no-observed-adverse-effect-level		
NOEL	no-observed-effect level		
NQO	nitroquinoline oxide		
NTP	National Toxicology Program		
	(USA)		
OCT	ornithine carbamyl transferase		
ODC	ornithine decarboxylase		

ANNEX 3
FORTY-FIRST JOINT FAO/WHO EXPERT COMMITTEE ON FOOD ADDITIVES

Geneva, 9 - 18 February 1993

MEMBERS

Dr S. Dagher, Associate Professor, Department of Biology, American University of Beirut, Lebanon

Dr C.E. Fisher, Head of Food Safety, Additives and Risk Assessment Unit, Food Science Division I, Ministry of Agriculture, Fisheries and Food, London, England (Joint Rapporteur)

Professor C.L. Galli, Professor of Toxicology, Institute of Pharmacological Sciences, University of Milan, Milan, Italy

Dr D.L. Grant, Chief, Toxicological Evaluation Division, Bureau of Chemical Safety, Food Directorate, Health Protection Branch, Health and Welfare Canada, Ottawa, Ontario, Canada

Dr D.G. Hattan, Deputy Director, Division of Health Effects Evaluation (HFS-225), Center for Food Safety and Applied Nutrition, Food and Drug Administration, Washington, DC, USA

Professor K. Kojima, Professor of Environmental Hygiene, Emeritus, College of Environmental Health, Azabu University, Kanagawa-Ken, Japan

Dr P. M. Kuznesof, Chief, Chemistry Review Branch, Office of Pre-Market Approval, Center for Food Safety and Applied Nutrition, Food and Drug Administration, Washington, DC, USA

Dr J. C. Larsen, Head, Department of Biochemical and Molecular Toxicology, Institute of Toxicology, National Food Agency, Søborg, Denmark (Joint Rapporteur)

Mrs I. Meyland, Senior Scientific Officer, Central Laboratory, National Food Agency, Søborg, Denmark (Vice-Chairman)

Dr B. Priestly, Scientific Director, Chemicals Safety Unit, Department of Health, Housing and Community Services, Canberra, Australian Capitol Territory, Australia

Professor F.G. Reyes, Professor of Food Toxicology, Department of Food Science, State University of Campinas, Campinas, São Paulo, Brazil

Ms A. Vongbuddhapitak, Principal Scientist, Department of Medical Sciences, Yodse, Bangkok, Thailand

Professor R. Walker, Professor of Food Science, School of Biological Sciences, University of Surrey, Guildford, Surrey, England (Chairman)

Mrs H. Wallin, Senior Research Scientist, Food Research Laboratory, Technical Research Centre of Finland (VTT), Espoo, Finland

SECRETARIAT

Dr K. Ekelman, #2 Additives Evaluation Branch, Division of Health Effects Evaluation, Center for Food Safety and Applied Nutrition, Food and Drug Administration, Washington, DC, USA *(WHO Temporary Adviser)*
Dr R. Goyer, Chapel Hill, NC, USA *(WHO Temporary Adviser)*
Dr Y. Hayashi, Director, Biological Safety Research Centre, National Institute of Hygienic Sciences, Tokyo, Japan *(WHO Temporary Adviser)*
Dr J.L. Herrman, Scientist, International Programme on Chemical Safety, WHO, Geneva, Switzerland *(Joint Secretary)*
Mr J.F. Howlett, Secretary to the Scientific Committee for Food, Foodstuffs Division, Directorate General III, Commission of the European Communities, Brussels, Belgium *(WHO Temporary Adviser)*
Dr. C.G.M. Klitsie, Chairman, Codex Committee on Food Additives and Contaminants, and Deputy Director, Quality Environment and Nutrition, Ministry of Agriculture, Nature Management and Fisheries, The Hague, The Netherlands *(WHO Temporary Adviser)*
Dr I.C. Munro, CanTox Inc., Mississauga, Ontario, Canada *(WHO Temporary Adviser)*
Dr P. Olsen, Head, Department of Pathology, Institute of Toxicology, National Food Agency, Søborg, Denmark *(WHO Temporary Adviser)*
Dr J. Paakkanen, Nutrition Officer, Food Policy and Nutrition Division, FAO, Rome, Italy *(Joint Secretary)*
Mr D. Schutz, Office of Toxic Substances, Environmental Protection Agency, Washington, DC, USA *(WHO Consultant)*
Professor P. Shubik, Senior Research Fellow, Green College, Oxford, England *(WHO Temporary Adviser)*
Professor A. Somogyi, Director, Max von Pettenkofer Institute of the Federal Health Office, Berlin, Germany *(WHO Temporary Adviser)*
Dr G.J.A. Speijers, Laboratory for Toxicology, National Institute of Public Health and Environmental Protection Bilthoven, The Netherlands *(WHO Temporary Adviser)*
Professor K. Tsuchiya, Food Sanitation Division, Environmental Health Bureau, Ministry of Health and Welfare, Tokyo, Japan *(WHO Temporary Adviser)*
Ms E. Vavasour, Toxicological Evaluation Division, Bureau of Chemical Safety, Food Directorate, Health Protection Branch, Health and Welfare Canada, Ottawa, Ontario, Canada *(WHO Temporary Adviser)*

ANNEX 4

ACCEPTABLE DAILY INTAKES, OTHER TOXICOLOGICAL INFORMATION, AND INFORMATION ON SPECIFICATIONS

Substance	Specifications[1]	Acceptable Daily Intake (ADI) and other toxicological recommendations — Acceptable Daily Intake
Antioxidants		
Dodecyl gallate	R	0-0.05 mg/kg bw (temporary)[2]
Octyl gallate	R	0-0.1 mg/kg bw (temporary)[2]
Propyl gallate	R	0-1.4 mg/kg bw
Flavouring agents		
Benzyl acetate	S	0-5 mg/kg bw (group ADI)[2,3]
2-Ethyl-1-hexanol	N	0-0.5 mg/kg bw
d-Limonene	R	Not specified[4]
α-Methylbenzyl alcohol	N	0-0.1 mg/kg bw
Quinine hydrochloride	R }	Current use levels of up to 100 mg/l
Quinine sulfate	R }	(as quinine base) in soft drinks not of toxicological concern
Flavour enhancers		
Disodium-5'-guanylate	R }	Not specified[4]
Disodium-5'-inosinate	R }	
Food colours		
Carotenes (algal)	R	No ADI allocated because of inadequate data
Carotenes (vegetable)	R	Acceptable, provided the level of use does not exceed the level normally found in vegetables
Sweetening agents		
Maltitol	S }	Not specified[4]
Maltitol syrup	R }	
Saccharin	S	0-5 mg/kg bw
Thickening agents		
Konjac flour	N,T[2]	Not specified (temporary)[2,4]
Processed *Eucheuma* seaweed	R	0-20 mg/kg bw (temporary)[2]
Propylene glycol alginate	R,T[2]	0-70 mg/kg bw
Miscellaneous substances		
ß-Cyclodextrin	N,T[2]	0-6 mg/kg bw (temporary)[2]
Sodium iron EDTA	N,T[2]	Provisionally considered to be safe in food fortification programmes[5]
Sucrose acetate isobutyrate	R	0-10 mg/kg bw (temporary)[2]
Urea	N	Use at levels of up to 3% in chewing gum not of toxicological concern

Contaminant	Provisional Tolerable Weekly Intake (PTWI)
Cadmium	7 μg per kg of body weight
Chloropropanols (3-chloro-1,2-propanediol and 1,3-dichloro-2-propanol)	Levels in hydrolyzed vegetable proteins should be reduced as far as technologically possible
Lead	25 μg/kg bw

Substances considered for specifications only

Substance	Specifications[1]
Alginic acid	R
Ammonium alginate	R
Ammonium polyphosphate	R
α-Amylase from *Bacillus stearothermophilus*	R
α-Amylase from *Bacillus subtilis*	R
α-Amylase and glucoamylase from *Aspergillus oryzae*	R,T[2]
Calcium alginate	R
Carmines	R
Cochineal extract (formerly cochineal and carminic acid)	R
Disodium pyrophosphate	R
Erythrosine	R
Ethyl hydroxyethyl cellulose	S,T[2]
ß-Glucanase from *Aspergillus niger*, var.	R
Hexane	S,T[2]
Lecithin	R
Lecithin, partially hydrolyzed	S
2-Nitropropane	S,T[2]
Oxystearin	S,T[2]
Petroleum jelly	S,T[2]
Potassium alginate	R
Sodium alginate	R
Sucralose (formerly trichlorogalactosucrose)	R
Tetrasodium pyrophosphate	R
Trichloroethylene	S,T[2]
Xanthan gum	R

Notes to Annex 4

1. N, new specifications were prepared; R, existing specifications revised; S, specifications exist, revision not considered or not required; and T, the existing, new, or revised specifications are tentative and comments are invited.

2. Details of further toxicological studies and other information required for certain substances are given in Annex 3 to the Report of the 41st meeting of JECFA (WHO Technical Report Series, in preparation).

3.   Group ADI with benzyl alcohol, benzaldehyde, benzoic acid, and benzoate salts.

4.   ADI "not specified" means that, on the basis of the available data (chemical, biochemical, toxicological, and other), the total daily intake of the substance arising from its use at the levels necessary to achieve the desired effect and from its acceptable background in food does not, in the opinion of the Committee, represent a hazard to health. For that reason, and for the reasons stated in the individual evaluations, the establishment of an ADI expressed in numerical form was not deemed necessary.

5.   The Committee provisionally concluded that sodium iron EDTA (ethylenediaminetetraacetate) meeting the tentative specifications prepared at the meeting does not present a safety problem when used in supervised food fortification programmes in iron deficient populations.

ANNEX 5
CORRIGENDA

World Health Organization
WHO Food Additives Series

No. 24
TOXICOLOGICAL EVALUATION OF CERTAIN
FOOD ADDITIVES AND CONTAMINANTS

Thirty-third meeting of the Joint FAO/WHO
Expert Committee on Food Additives

Page 165, line 2 under Absorption, distribution, and excretion:

"...Cadmium deficiency..." should be changed to "...Calcium deficiency..."

Page 192, line 2:

"...excreted and also that 0.005% of the total body burden is excreted daily"
should be changed to "...excreted daily"

No. 26
TOXICOLOGICAL EVALUATION OF CERTAIN
FOOD ADDITIVES AND CONTAMINANTS

Thirty-fifth meeting of the Joint FAO/WHO
Expert Committee on Food Additives

CORRIGENDA

Page 30, line 2 under 2.2.2.1 Rats:

"...equivalent of 0.25, 100 ..." should be changed to "...equivalent of 0, 25,
100..."

Page 37, line 8 in second paragraph:

"...days 7 and 24 were..." should be changed to "...days 7 and 14 were..."